PRACTICAL HINTS ON ABSORPTION SPECTROMETRY (ULTRA-VIOLET AND VISIBLE)

PRACTICAL HINTS ON
ABSORPTION SPECTROMETRY
(ULTRA-VIOLET AND VISIBLE)

J. R. Edisbury
D.Sc., Ph.D.(Liv.)

*Consultant. Lately of Unilever Research; Previously
with Medical Research Council; Sometime member
League of Nations Accessory Food Factors Vitamin-A
Sub-Committee; Co-founder and first Chairman
Photoelectric Spectrometry Group, 1948-50; editor
P S G Bulletin; Inter alia, Member Physical
Methods Group Committee, Society for Analytical
Chemistry, 1946-48; Chairman North of England
Section, S A C, 1959-61; Vice-President S A C,
1961-63.*

PLENUM PRESS
NEW YORK
1967

First published in the U.S.A. in 1967 by
PLENUM PRESS
a division of
PLENUM PUBLISHING CORPORATION
227 West 17th Street, New York, New York 10011

Library of Congress Catalog Card No. 67-28581

Published in Great Britain by
Hilger & Watts Ltd, 98 St Pancras Way, London NW1

Printed in Great Britain by Bell & Bain Ltd, Glasgow

DEDICATED

to

TYCHE, *alias* **FORTUNA**

the

GODDESS OF CHANCE

whose random

WHIMS

unobtrusively govern so many

PHENOMENA

for which we flatter ourselves

we are responsible

PREFACE

According to the Bible, Spectroscopy began when the Flood ended
DR WM F. MEGGERS (NBS, U.S.A.)

Probably many people—I know some of them—could have written this book better than I. They just haven't done so.

This book is a selection of practical hints on absorption spectrometry, garnished with what I hope is just enough theory for their intelligent appraisal. It is meant to ' live ' on the bench or desk, to bridge the gap between the school textbook and more scholarly works, and to supplement rather than to supplant them. It is directed at the intelligent School-Leaver and also the Occasional Spectroscopist, who wants to use a spectroscope now and then but has little idea, or wrong ideas, of what can and what cannot be done.

The deeper theoretical aspects—valence bonds, ligands, orbitals, energy levels, and the like—I gratefully entrust to those who understand such things and can make them sound convincing even amid the Babel of rival theories. I prefer not to take sides. If, in passing, I mention a theory that happens to illustrate my theme but is currently out of favour, by all means substitute whatever alternative you consider more appropriate: it won't affect the smooth working of your spectrophotometer or the shape of the absorption spectra. Specialist books and textbooks are available that deal with the current fashions in theory at almost every educational level.

Practical hints, on the other hand, as valid now as they always have been and probably will continue to be until complete automation takes over, are scattered far, wide, and thinly. It would be an interesting though strenuous exercise to make a comprehensive collection of them, but this would fill a volume too bulky for any normal workbench.

Here I have attempted a modest compromise based mainly on personal experience. Although not exhaustive, it should provide the reader with enough of the ' staple philosophy ' of absorption spectrometry to enable most problems within the range 200–800 mμ to be tackled intelligently, and the occasional failure to be plausibly explained away.

When I was asked in 1938 to start a new spectroscopy laboratory, I installed a wavelength spectrometer for work in the visible, and a medium quartz spectrograph taking 10×4 inch (25×10 cm) glass negatives for the ultra-violet. Only ' spec lab ' staff (myself and one young assistant) were allowed to touch the precious equipment. This specialization had its advantages. One of us had already had some years of experience and so knew what could and what could not reasonably be expected; and the Junior Member, with no other instrument to master except a balance, soon became more proficient than I at their routine handling. Specialization also had its drawbacks: absence of one staff member for a few days resulted in chaos. Some enlightened ' occasional spectroscopists ' were needed.

Nowadays, after ten minutes' instruction on the best order in which to press the various buttons, almost any intelligent school-leaver, with little knowledge of what goes on inside, is allowed the full run of far more sophisticated boxes of mystery. That so little harm comes to sensitive instruments under these rigorous conditions is a tribute to the manufacturers. That the results are not more often disappointing is a minor miracle, repeated daily but seldom acknowledged.

If any experienced spectroscopists ever read this book and find some favourite ideas mentioned casually without acknowledgement, as if they were my own, please forgive me: either I thought of them too (faced with the same problems, people do tend to think up similar solutions) or else your ideas made such an immediate appeal that my subconscious quietly ' scooped ' and stored them for future use. If you provide me with chapter and verse I will try to make amends. I shall also be glad to hear from anyone who can fill any of the inevitable gaps in the present narrative with Further Practical Hints, which will be properly acknowledged if or when they ever reach print.

Long before this possible future stage, there is one debt of gratitude I am delighted to acknowledge here and now: that is to my first Chief and very staunch friend Professor R. A. Morton, F.R.S., under whose kindly guidance I was privileged to work for six post-graduate years on some unusual applications of absorption spectrometry.

I must also thank my wife Mabel for, incredibly, still putting up with me, despite everything; and my daughter Ann, who valiantly disentangled and re-typed the entire illegibly multi-corrected monograph in a quarter of the time it would have taken me.

J.R.E.

CHESTER
March, 1966

A*

CONTENTS

xi

CHAPTER 1

FIRST PRINCIPLES

When thou shalt contemplate, starry-eyed, some wondrous new instrument, thou shalt ask thyself ' Who have we that can make it work ?   CONTROL 1962 Sept.

Imagination is often as important as knowledge
                                        ALBERT EINSTEIN

In passing through translucent material, solid or fluid, a ray of light loses some of its original intensity. Part gets through; part does not. Absorption spectrometry concerns a specific portion of the part that does not, that portion which is *absorbed* by the material rather than scattered by dirt or cloudiness, or reflected, or refracted at the surfaces of entry and exit. A graph of a series of corrected light absorptions, plotted against the corresponding wavelengths (or frequencies), is called the *absorption spectrum* of the material in question. This book deals mainly with how to obtain dependable absorption spectra within the wavelength range 200–800 mμ. The need for the qualification ' dependable ' will become clear later.

The normal human eye responds usefully to electromagnetic radiation between 400 and 800 mμ, the ' visible region ' of the spectrum (Plate 1). Maximum sensitivity is at 555 mμ, or thereabouts, in the green. Around 400 mμ (extreme violet) and 750–800 mμ (deep red), sensitivity tails off to almost zero for most people.

The ultra-violet (' beyond violet ') is conventionally regarded as covering 200–400 mμ. There is, of course, no sharp demarcation at 400 mμ between visible and ultra-violet (UV), any more than there is between adjacent colours of the rainbow: Isaac Newton was over-optimistic when he told his young assistant to mark ' the confines of the colours ', though one sees what he meant. Many people can see no further towards the UV than 420 mμ, and what they do see is probably stray light (q.v.). Others, more gifted and (it is said) usually young and lightly pigmented, can see the

1

365 mμ line of mercury in the near UV. If any such blond(e) youngsters ever read this, I hope they will tell me what ' colour ' they see at 365 mμ.

Analogy with music suggests that the visual impression should be ' a sort of red ', in much the same way that each note in the scale has a recognizable affinity with its octave(s). Half of 365, 182·5 mμ, is well beyond any human reach, but twice 365, 730 mμ, is in the easily seen deep red.

WARNING

NEVER expose the eye for more than a moment—even from the side—to light from any form of UV lamp. You may not notice anything at the time except a tell-tale smell of ozone; but you are apt to wake up in the small hours with a feeling of sand in your eyes which can persist for days and might need medical attention.

Viewed through a glass-train wavelength spectrometer, the isolated 365 mμ mercury line is probably sufficiently attenuated to be safe over a brief period; but I would not recommend frequent sessions without knowledge of the real intensity (determined photographically or by a meter). Incidentally, the red glow of a Wood's-glass-covered lamp is due to an ' optical leak ' in the far red part of the spectrum, too slight to spoil UV irradiation experiments but still strong enough to invalidate any rash attempt to see the UV directly through Wood's glass.

COLOUR

The sensation of colour is entirely subjective and can be produced by a variety of causes, including pressure on the eyeball (e.g. ' seeing stars ') as well as by the more comfortable and conventional retinal response. Received in certain proportions, several combinations of radiation between 400 and 800 mμ produce a sensation

PLATE 1

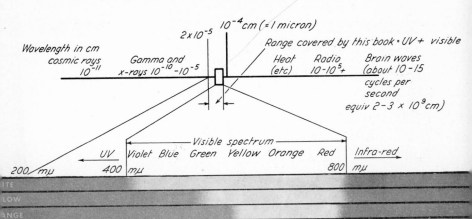

Simplified electromagnetic spectrum (adapted from Brode, 1955). Only the small range in the little window, here enlarged, can be seen direct. Some of the remainder can be *felt* (heat, UV burns, etc.) and the rest detected by various forms of apparatus. In the lower part of the diagram, the blank areas represent transmitted visible light; the shaded portions are either invisible or have been absorbed or attenuated. Many variants are possible. A few are given here.

White No selective absorption at all, as here, *or* a carefully balanced selection of colours that blend to look white.

Yellow Violet and blue absorbed or attenuated. Red plus green cancels out in the eye to give the net effect of yellow.

Orange Violet and blue absorbed. Red, orange, and yellow transmitted. Red plus yellow looks orange; hence the appearance of orange.

Purple Only red and blue transmitted, together making purple.

Blue All except blue absorbed or attenuated. Attenuation in the orange-red alone also gives an impression of blue; transmitted red plus green cancels out in the eye, leaving blue.

Green Blue, yellow, orange, red, all absorbed; only green remains. Compare Fig. 1.2 (chlorophyll).

The diagram incidentally explains why photographic colour negatives look so peculiar and why the colour of carotene solutions changes from pale yellow, through orange, to red as the solvent is changed from light petrol to chloroform to carbon disulphide, while the absorption maximum shifts from the blue-violet to longer wavelengths.

of white; any imbalance in these proportions produces colour. The emission from a sodium lamp looks yellow because it is dominated by the high-intensity D-lines in the yellow part of the spectrum; these conceal the rest of the fairly complex sodium spectrum by sheer overwhelming dazzle, unless they are first segregated by a spectroscope or light filter. A leaf looks green because chlorophyll absorbs red and violet, leaving most of the yellow, green and blue,

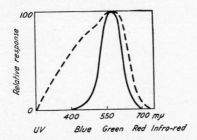

Fig. 1.1. The spectral response of an average human eye compared with that of a typical photocell (broken line) as used in photographic exposure meters. A pale khaki-green 2 × light filter modifies the overall response of the photocell to agree with the eye almost exactly. Maximum eye-response is in the green, tailing off to *almost* nil at 400 to 700 mμ, but reflex opening of the iris may allow rather attenuated vision beyond this. (Photocell curve by courtesy of Evans Electroselenium Ltd.)

which together add up to green, the colour to which the eye is most responsive (Figs. 1.1 and 1.2). Autumn tints are largely due to the selective fading away of the chlorophyll well before the chemically more stable red/orange/yellow pigments, such as carotenoids; these, hitherto masked by the more intense chlorophyll, now get a chance to show themselves for a while until they, too, decompose and fade.

In the opposite direction from the UV, the infra-red ('below red') extends indefinitely and, in apparent defiance of etymology, *up*wards from about 800 mμ; etymological integrity is restored by remembering that longer wavelengths imply lower frequencies. Again any quoted 'boundaries' are arbitrary, mere convenient fictions. But, as someone is said to have said, 'You've got to draw the line somewhere. Otherwise, where are you going to draw the line?' Our excursions out of the 200–800 mμ range will therefore be rare. Let Dr Chapman (1965) introduce you to the outer regions and their possibilities.

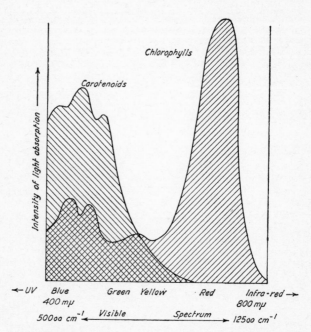

FIG. 1.2. Sketch showing very diagrammatically the absorption spectra of chlorophyll(s) and typical carotenoids, and why many leaves change colour from green in summer to red in autumn. The carotenoids absorb the blue part of the spectrum and transmit the rest more or less freely; the stronger the solution, the less free the transmission, so that really strong solutions look red (because everything else has been absorbed) and weak solutions look pale yellow (because, roughly, in a mixture of red, yellow, and green, the red and green cancel each other out). Similarly, chlorophyll looks green because it absorbs strongly in the red, and rather less in the blue, and transmits most of the yellow-green region between. In summer, chlorophyll dominates the spectrum; when the leaves die, the chlorophyll fades first and the carotenoids temporarily take over.

The shaded area below the curves represents light that has been absorbed; areas above the curves, light that has been transmitted. Inverted, the curves become transmission spectra.

INSTRUMENTS

The equipment needed to produce an absorption spectrum comprises essentially:

1 A steady source emitting the required range of radiation.

2 A means of reproducibly selecting a number of appropriate small portions of this range.

3 A precisely aligned mount or container for the solid or fluid specimen under examination.

4 A radiation detector with predictable response characteristics.

5 Some means of adjusting the intensity of radiation falling on the detector, so as to provide a zero-setting (e.g. nominally 100 per cent light transmission) or a reference-datum whereby intensities can be compared before and after traversing the specimen.

For work in the visible and the near fringe of the UV, a prefocused incandescent filament lamp is understandably the most popular light source. In the UV itself, the glow from an electric discharge through hydrogen at low pressure provides good intensity where the filament's performance falls off; it is not as good as the filament at wavelengths higher than about 400 mμ. That is why the more versatile spectrophotometers, covering both UV and visible, are equipped with a filament lamp and also a hydrogen or a deuterium lamp.

How the wavelength is selected depends on the degree of selectivity required. For some purposes, simple apparatus containing a series of light filters, each of which transmits only part of the spectrum, is adequate and, in certain circumstances, can even be preferable to more selective devices; for one thing, ' adjustment ' is permanent and does not depend on the variable skill of an operator. Such instruments are often called ' abridged spectrophotometers ' or, more correctly, ' absorptiometers '. They are not designed for the determination of absorption spectra. Their correct use is to replace the older types of visual colorimeters by something more objective and less tiring. Optical density (absorbance) readings obtained on them are reliably related through a constant factor to the more nearly absolute values given by a spectrophotometer. For quantitative analyses, a calibration curve is constructed by comparing the readings obtained with different dilutions of the material(s) under assay.

Genuine spectrophotometers range in complexity from the simplest assembly based on an inexpensive plastics replica grating, through the conventional single-prism or high-resolution grating, to recording instruments with a couple of complete spectrometers in series, ' double monochromators '. Each type has its appropriate applications. Each can be misused to give misleading yet reproducible results.

CHAPTER 2

DEFINITIONS

It depends what you mean by . . .
PROFESSOR C. E. M. JOAD
(BBC Brains Trust, 1940s)

This explanatory chapter is arranged in a more or less logical order rather than alphabetically, mainly because it is easier to read a continuous sequence of related items than a dictionary, even a short one. Experts don't, or at least shouldn't, need this selection, and they can certainly add several pages; but they will probably find enough iconoclastic, though truthful, remarks to start an argument.

Spectroscope, literally ' spectrum viewer ', is used correctly to mean only an instrument through which one can directly *see* and examine a spectrum, but also—loosely but widely—for any device that resolves mixed radiations into an orderly spectrum.

Spectroscopy (' spectrum viewing ') therefore, although strictly meaning only work with a spectroscope, is also used loosely to cover the entire science of spectra; *spectrology* (logos = discourse, knowledge) would be more appropriate, despite the existing supernatural connotation; or perhaps *spectronomy* (nomos = law; nemein = manage, wield).

Spectrograph, on the other hand, is customarily reserved for a combination of a ' spectroscope ' and a camera to record the spectrum photographically.

Spectrogram, a photograph of a spectrum. There seems no semantic reason why this should not be extended to include other permanent recordings of spectra (charts, etc.). *Photogram* is used by the Upper Echelon of the camera world to describe what lesser mortals call a photograph. (' Spectrograph ' is, understandably, often misused by the lay press—as when a well-known gentleman took a few stellar spectrograms to show to fellow

7

members and was reported as having ' walked into the meeting with a briefcase full of spectrographs '.)

Photometer, literally ' light measurer '.

Spectrophotometer, apparatus for measuring light intensity from selected parts of a spectrum—a combination of a spectroscope and a photometer. In this context the spectroscope is often euphemistically called a monochromator (q.v.).

Spectrometer, increasingly used as a briefer synonym for spectrophotometer. Some purists claim that it should be reserved for the monochromator itself. But ' spectrometer '=' spectrum measurer ', which neither specifies wavelength nor specifically excludes intensity, and thus seems justified on grounds of both convenience and etymology.

Monochromator, literally ' one-colour producer ', means ideally a device for selecting a single wavelength, and in practice a ' spectroscope ' with good resolving power capable of isolating really narrow spectral ranges, each not more than a few angstroms wide. True monochromatism implies the isolation of one emission line, which can in some circumstances be achieved just as well by a light filter as by a spectroscope; but the choice of sufficiently uncrowded lines, unaccompanied by background, is limited and it is a very lucky chance indeed to find one just where you want it, certainly not a large enough number of isolable lines to plot a complete spectrum.

Light Filter, a device that intercepts unwanted radiation and transmits only a selected portion of the spectrum. *Pigmented* filters, which may be solid or liquid and might not even be coloured (for instance, true UV filters), typically transmit bands 50–150 mμ wide. *Interference* filters, less robust and more costly, approach closer to monochromatism with 5–20 mμ, plus one or two tiny side-bands which modern techniques have almost eliminated. At the expense of slightly broadening the main interference band, the effective mid-point or ' optical centre of gravity ' can be adjusted over a few mμ towards *shorter* wavelengths by bodily tilting the filter. (Although the effective separation between the interfaces thereby increases, the difference between path-lengths—which is what matters here—becomes smaller). Tilting is usually discouraged because, unless carefully controlled and calibrated, it not only spoils the designed narrowness of the band transmitted but also displaces the light beam sideways to a not always easily predictable extent. Either fault can vitiate the performance of a blameless and well-calibrated absorptiometer.

Absorptiometer (or '*abridged spectrophotometer*'), is an assembly comprising a photometer that receives light through any one of a number of light filters, each of which isolates a known part of the spectrum. Intelligently calibrated, such an instrument copes with some situations better than a fully-fledged spectrometer—for instance, those colour reactions which do not show a definite absorption maximum—and the complication of precisely pre-setting a wavelength adjustment is neatly evaded. Often the colour is such that the most suitable wavelength is critically poised on the edge of a rising curve, and a mμ or two either way profoundly affects the photometric reading.

Absorbance (=*Optical Density*), is the logarithm of the ratio between the intensities of the light beam before entering and after leaving a sample, $\log_{10}(I_0/I)$. Abbreviated E (for '*Extinction*'), or A, or a, or OD. (See Chapter 3.)

Extinction is—at least temporarily—outmoded, but it is, I think, far preferable to 'absorbance', which always strikes me as more appropriately applicable to the hydraulic properties of a mop, sponge, or towel than to the attenuation of light. 'Density' is overworked, though the context avoids ambiguity. If *extinction* (=*OD*) is not already beyond recall, let's try to revive it. If we can't, will someone please coin a word based on 'to dim'? Meanwhile, I try to go (at least for part of the time) with the stream . . . But only half-heartedly, as an inelegant variation for those who like current fashions.

Absorptivity, $E(1\%, 1\text{cm})$, or E-value, is the absorbance divided by the product of path-length and concentration (in cm and %w/v). Also written E_1^1, pronounced 'E one one'.

Absorption spectrum is a graph or chart plotting absorptivity as ordinate against wavelength or a function of frequency as abscissa. *Maxima*, *minima* and *inflexions* are self-explanatory; but remember that an absorption maximum is a transmission minimum. See Figs. 2.1 and 19.1.

Spectral slit-width is the range of spectrum, typically a few AU, emerging from the exit slit of a spectrometer at a given (nominally monochromatic) wavelength. The wavelength control moves the complete spectrum—a few inches long and a few mm wide—across the pair of exit slit jaws: their separation, normally well under one millimetre and perhaps as little as 0·01 mm, governs (*a*) the width of spectrum that gets through alongside the nominal wavelength, and hence also (*b*) the maximum illumination of the detector.

Continuous spectrum or *spectral continuum* is a spectrum unbroken by emission lines. *Line spectra*, due to quantum jumps by excited atoms (e.g. metal arc or spark), show a more or less distinct background between the lines. An ideal continuum may

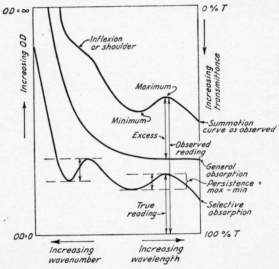

FIG. 2.1. The curve that is plotted or recorded is the summation of the spectra of all light-absorbing substances present. Irrelevant absorption must be removed or allowed for; otherwise the substance under test will be over-estimated.

be said to be all background. Within their useful ranges, incandescent filaments and an electric discharge through hydrogen at low pressure give good continuous spectra. Outside their useful ranges, intensity falls and the gas continuum develops lines, which, incidentally, can be useful for quick wavelength calibration. A spectral line is an image of the entrance slit, and its width varies accordingly. The true, physical, width of a line is a more complicated matter. Professor Moon (1965) gives a good popular account.

Spectral impurity is the inevitable consequence of a finite slit width, and consists of a small range of neighbouring wavelengths accompanying the nominal wavelength. This is not to be confused with stray light.

Stray radiation (or *stray light*) is light emerging through the exit slit from any but the chosen region of the spectrum, not merely the small range due to finite slit width. An extreme example would be daylight admitted through a defective cover—the spectroscopic equivalent of pin-holes in a camera bellows. Usually, the entering ' unsorted ' ray from the light source is scattered by the dust or corrosion on internal baffles, or reflected from bright patches that should be matt black. It is more often a result of neglect than of bad design or workmanship.

Cuvette is a useful synonym for absorption cell. The word ' cell ' is over-worked in scientific literature. Out of context, an adjective or other description of the cell is essential.

Beer's law is the popular name for the Beer-Lambert-Bouguer set of rules governing the partial extinction of light by absorption, and forming the basis of quantitative absorption spectroanalysis. Briefly, *absorbance* (or *optical density* or *extinction*) is proportional to the number of absorbing entities (molecules, ions, etc.) in the light-path, and remains unchanged so long as the entities themselves remain unchanged. Thus, for instance, at half the path-length and twice the concentration, the reading should stay the same. If—as often happens—it does not, Beer's law has not failed: deviation means merely that the conditions have somehow changed. Ionization or association or interaction between the absorbing material and the solvent has altered the number of entities of the original ' absorbing molecular species ' in the light-path; or fluorescence or stray light are interfering; or the light beam is excessively non-parallel; or something else is obscuring or exaggerating the effect that would be obtained under ' neutral ' conditions. In quantitative work much can be learnt from apparent deviations from Beer's law (e.g. Lothian, 1963). And, as a matter of routine, the behaviour of any material under assay should be thoroughly studied under all conditions likely to be encountered. Lack of proportionality need not cause panic; a calibration curve can be constructed. But it is as well to be prepared.

Phototube or Photoelectric Cell, typically a transparent near-evacuated vessel containing two insulated electrodes, one of which, the *photo-cathode*, is coated with an alkali metal or mixture (e.g. Cs–Sb) that emits electrons in proportion to the light energy falling on it. The anode is a positively charged grid of fine wire arranged so as to intercept electrons but obstruct very little light. The microcurrent thus available can be amplified to operate the pointer of a galvanometer or—through a servo—the pen of a recorder. Under conditions of no illumination there is still some slight residual (thermal) emission of electrons, the so-called *dark current*. It is convenient to balance-out this before taking readings by a similar, but calibrated, potentiometric process. A sample reading is thus in practice a comparison between two lengths of potentiometer wire, one length representing nominally $100\% T$ (or zero OD) for the blank. In a silica envelope, the Cs–Sb (' blue sensitive ') surface responds well to the radiation range 200–600 mμ; above, say, 650 mμ, the ' red sensitive ' caesium oxide type is usually preferable.

Photomultiplier, a development of the phototube based on the fact that if the photo-emitted electrons are accelerated by an applied potential of about 80–160 volts and made to bombard another electrode (' target ') of suitable material, each electron liberates a few more electrons (' secondary emission '), which bombard the next target. A cascade of several such ' dynodes ' thus provides useful initial amplification, perhaps a million-fold, before the signal reaches the detector of the main amplifier. The well-tried 1P28, with 9 dynodes and a Cs–Sb photo-surface, is sensitive from below 200 to upwards of 650 mμ if it is fitted with a silica window.

Barrier-layer photocell, known also as a *rectifier* or *photo-voltaic cell*, consists usually of a sandwich of β-selenium between two electrodes: (1) a metal base-plate, and (2) a metal or metal oxide film, thin enough to transmit light, but thick enough to carry a current of a few milliamperes. Many photographic exposure meters are based on this cell because the voltage generated is sufficient to operate a milliammeter directly. Over a useful range of illumination, response is rectilinear, so the meter can be conveniently calibrated $0–100\% T$ in equal divisions for use in absorptiometers. Best response is in the mid-visible region, 500–600 mμ, tailing off to 300 and 800 mμ.

Servo or servomotor, a device for multiplying mechanical effort without losing range of movement (as occurs in normal leverage). The range can in fact be increased, and often is. The essential feature here is that the final amount of movement shall be

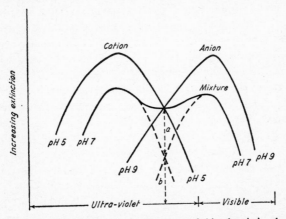

Fig. 2.2. Diagrammatic explanation of 'isosbestic'. As a simple example, imagine an acid/alkali indicator that is colourless in acid, coloured in alkaline solution, and faintly coloured at neutrality. Phenolphthalein behaves like this. The red-coloured anion absorbs all visible light strongly, except red; the colourless cation absorbs strongly in the UV, but not at all in the visible. Their respective absorption spectra are shown for pH 9 and pH 5 (pH is the logarithm of the total number of litres of aqueous solution that between them accommodate one gram of hydrogen ions). At intermediate pH values, both forms are present, showing both maxima more or less vestigially according to how far the equilibrium is from one extreme or the other. All curves (only three are shown for clarity) pass through one point, the *isosbestic* point. The intermediate curves can be roughly resolved freehand into their components if you remember that it is their summation curve that forms the observed spectrum; the distances *a* and *b* must be made equal. The two maxima may or may not be shifted 'inwards' by a mμ or so.

predictably governed by the initial effort and/or displacement. Choice of motive power is a matter of convenience. In a recording spectrophotometer, amplified electrical imbalance is usually chosen.

Chromophore, a group of atoms in a molecule responsible for its light absorption. Adjacent chromophores (e.g. conjugated double bonds) can interact to give more than an additive result quantitatively (higher extinction) and often completely new effects qualitatively (new wavelengths). In colour tests, visible chromophores are produced by reactions involving *chromogens*, which may themselves be coloured or colourless. An *auxochrome* enhances the light-absorptive performance of a chromophore; a *bathochrome* shifts its peak absorption (' absorption maximum ') to a lower frequency. The prefix ' chrom- ' is loosely extended to cover the entire spectrum, although it was originally restricted to the visible region of interest to dyers and colourists. See also Brode (1949).

Isosbestic: When a dissolved substance can exist in two or more light-absorbing forms in equilibrium (for instance, ions and undissociated molecules) the spectra of the forms often differ. At some point or points the curves cross, and the light-absorption properties are here, but only here, identical. In a series of such curves representing a ' family ' of different equilibria, one maximum rises and the other falls as the equilibrium shifts; but the intersection remains constant and is known as the *isosbestic* point, often misspelled ' isobestic ' (Fig. 2.2). The derivation is from the Greek: isos, equal; sbestos, extinguished—compare asbestos. The pseudo-humourist who coined the word evidently had more regard for etymology than for euphony. Because an isosbestic point is insensitive to changes in equilibrium, E-values are sometimes better measured here than at a maximum; but much greater care is needed in establishing and subsequently using the exact wavelength. A mμ either way might mean a few percent error in E-value. If the equilibrium can be reversibly displaced to either extreme, measurements are then more safely made at one of the (relatively) wavelength-insensitive maxima. *Cis-trans* equilibria also often show isosbestic points in their spectra.

CHAPTER 3

UNITS AND NOTATION

Lord, what fools these mortals be
MIDSUMMER NIGHT'S DREAM, **II** ii 115

Except when re-emission occurs (by fluorescence, for instance) the wavelength of a light ray does not change as a result of absorption. The intensity does.

Let the light incident on a sample be of intensity I_0, and the emergent light I. Then the *fraction transmitted* $T=I/I_0$, and the *percentage transmittance* $\%T=100\ I/I_0$.

Suppose that the first millimetre thickness of a uniform sample, such as a solution, absorbs $\frac{1}{3}$ of the light incident upon it. Each subsequent mm will also absorb $\frac{1}{3}$ (and so transmit $\frac{2}{3}$) of the attenuated light it receives, independent of the absolute intensity (Lambert's law). Together, in tandem, the first first 2 mm will therefore absorb $\frac{4}{9}=(\frac{2}{3})^2$; 3 mm, $\frac{8}{27}=(\frac{2}{3})^3$; 4 mm, $\frac{16}{81}=(\frac{2}{3})^4$; ... 1 cm, $(\frac{2}{3})^{10}$; and so on. More generally, if $T=1/x$ for a given thickness, it will be $1/x^n$, i.e. x^{-n}, for n times that thickness. Double (etc.) the thickness and you double (etc.) the index n. Subject to Beer's law, the same is true of concentration.

Calculations on a basis like this, particularly if n is not an integer, are vastly simplified by the immediate use of logarithms. [Try to work out even $(\frac{2}{3})^{10}$ long-hand in a hurry.] So it comes about that *extinction, absorbance,* or *optical density* (OD) is defined right away in terms of logarithms, not out of mathematical caprice, but to make things easy:

$$OD=\log_{10}(I_0/I)$$
$$=\log(1/T)$$
$$=-\log T$$
$$=\log 100-\log(\%T)$$
$$=2-\log(\%T)$$

In the above example (%T=66·6 per mm) the *OD* is 0·176 per mm, or 1·76 per cm. If 1-mm and 1-cm cuvettes are both available, a stringent but conveniently quick check on photometer+cuvettes is to take readings on the same solution at both thicknesses. Don't expect perfection, but any deviation from a 10:1 ratio should not exceed two units in the third digit. Beer-type complications are completely absent.

Contrary to anything you may read or hear elsewhere, the expression *OD*=2—log (%T) does *not* mean that absorbance readings can never exceed 2·0. This myth, widely believed, probably arose from the pardonable illusion that log 0 is zero (instead of —∞). If %T is less than 1·0 (the logarithm of which *is* zero), log (%T) becomes negative. Thus at 0·5%T,

$$OD = 2 - \log_{10} 0.5$$
$$= 2 - (\bar{1}.699)$$
$$= 2.301$$

Only an initially good and thereafter well-maintained instrument will give dependable *OD* readings above 2. Many fail below this. The readings may be clear, but they won't mean anything quantitative, and may even be misleading qualitatively by indicating a non-existent absorption band. (See Chapters 12 and 17 and Figs. 7.1 and 17.1.)

The permanent relationship between %T and *OD* is shown in the adjoining table. The exact equivalence 39·90 %T=0·3990 *OD* is worth noting: it can be useful in checking the integrity of the linkages (etc.) in recording instruments with ' switching ' between the *OD* and %T modes of operation. (See Chapters 6 and 11.)

E-VALUES

Four standard expressions for the comparison of absorption intensities are in current regular use: (1) ϵ; (2) log ϵ; (3) $E(1\%$, 1 cm) or E_1^1; (4) Specific α.

(1) ϵ, the Greek epsilon, is called molecular (or molar) extinction, and is used mostly in academic work.

   $\epsilon = OD/$(cell thickness in cm × molar concentration)

(2)   log ϵ=logarithm (to base 10) of above.

CONVERSION TABLES
Optical Density (Absorbance or Extinction)
and Percentage Transmittance

OD	%T (approx)	%T	OD
Infinity	0	0	Infinity
2·6	0·25	0·5	2·301
2·0	1·00	1	2·00
1·7	2·0	2	1·699
1·5	3	5	1·301
1·45	3·5	10	1·000
1·4	4	15	0·824
1·35	4·5	20	0·699
1·3	5	25	0·599
1·25	5·6	30	0·523
1·2	6·3	35	0·456
1·15	7	40	0·398
1·1	8	45	0·346
1·05	9	50	0·301
1·00	10·0	55	0·260
0·95	11	60	0·222
0·9	13	65	0·187
0·85	14	70	0·155
0·8	16	75	0·125
0·75	18	80	0·097
0·7	20	85	0·071
0·65	22·5	90	0·046
0·6	25	95	0·022
0·55	28	100	0·000
0·5	31·5		
0·45	35		
0·4	40	Basic Equation:	
0·35	45	$OD = 2 - \log_{10}(\%T)$	
0·3	50		
0·25	56	It is worth noting that	
0·2	63	$0·3990\ OD = 39·90\%T$	
0·15	71	and that	
0·1	79·5	$0·5\ OD = 10\sqrt{10\%T}$	
0·05	89		
0	100		

(3) $E(1\%,\ 1\ \text{cm}) = OD/(\text{cell thickness in cm} \times \text{concentration} \%\text{w/v})$. This was originally written

$$\mathsf{E}\genfrac{}{}{0pt}{}{}{}\begin{array}{l}1\% \\ \dots\ \text{m}\mu \\ 1\ \text{cm}\end{array}$$

the three parameters of concentration, wavelength, and cell thickness (path-length) occupying the three prongs of a large capital E (for extinction). The form $E(1\%,\ 1\ \text{cm})$, as used here with or without specifying wavelength, is typographically more convenient and increasingly used in print. Sometimes, perhaps ambiguously, it is over-abbreviated to E (which should be reserved for extinction, the OD reading itself) and is currently pronounced *absorptivity* or ' E one one '.

(4) Specific α or specific alpha$=OD/$(cell thickness in cm $\times$ concentration in g/litre). This has been much used in American literature, and is synonymous with $E(0\cdot1\%, 1\ \text{cm})$.

The expressions are therefore related thus:

$$E(1\%,\ 1\ \text{cm})=10\times\text{specific }\alpha=10\epsilon/\text{molecular weight}$$

$$\log\epsilon=\log(\text{specific }\alpha\times\text{molecular weight})$$

$$=\log(E_1^1\times\text{molecular weight})-1$$

Probably because a is sometimes used as one of the symbols for absorbance, the expression $a(1\%,\ 1\ \text{cm})$ occasionally replaces $E(1\%,\ 1\ \text{cm})$. The literature abounds with such manifestations of rugged individualism; but, although they may be regrettable, they are unlikely to confuse the observant and alert reader.

Log ϵ and ϵ have the advantage, which is sometimes more than academic, of providing truer direct comparisons between related compounds, particularly in homologous series, where many minor differences are automatically eliminated by including the molecular weight in the calculation. Transparent groupings, which act absorptiometrically as mere diluents, become in a mathematical sense part of the solvent.

If the molecular weight (MW) is unknown, or if a mixture is involved, ϵ obviously cannot be used, and E_1^1 or specific α is appropriate. Either of these is equally useful as a method of reference for assays in terms of either the pure substance (known MW) or a standard preparation or concentrate of it (unknown mean MW)—subject always to the need to remove or to allow for other substances whose light absorption can interfere. It is enough to say that the observed OD is the sum of all the contributory ODs at the wavelength concerned.

A ' straight ' or direct extinction reading in fact sets an upper limit to your estimate of an absorbing substance. The preparation can't possibly contain more of the substance than is represented by the reading, so the presence of contaminants leads to an over-estimate. In a colour reaction, on the other hand, which provides an indirect estimate through the action of a chromogen (see p. 14), the reading is sometimes inhibited by contaminants (alcohol or acetic anhydride in more than minimal quantities will prevent the blue colour from developing when vitamin A is treated with antimony trichloride) and can then represent a lower limit. You can't generalize.

There is therefore much to be said in favour of preliminary isolation of the pure absorbing substance (by chromatography, for instance) rather than attempting to apply corrections for irrelevant absorption, even though corrections are inherently much quicker. But take each case on its own merits. If there is any doubt, try for yourself to see what best suits the circumstances. Armchair theory doesn't cover everything. Corrections are however so often so unintelligently used, despite careful instructions, that one hesitates to recommend them as general practice (cf. Taylor, 1955; Lothian, 1958).

E-values (which usually mean absorptivities) of pure substances often run up to a few thousands; ϵ is of course even higher—one-tenth of the molecular weight times higher. Remember when you light-heartedly say 'Absorptivity$=840$' that this is the *logarithm* of a number, the number itself being the enormous ratio, 10^{840} in this case, between incident and emergent light-intensities, cal-culated by simple proportion to arbitrary (1%, 1 cm) conditions and not directly measurable by any conceivable means. In quantitative spectro-analysis, what you do in practice is to deter-mine how much you have to dilute the sample to produce an OD reading within the useful range of the photometer; then you reasonably assume proportionality only within this restricted range. Compare Andersen and Nightingale's 'dilution test' (p. 197). The same principle applies throughout analytical pro-cedure; but sometimes (e.g. Pritchard and Ward, 1957) the proportionality extends over a usefully wide range.

A notation sometimes found convenient with clear liquid glyceride oils, specific gravity 0·92, is $E(92\%, 1\ cm)$. The oil is regarded as a 92 per cent solution of itself. *Mutatis mutandis*, this principle can be extended to other materials.

WAVELENGTHS

Units of wavelength are needlessly wrapped in mystery, perhaps partly because most typewriters do not carry the appropriate symbols. Some typeface letters can be altered by hand to look like Greek; Greek letters can also be spelt out in full; but whole words are out of place in equations and are in any event apt to be misspelt (see below). The general scheme is, however, simple:

Angstrom Unit, Å or AU$=10^{-10}$ metre, hence the alternative older name ' tenth-metre '.

Micron, $\mu=10^{-6}$ metre$=10^4$ AU$=1000$ mμ. A micron is a millionth of a metre, or a thousandth of a millimetre, and is also—misguidedly, though logically—called a ' micrometre ', μm. To avoid obvious probable confusion between a measurement and a precision measuring instrument, a terminal -tre (never -ter, friends in U.S.A. please note) and accented first and third syllables (never the second) are essential. This applies generally—km, dm, cm, mm, nm—but in none more strongly than in micrometre. Preferably (*pace* the British Standards Institution and their excellent B.S. 1991) don't use it: someone is sure sooner or later to confuse it with ' micrometer '. ' Micron ' has had wide acceptance for many years. Don't change it.

Millimicron or *millimu*, m$\mu=10$ AU$=10^{-6}$ mm. All too often mμ is mistyped mu (which is the phonetic spelling of μ) instead of the permissible but clumsy mmu. A convenient symbol for mμ slowly coming into wider use is *nanometre* or *nanon* (10^{-9} m), abbreviated nm. This has obvious typographical advantages; but already it is occasionally mistyped nM, which (if it means anything at all) is ' nanomega ', i.e. an absurdly long way round to spell ' milli ' ($10^{-9}\times10^6=10^{-3}$).

To summarize:

$$m\mu=nm=10 \text{ AU}=10^{-9} \text{ m}=10^{-3}\mu$$

(The range covered by this book could therefore be written $0\cdot2$–$0\cdot8$ μ instead of 200–800 mμ.)

In some contexts, particularly astrophysical, the unit AU is understood and therefore omitted, and the wavelength prefixed by the Greek lambda ($=$length): thus λ 5461 means 5461 AU, or $546\cdot1$ mμ. This is a handy convention—if you have a λ on your typewriter.

FREQUENCIES AND WAVENUMBERS

It is often expedient to work in terms of (though not necessarily directly *with*) frequencies instead of wavelengths (Fig. 3.1). Absorption spectra plotted or charted on a rectilinear frequency scale—even though the calibrations themselves may be labelled in wavelengths, and therefore be spaced unevenly, as on the Ultrascan charts—reveal more obviously any regularities or patterns in band-spacing. And there are theoretical as well as practical advantages, a brief but penetrating summary of which is given by Wilkinson (1957) and fuller accounts by Lothian (1958) Rao (1961), Walker and Straw (1962), and Bauman (1962). See also Figs. 19.3 and 19.4.

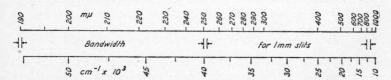

Fig. 3.1. The wavelength scale of a typical quartz-prism spectrometer compared with the same scale expressed in wavenumbers. The diagram also shows how spectral bandwidth varies throughout the spectrum when the width of the exit slit is fixed. (By courtesy of Unicam Instruments Ltd.)

Because wavelength × frequency = velocity of light (symbolized c, 3×10^{10} cm/s) the frequencies characterizing radiations in the visible and UV run into cumbersome numbers. Thus, the frequency (v, Greek nu for number) corresponding with 500 mμ (that is, 500×10^{-7} cm) is $(3 \times 10^{10})/(500 \times 10^{-7}) = 6 \times 10^{14}$ cycles per second, or 600 megamegacycles/second, or 600 MMc/s.

Apart from the last, the human mind finds such figures hard to grasp. The *fresnel* ($f = 10^{12}$ c/s or 1 MMc/s), named after the physicist famed for his work on interference fringes, brings visible and UV frequencies down to a human level, but has two drawbacks: (1) it involves assumptions about the value of the speed of light (an academic objection unless measurements are significant to more digits than are normally justified in routine absorption spectrometry); and more seriously, (2) for wavelengths below 300 mμ, f requires four digits, which is the same practical objection that makes many people prefer mμ or nm to AU for describing

B

the wavelength of an absorption maximum. 302 mμ means 'between 301 and 303 mμ'; 3020 AU or λ 3020 could reasonably—though quite wrongly in most absorption spectra contexts—be taken as 'between 3019 and 3021 AU', especially by an unguarded astrophysicist or a user of atomic spectra data, to whom four digits are customary and significant. Fresnels are not often used in describing UV and visible absorption spectra. For the record, however, in case you ever come across f in the literature (and here I use ' = ' in its looser sense of 'equivalent to'):

$$1500 \text{ f} = 200 \text{ m}\mu; \quad 666 \text{ f} = 450 \text{ m}\mu; \quad 375 \text{ f} = 800 \text{ m}\mu.$$

A much more useful alternative, avoiding any controversies concerning c, is the *wavenumber*, cm^{-1}, which is the number of wavelengths contained in 1 cm and is properly (though rarely) pronounced 'reciprocal centimetre':

wavenumber = frequency/speed of light = 1/wavelength in cm

Wavenumber is thus neither a wavelength nor a frequency but is closely related to both, inversely to wavelength, directly to frequency. Deep down, everyone knows this, but it rarely comes to the mental surface. As Bauman says: 'The concept of frequency is so firmly implanted in the literature and thinking of spectroscopy that the wavenumber has not displaced it but only become scrambled with it.' He further comments that to refer—as I have heard graduates refer—to a 'frequency of so-many wavenumbers' is 'about as appropriate as speaking of a lifetime of 10 wavelengths'. Anyone who (understandably) finds the oddly-displaced $^{-1}$ index a barrier to clear thought may be helped by remembering that a wavenumber of 10 cm^{-1} is equivalent to a wavelength of 1 mm, because 10 mm = 1 cm.

Various symbols have been proposed and/or used for the reciprocal centimetre, ν', $\bar{\nu}$, σ, B, and K (B for *balmer*, after the discoverer of the relationship behind a well-known series of atomic hydrogen lines; K for *kayser*, after the author of the *Handbuch der Spektroskopie*, 1905). All these symbols are already over-used and misused (what symbols aren't?), and none has achieved the respectability of unequivocal official sanction. K and B have their points, however, being not only type-able and pronounceable but also lending themselves to convenient multiples and sub-multiples—kK and kB for kilokayser and kilobalmer, for instance.

(Compare kW for kilowatt, often miswritten KW or even Kw.) This could, as Wilkinson (1957) points out, be one way out of the difficulty that 200–800 mμ is 50 000–12 500 cm^{-1}, involving the inevitably misleading use of five digits for what is essentially barely three-digit information. 200–800 mμ modestly becomes 50–12·5 kK, or 50–12·5 kB. Alternatively, without solving the pronunciation problem but also without adding to the number of symbols to be memorized, 50 000 cm^{-1} could well be written (and I think should be written) 500oo cm^{-1}. This is self-explanatory and at the same time brings things back to earth. I propose its general adoption.

Two other versions (still legitimately ' wavenumbers ' inasmuch as they represent numbers of wavelengths per unit length) are mm^{-1} and μ^{-1}. In the UV and visible, mm^{-1} requires four digits, like AU, and so is rarely appropriate; μ^{-1}, on the other hand, goes even further than kK and kB, and seems the best *self-explanatory* compromise in current use for the visible and UV regions:

$$200\text{–}800 \text{ m}\mu = 5\cdot0\text{–}1\cdot25 \ \mu^{-1}$$

As μ^{-1} means ' number of wavelengths per micron ' the names *permu* and *permicron* (no plurals) have been proposed. Whether either is sufficiently self-explanatory is debatable, but I think worth debating. Permicron is or is not self-explanatory according to how you pronounce it: accent on the second syllable with a long i is my own choice (I never did hold with mickro-anything). The symbol μ^{-1} certainly needs no explanation. This in itself is a point in favour of any word or symbol. And, far from being a drawback, decimals have a positive advantage: they impart flexibility. They can be cut short wherever appropriate. A vague maximum somewhere between 380 and 390 mμ can be honestly expressed as 2·6 μ^{-1} or even 2½ permicron; 383 mμ as 2·61 μ^{-1}; 3836 AU as 2·607 μ^{-1}; and so on. The same principle applies to kB and kK.

To preserve true continuity with the mμ and nm 3-digit tradition, however, what is needed—despite the cornucopian abundance (or Pandora's Boxful, according to how you look at it) of existing symbols—is a symbol meaning 10^{-2} cm. The obvious abbreviation ccm is already widely misused in place of cm^3, and the euphonious *decimillimetre* abbreviates inelegantly but logically and understandably to dmm. But dmm^{-1} *could* be pronounced decikilobalmer, 200 dkB=500 mμ, etc ... I pursue the matter no further. However, if ever you have the temerity to use any novel names or symbols, do please have mercy on your readers and define everything, clearly.

To summarize (again using ' = ' to mean ' equivalent to ' rather than ' equals '):

$$m\mu = nm = 10AU = 10^{-3}\,\mu = 10^7\,cm^{-1} = 10^6\,mm^{-1}$$

$$= 10^3\,\mu^{-1} = 3 \times 10^5\,f = 10^5\,dkB$$

At this juncture, a remark variously attributed to Sam Goldwyn, Mark Twain, Will Rogers and a Bishop of Pittsburgh (among others), seems relevant: ' Why be difficult, when with only a little extra trouble you can be impossible?'

CHAPTER 4

GENERAL WORKING INSTRUCTIONS

PHOTOGRAPHIC INSTRUMENTS

The camera cannot lie
POPULAR SUPERSTITION

The handbook supplied by most manufacturers provides enough detailed information for the operator to obtain an absorption spectrum without further aid. This chapter gives a more general background, partly personally reminiscent, not restricted to one specific instrument, but *mutatis mutandis* broadly applicable to most: any brief instrument descriptions are intended to illustrate an application of a principle. Some of the older but still usable instruments, which have been donated to a school or technical college, are probably unaccompanied by any handbook at all. Students may find some evocative hints useful, perhaps thought-stimulating to the point of action.

There are more spectrographs still scattered around the globe than is generally realized. Some of them lie mouldering in instrument ' boneyards ' awaiting break-up or donation to local evening classes; some repose under dust-sheets in laboratory corners where they were carefully enshrouded when the new photoelectric instrument arrived; any that are not too expensively restorable to working order are worth putting back into limited service, not only for educational purposes but for real ' use '.

No one who has enjoyed the convenience of a modern photoelectric instrument would willingly go back to the old spectrograph for quantitative absorption spectrophotometry; but there are times when a tangible spectrogram can be valuable to convince the sceptical layman or jury, or as a semi-quantitative spare in emergency, or—most effectively of all, in my own opinion—after conversion to moving-plate operation (*vide infra*) as a valuable qualitative accessory.

The straightforward photographic spectrographic spectrophoto-meter comprises (*a*) light source, (*b*) optical photometer or attenuator, and (*c*) spectrograph. Unless the photometer is of unusually long focus, an open arc-light source 'wanders' too much to be useful, even qualitatively. This is a pity, because an arc is almost silent and is intense enough to allow the use of a narrow slit. Quite the nicest spectrograph I have ever handled was an E3 Medium Quartz, made in 1916 by Adam Hilger Ltd. This held 10×4 inch (25×10 cm) glass plates, was made mainly of wood, and produced man-sized spectra which, though (I'm told) open to theoretical criticism, were in practice a delight to look at, gave good results, and did not strain the eyes. More modern versions are decidedly better for producing emission spectrograms from which line intensities can be measured quantitatively with a microdensitometer, but less satisfactory when spectrograms are juxtaposed in pairs for absorption spectrometry, which is what concerns us here.

With the old E3, we used a long-focus sector photometer with a d.c. arc between a pair of horizontally-mounted electrodes of iron and nickel, located a couple of metres away from the entrance slit and encircled by movable anti-dazzle screens with a hole facing the slit. After adjusting the gap to about 3 mm, we struck the arc by briefly bridging the gap with a metal rod, and then if necessary moving the whole assembly slightly until the slit bisected the small round image formed by the photometer lenses. The position of the arc itself was delightfully uncritical: $\pm \frac{1}{2}$ cm in any direction was an allowable tolerance. And you could *see* when it was right without trial. But these were leisurely days, and a single 'plateful' took 25 minutes, plus photographic processing and subsequent plate reading (Baly, 1924, 1927).

The sector photometer, as used with such a light source, is a simple device usually comprising two rotating disks, one with a fixed aperture (or, rather, two balancing fixed apertures of 90°), the other adjustable and calibrated in percentages of the fixed one. The test-solution cell (we didn't hear the word 'cuvette' till nearly twenty years later) is mounted in line with the fixed aperture(s), the compensator or blank or control cell, containing solvent only, in line with the variable aperture(s). A lens system brings the two spectra, sample and control, side by side on the photographic plate. By running a series of exposures—from, say,

0·2 to 1·5 extinction, i.e. 63 to 3·2 % T—of varying duration such that an equal total amount of light passes through the adjustable aperture(s) at each setting, one gets a series of nominally identical control spectra for comparison with interleaved adjacent spectra that have been attenuated here and there by the solution. Equal photographic blackening occurs at points of equal attenuation. We know from the routine photometer settings the degree of uniform attenuation in each control spectrum, so we infer the attenuation produced by the test solution at adjacent points of equality. From the known concentration and cell thickness of the solution we can therefore calculate, point by point, the $E(1\%, 1 \text{ cm})$ or ' absorptivity ' values, etc., for plotting on graph paper:

$$E(1\%, 1 \text{ cm}) = \frac{\text{Reading}}{\text{concentration per cent} \times \text{cell thickness cm}}$$

If the routine exposure times have been suitably chosen, the control spectra are all uniform and nominally correct in a photographic sense. The sample spectra vary along their length from grossly under-exposed to grossly over-exposed, and are correctly exposed only at and near the match-points. Over-generous photographic latitude spreads the match-points into indeterminacy. Excessive contrast contracts them into invisibility.

Because light from a single source is split into two beams that pass simultaneously through both control and sample solution, minor changes in source-intensity—due, for instance, to mains fluctuations—do not affect the final result so long as the blackening at the match-points is neither too faint nor too dark for OD changes to be detectable. But serious unevenness in the control exposures spoils the appearance of the plate.

As a relief from the two-sector theme we have single sectors with two sets of apertures, one fixed, one variable, at different radii from the axis of rotation; single sectors with adjustable apertures for the control and only the sample in the other light beam; and an ingenious assembly embodying a pair of echelon cells (Plate 2) covering 1 mm to 1 cm in ten logarithmic steps, arranged as in Fig. 4.7. One cell contains solvent, the other the sample solution, and the alignment is such that the ten pairs of very narrow spectra alternate in the complete absorption spectrogram. Whereas the conventional spectrogram reads Control, Sample, Control, Sample, C,S,C,S, . . ., the echelon spectrogram reads C,S,S,C,C,S,S,C, . . . To an operator accustomed to the conventional arrangement, this alteration is mildly irritating; and the fact that it simplifies an inevitably complex construction brings no comfort to the user. Nevertheless, if anyone keen on ' make-do-and-mend ' finds such an outfit lying idle, I think it would be well worth while to rig it up with a hydrogen light source, without any special stabilizing circuit, and to use it with a fixed setting of 1·2 extinction (6–7% T),

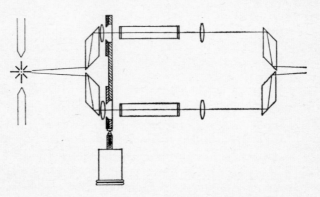

FIG. 4.1. Optical system of the Spekker photometer (see text). A calibrated drum varies one aperture to a known proportion of the other through a screw thread.

which gives about the optimum plate-reading conditions. The dynamically balanced single sector, mounted directly on the motor shaft, rotates at high speed and is unnervingly close to the fragile and costly cells. *Pace* the experts, I do not believe this high speed is necessary: what *is* necessary in quantitative sector spectrometry is that the total number of revolutions shall be large enough for one more or less not to be significant. The idea of using a single sector, instead of wasting 50% of the light against the blank area of a second sector, is however a welcome break-away from tradition and, so far as I can see, makes no difference in practice except to halve the necessary length of exposure.

The coming of the Spekker photometer practically ended all experiments of this nature. Here a condensed spark light source, between alloy steel electrodes to give long life and a multitude of emission lines, is mounted as in Fig. 4.1 near a pair of beam-splitting rhombs. The twin beams pass through two stationary rectangular apertures, one adjustable and in line with the solvent cell, the other fixed and aligned with the sample. Unless it was to simplify drum-calibration, I have often wondered why rectangular apertures were chosen; the adjustable aperture is markedly off-centre at high absorbance readings. A pair of V-notched slides, giving a diamond-shaped aperture central at all settings, seems preferable. But the simpler rectangle certainly works well in practice, and being out of focus its position is uncritical. Both beams are focused and brought side-by-side on the entrance slit of the spectrograph. Exposures are measured in seconds instead of minutes, which is just as well, because the noise is shatteringly loud even when the spark is boxed-in.

REFINEMENTS TO THE SPEKKER PHOTOMETER

On the principle that things seem to need less attention when they are easy to get at, I advise mounting the electrodes, as shown in Plate 2, on a stationary lead-lined *lid* with a detachable *box* rather than vice versa. The culmination of sundry refinements introduced over a period of ten years is shown in Fig. 4.2 and Plate 2, and has been published in detail (Edisbury, 1948). One of the more important features is the electrode ' grip ' by means of a spring mounted well out in the relatively cool laboratory air away from the heat and corrosive fumes generated by the spark. The outboard springs do not tire and the electrodes no longer work loose and slide out of adjustment as a result of over-heating. Only spark erosion of the electrode chisel-edges causes any drift from good adjustment, and this is slow.

The accessory shown in Plates 2 and 3 simplifies adjustment of the gap. This device would, of course, be almost useless without the help of an optical bench photometer mounting, like the Barfit Accessory Bar, to enable the photometer to retain alignment with the spectrograph. Slide the Spekker photometer bodily a few cm away from the slit and view the spark gap through the eyepiece (in this case borrowed from a wavelength spectrometer). Compress the springs on the electrode holders in turn, remove each electrode and grind both ends to a blunt chisel shape: an unworn end is then available when wanted, at a moment's notice. Replace the electrodes and gently ease them into the position that gives an

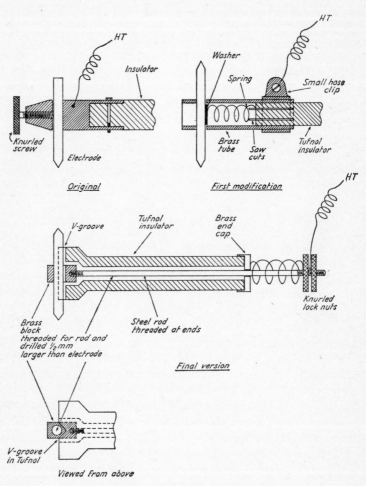

Fig. 4.2. Evolution of an electrode-holder.

image in the eyepiece looking like Fig. 4.3. Then withdraw the 'periscope', replace the silencing box, and slide the photometer back into position.

The on-off switch for the spark is, of course, in the primary circuit of the transformer (an out-door neon sign transformer is recommended for ruggedness). The best switch, I found, was a tilting mercury switch, ' on ' in the horizontal position with the little pool connecting the terminals, and ' off ' when lifted at one end. On an a.c. supply there is no arcing. Ordinary metal contacts wear out and/or corrode very quickly; the mercury surface renews itself and operates in an inert atmosphere.

On each plate there are several exposures. Eight of them are expended in photographing a photometric standard (q.v.). This sacrifices about a quarter of the available photographic area but is well worth while if quantitative work is being attempted. I

Idealized   As observed

FIG. 4.3. Image of spark gap seen through eyepiece.

recommend the following procedure as being in the long run less irksome and more dependable than others I have tried:

(1) Adjust electrodes as above.

(2) Check adjustment photographically by running a few exposures, at absorbance intervals of 0·05, below and above the nominal value of the standard. Develop the plate and read off the ' zero error ' to be applied to the next set of exposures. If the reading does not differ from the nominal by more than 0·02, proceed with the next plateful of ' real ' exposures on a genuine sample, *without touching the electrodes*.

(3) When this plate is completed, inspect the electrodes as above, and readjust them if necessary. Mere inspection does not alter the adjustment. Then run another four exposures on the standard, the two middle ones being aimed at ' bracketing ' (i.e. lying just above and just below) the nominal.

(4) Photograph a wavelength scale at the top and bottom of the plate.

(5) Develop the plate and examine it. Regard the last exposures on the standard as belonging to the *next* plate. More often than not, this standard will again be acceptable (within ± 0.02 of nominal). If so, carry on with the next plate, without upsetting the adjustment. If not, readjust and start again at (2) above. The first half of the plate just completed was probably reliable, being covered by the standard on the previous plate; the second half is open to grave suspicion and should be repeated after an acceptable set of standard exposures has been obtained.

The whole exercise depends on the sandwiching of a series of 'sample' exposures between two standard sets, without any intervening adjustments. The likelihood that the spark gap will wander out of adjustment, and then spontaneously drift back again to normal in time for the second standard, is sufficiently remote to lend confidence.

That is why I called our much-used standard a 'Link with Sanity' (see Chapter 15).

The photometric (or *OD*) standard that I used in this way for many years was made for me by Hilger's from an optically good piece of Wood's glass, showing the usual transmission band at 360 mμ. It was ground and polished to such a thickness that the extinction at peak transmission was just under 1·2, and then sent to the National Physical Laboratory, Teddington, for calibration. (In the U.S.A. the appropriate official body would be the National Bureau of Standards, Washington, DC). The NPL Certificate confirmed that, subject to an almost insignificant temperature gradient affecting the third decimal place, the extinction was 1·18 at 360 mμ at 20°C. So in standardizing plates the photometer was set at 1·10, 1·15, 1·20 and 1·25, and the transmission peak had to fall between the two middle exposures before the adjustment of the electrodes was accepted as suitable for absorption spectrometry. If the *OD* reading was an estimated 1·18, readings on the rest of the plate were taken at their face value, uncorrected; if the standard showed, say, 1·16, a correction of 0·02 was added to each reading. This was fairly sound in theory and worked well in practice. Plate readings outside the range 0·9–1·3 were never taken seriously because of obscure photographic and probably also physiological idiosyncrasies. I imagine that limitations of eye-response were as much to blame as any vagaries of the silver halide emulsion.

PLATE READING

When reading a plate I never found any advantage in using a microdensitometer for matching intensities. A photographic absorption spectrogram is very different from an emission spectrum, where a microdensitometer is essential for quantitative comparisons of pairs of lines. Maybe, under ideal conditions of leisurely processing, match-points could be dependably picked out by a photocell and galvanometer; but certainly not under wartime stress and hurry in a commercial laboratory. The trained eye

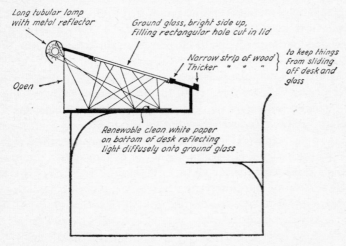

FIG. 4.4. Viewing stand made from an old school desk. Intensity of light is varied by a rheostat at the side of the desk. The metal reflector is adjusted to give as nearly as possible uniform illumination of the white paper or a flat sheet of bright metal.

can make allowances for specks of dirt, developer stains, imperfections in the emulsion; a detecting instrument can't; it takes things too literally as it finds them.

For ease of plate examination, a so-called viewing stand was made, to provide a bright uniform surface as a background for the spectrograms. Over the years modifications were, of course, introduced without altering the basic principle. Fig. 4.4 shows the sort of thing I would design now. An old school desk forms the starting point. The plate rests in a shallow recess just larger than itself, with a sheet of ground glass beneath, plain side up.

Below this, at an appropriate angle, is a domestic mirror or (in a well-endowed laboratory) a sheet of polished stainless steel. Behind and out in the cooling air is a long festoon bulb with a metal reflector beyond it, spreading the light into a roughly rectangular pattern on the mirror, and thence to the lower surface of the ground glass, without any measurable heat. A rheostat controls the illumination to suit the external conditions. If someone could devise a means of controlling the intensity of a fluorescent strip light, that would be better still. Much could be done by interposing further sheets of ground glass or ' milk ' glass, even tracing paper. The ' best ' degree of brightness is a matter of personal opinion, but everyone agrees that uniformity is desirable. Some, too, like the spectrogram magnified: $2\times$ is suitable, as provided by those 4-inch (10-cm) lenses on three legs that are sold for elementary biology classes.

As often as not, plates are examined either wet or after hurried near-drying with acetone. Hold the plate horizontally, ' balance ' a few ml of acetone on the wet emulsion, tilting the plate slightly this way and that for even distribution and to prolong contact with the acetone; drain off; repeat if necessary. Evaporate the residual acetone with a jet of *just*-warm dry air, or by judiciously ' fanning ' the plate through the air of the laboratory. Heat melts photographic gelatine into interesting but so far unprofitable patterns. Match-points are ' spotted ' with a nearly dry nib carrying ordinary ink. An acetone-dried plate can be ' spotted ' immediately as successfully (and as irrevocably) as a ' properly ' dried plate; the spots are larger but not so large as to mislead. Each spot confirms and is confirmed by its neighbours, and they all lead the eye round to the maxima and minima just as if they had been plotted on graph paper. I believe in leaving the exposures at and near the peaks clear of spots on the gelatine side, and spotting those exposures only on the glass side of the plate, in case someone (perhaps myself) wants to have another unprejudiced look. The glass has to be as dry and grease-free as possible to keep the spots small. Parallax makes spotting on the glass side more difficult than spotting directly on the gelatine, and as the estimates of two observers can differ by a mμ or two, and maybe 0·03 extinction, you have to choose between permanently marking a plate, and so prejudicing future observers, or taking the mean of several estimates. This, I think, is the better method if you have time.

Ink spots can be easily wiped off glass, but they take gelatine with them.

As an aid to quick extinction reading I advise cutting a slit, say 7 cm × 3 mm, in a thin card and laying the card flat on the dry gelatine side of the plate with this slit bisecting the relevant absorption band. You can then see more distinctly where the changeover occurs from light above, dark below, to dark above, light below, and where the sample lets through the same fraction of radiation as the attenuating member of the photometer (i.e. the adjustable sector, aperture, etc.). The intact area of the card obscures the eye-distracting sections of spectra where the differences between sample and control are glaringly obvious, and allows better mental concentration on the small wavelength range wherein the changeover occurs.

For reading wavelengths, sacrifice an entire plate by photographing on it half-a-dozen wavelength scales. After processing, cut it lengthways into narrow strips, each bearing one scale. These mobile scales can be laid flat on the plate which is to be wavelength-tested, gelatine-to-gelatine to avoid parallax. Use the emission lines on the plate as guides: the conspicuous 3100 AU triplet iron line is particularly convenient. In the complete absence of identifiable lines, scribe a mark right across the plate between two corresponding calibrations near one end of the scales already on the plate, for instance, at the visible end if the spectrum concerns the UV: the gelatine marks easily enough if scratched with a fine point guided by a ruler.

Incidentally, the do-it-yourself enthusiast who has a spare hydrogen lamp can improve the Spekker photometer almost beyond recognition. Some (e.g. Lothian, 1958) claim that the lines in a normal emission spectrogram help in locating match-points. Maybe they do, for some people. I find them distracting, and I prefer continuous spectra for ease of spotting both band-peaks and match-points. Tastes differ. Try for yourself. Remove the entire spark-gap and silencing-box assembly, and mount the hydrogen lamp in spring clips which are themselves mounted on a vertical rod attached to a stiffly-jointed horizontal arm (Fig. 4.5). With the lamp cold, view it through the periscope and manipulate it so that the little aperture in the internal metalware, through which the radiation emerges when the lamp is on, straddles the ' horizon ' midway in the eyepiece field, equally above and below, analogously to Fig. 4.3: part of the aperture will be seen twice over. After gripping the lamp to move it up and down, be careful before using the lamp to wash away any fingermarks from the portion of the envelope in the light-path. The heat of the discharge is apt to bake fingerprints into the surface almost irremovably. The same applies to tungsten lamps. Wipe gently with a clean cloth dipped

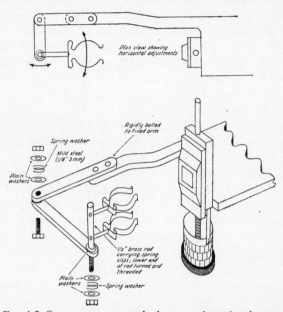

FIG. 4.5. One way to mount a hydrogen or deuterium lamp on a Spekker photometer. The screw on the fixed arm can be tightened and left tight as soon as the position of the lamp along the axis of the photometer has been settled, e.g. from the original electrode position. The nut under the clip-holding rod is slackened slightly to move the lamp sideways. Vertical adjustment of the lamp can be refined by introducing a screwed fitting as in Fig. 7.6; but this is a luxury; this lamp is adjusted while cold and easy to handle.

in detergent, followed by alcohol. (Compare Figs. 7.6 and 7.7, where the lamp has to be moved while hot.)

DIAGNOSTIC USE OF HOLIDAY CAM OR ECHELON CELLS

A qualitative set-up that produces excellent results can be based on the Holiday Logarithmic Cam (1937). Dr Holiday's original

PLATE 2

Above A completely removable spark-silencing box, and the appearance of the electrodes correctly separated after adjustment.

Left Notched echelon cell made by Adam Hilger Ltd, but not manufactured nowadays. (About twice actual size.)

PLATE 3

New design of clamp for modified electrode-holders.
A dismantled clamp is in the foreground.

Eyepiece and mirror through which the image shown in Fig. 4.3
is seen when the electrodes are brought together and illuminated
from behind.

idea was ingenious and superficially simple, but (I believe) over-
ambitious for routine extinction measurements. The principle is
this: Over a fairly wide range, the blackening of a photographic
emulsion is proportional to the logarithm of the intensity of
illumination. If, therefore, a plate moves with logarithmic
acceleration perpendicularly across a spectrum, the blackening is
proportional to, and predictable from, the distance traversed, up
to the point where the effective exposure becomes too short. The
difference between the predicted blackening and the actual
blackening, as assessed by a traversing microdensitometer, is a
measure of attenuation by the sample.

In practice, this demands a degree of photographic expertise
rarely encountered in a laboratory, and I have never attempted
quantitative extinction measurements by this technique. Instead,
I have confined myself to wavelength measurements on complex
spectra. I seriously recommend that as a wavelength-diagnostic
tool the moving plate is worth reviving wherever an old spectrograph and a continuous UV light source are available. Having
realistically abandoned any attempt at quantitative extinction
measurements, there is no point in insisting on accurately logarithmic acceleration. *Smooth* acceleration is however desirable, if only
for the sake of a more pleasing negative. Wavelength accuracy is,
of course, essential, for the whole scheme depends on correctly
spotting and comparing, perhaps after a considerable time interval,
patterns of wavelengths.

Sanders and I (Unilever Research, Port Sunlight; unpublished
work) brashly sought to improve on Holiday's moderate 10:1
velocity ratio by using a 100:1 cam. This understandably imposed
enormous sideways stresses on all parts of the mechanism whenever the high-speed section of the cam contour was reached. So,
after one or two blow-ups, we arranged for the cut-off switch to
operate at about 60:1. We turned out some magnificent plates.
Impure light petroleum, for instance, showed many of the fine
structure features of benzene *vapour* despite the fact that the
benzene was in solution.

Looking back, I can't figure out why we didn't think of running
The Thing backwards, using the 100:1 cam merely to restrain and
decelerate the plate carrier as it tried to fall under gravity, plus
perhaps a little assistance from a light spring. The resulting
' decelerative spectrogram ' would look just the same as an

C

' accelerative spectrogram ' turned over; they should in fact still be directly comparable by superposition as usual, but with one plate the wrong way round. Someone should try it.

To read this general type of spectrogram you spot the mid-points of the pale patches where they become narrow, that is, near the peaks of the absorption bands. (Some prefer to make positives from the spectrograms on paper. By so doing you can vary the contrast to your liking. In this case, the bands show as dark patches. You can also spot any number of prints without spoiling the negative, a fact which can have its advantages.) With a sharp

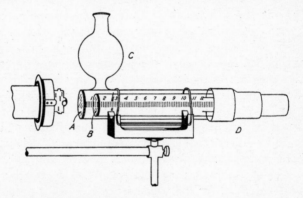

Fig. 4.6. The Baly tube, ' trombone ', or ' trombo-cuvette ', with pre-Barfit mounting.
A   End window, fixed
B   End window, on sliding member
C   Reservoir, corked for volatile liquids
D   Sealing sleeve, needed only for very long path-lengths

point scribe a line across the gelatine side of the whole plate between two corresponding calibrations near one end of the photographed wavelength scales (or rule a similar landmark on a print). Lay one of your mobile scales on the plate or print, gelatine-to-gelatine, using the line as a guide to locate the scale endways. Read and record the wavelengths of the spots.

In identification work it is convenient to cut strips of transparent (tracing) paper and mark on them little vertical lines to show the exact position of the spots, which you can see through the paper. Vary the lengths of the lines as a rough assessment of the relative intensities of the bands. Label the end of each strip with details, including the plate serial number in case a second look is wanted. Comparison of strips is easy because they are transparent, and similarities and differences can be detected in a moment by superposing the strips against a bright background such as on the viewing stand (above).

This sort of qualitative spectrometry is essentially 'single-beam' work; there is no place here for control cell or cuvette filled with solvent alone. For the solution, an adjustable cell is most convenient. I had excellent results from the Baly Tube, which we irreverently but aptly called the 'Trombone' (Fig. 4.6). The calibrations, from 1 to 100 mm, are accurate to unexpectedly fine limits, allowing reproducible settings to be made, and the cell is easily cleaned unless it has been carelessly left dirty and the

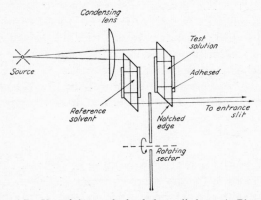

FIG. 4.7. Use of the notched echelon cell shown in Plate 2.

solution has dried between the sliding surfaces. Always dismantle and rinse the cell before putting it away, and keep the dismantled parts separate while stored. To hold the cell in its trough in the light-path, an elastic band is simple to apply and prevents the cell from rotating and spilling its contents. Spontaneous sliding can be stopped by a second elastic band. This is preferable to the rubber sleeve shown, which is usually not needed even at extreme extension and which could contaminate the solution.

An idea that I toyed with but never got round to putting into practice was to mechanize the 'Trombone' and link it with a moving plate (compare Sutton, 1950). As I see it, accelerated motion would not be needed, just a pair of synchronized screw threads moving both the plate-carrier and the sliding member of the 'Trombone' at a uniform rate of a couple of cm/min. On the E.528 the plate could be moved mechanically through the manual wheel with its '1-mm click' feature inactivated. If anyone tries this, please let me know.

Less elegant than the Holiday Cam but covering a vastly greater absorptivity range is an unorthodox but highly practical use of the notched echelon cell (Fig. 4.7) in conjunction with a continuous light source. Three complete sets of exposures can be accommodated on one plate. At a single setting of 1·2, to give optimum photometric performance and ease of reading, use the original solution and two dilutions of 2·5 ml in 20 ml (8:1, to allow overlap with the 10:1 of the echelon cell's path-length range of 1 mm–10 mm). This gives on a single plate 30 pairs of spectra, sample and reference in each pair, covering an absorptivity range of $8 \times 8 \times 10 = 640{:}1$. Frankly, when I tried this I shied away from making any extinction measurements; but anyone who can interpret echelon cell spectrograms conventionally would have no difficulty. Its most practical use is as with the Holiday cam plate— qualitative 'spotting' of patterns of fine details.

PROCESSING

Photographic details are largely a matter of personal choice. My own preference is for the nearest present equivalent to the old Ilford Iso-Zenith plate, developed fairly vigorously to give medium contrast. Much depends on what is available locally. Certainly very high contrast and very soft gradation should both be avoided. Each box of plates carries adequate printed instructions for processing. I favour, unless they are specifically contra-indicated, a dilute acetic acid rinse or 'short stop' between the alkaline developer and the acid fixer (to 'kill' the developing action and prolong the life of the fixer) and a little formalin in the fixing bath to toughen the gelatine.

One thing that is not a matter of choice but of stern necessity is to keep a permanent register of every plate—ideally (though I never did this myself) in duplicate, in case the register gets mislaid. Keep the cleaner version in the laboratory office. Before developing a plate, write its reference number in pencil on the gelatine in one corner. This is easily done ' by feel ' after a little practice, even in the total darkness demanded by panchromatic plates. The final digit is enough at this stage; write the number in full later, when you are spotting the finished plate in ink. At this time also write on some bare patch of the dry gelatine all other relevant details, copied from the register, which should have columns headed: Plate Number, Date, Sample Description and/or Reference, Concentration, Cuvette thickness, Solvent, Remarks (a wide column), Operator's Initials.

The fully dried plates can be stored in their original boxes. A box that held a dozen wrapped plates will hold twenty unwrapped. Write the numbers on both ends of the boxes: 1–20, 21–40, etc. When you get as far as 999 you can decide whether to go on to an alphabetical prefix or continue with digits. It depends on how many plates you get through per month.

Be sure to keep the plates dry. If they stick together through damp, salvage may be impossible, but it is worth trying because they are useless while they remain stuck. Immerse them in *cold* water containing a little detergent or other wetting agent and leave them overnight. They should slide apart. If they do, wipe them gently with thoroughly wet cotton wool, dry overnight, and this time take better precautions for dry storage.

Now that recording spectrophotometers, or at least some of them, have reached new heights of resolving power, there is less need for the moving photographic plate (or echelon cell) except as a standby. The only way to tell is to try for yourself. Run a very small droplet of benzene down one of the two inner (ground) side faces of a 10 mm cuvette, blow gently across the top to vaporize the liquid, seal with a lid and record from 240 to 280 mμ, using the single-beam mode of operation, a slow scanning speed, and a narrow slit. Examine especially the 260 mμ region. Here there should be at least a couple of needle-sharp peaks a little more than 10 AU apart, with—if you are lucky—another just visible between them. If the recorder chart doesn't show this degree of resolution, a moving plate with ' trombo-cuvette ' (or a pair of echelon cells) plus a continuous light source is probably worth while.

CHAPTER 5

GENERAL WORKING INSTRUCTIONS

VISUAL INSTRUMENTS

Seeing is believing
OLD SAW

At first sight there is little obvious need nowadays ever to use a visual instrument for absorption spectrometry, but the wavelength spectrometer is such a highly versatile device that it should never be thrown out unless space is very short indeed when the laboratory ' goes all photoelectric '. Even the oldest model can, time permitting, be put to good use as a supplement to more modern equipment. Among other things, it can prove yet another comforting ' link with sanity ' when a recorded chart of the visible region shows unexpected features. Maybe they will still strain the credulity; but if you can see them as well as record them, they are probably real.

The operative words above are ' space ' and ' time permitting '. Unless you have plenty of time and space to spare, don't attempt to reconstitute an old spectrometer if the units are not mountable on an optical bench (e.g. the Hilger Barfit accessory bar). Your success will last only until someone dusts the apparatus. As an exercise for students, optical alignment is, of course, magnificent in a soul-searing sort of way; but it is out of place in a routine laboratory, where day-to-day problems provide more than enough chastening experiences.

Having rescued a properly mounted or mountable wavelength spectrometer in dirty but otherwise sound condition, the first thing to do is to look for the reference number and ask the manufacturers for the relevant instruction book. In most cases this will be very rewarding. These notes are intended merely as a supplement.

PREPARATION

Clean the prism and lenses with re-distilled methylated spirit and/or distilled water containing a little detergent on a wad of cotton-wool, taking care not to touch the operative light-faces with the fingers. It might be worth asking for an opinion on ' blooming '. Probably you can see a faint outline of where the prism should stand on the detachable prism table. If it has moved, slack off the securing clamp, move the prism back by hand to as nearly as possible the original position, insert a thin piece of cork under the clamp, tighten the clamp very lightly, and gently tap the prism into position with a pencil. Don't tighten fully until you have checked the wavelength at three points, and even then let it be only finger-tight. Take particular care to prevent the operating arm of the slow-motion table from springing back against the point of the operating screw on the wavelength drum spindle. This can upset the adjustment by several $m\mu$, and might mean having to renew the spindle.

Wavelengths, as read off from the calibrated drum, should agree with the position of the little pointer seen in the eyepiece. This pointer is illuminated at will from above by swivelling a small mirror mounted on top of the eyepiece and sliding one of a selection of coloured filters into position. The plane of the pointer is fixed. Within this plane it can be moved vertically to just ' nick ' the lower edge of the spectrum, and sideways for the final fine wavelength adjustment. The pointer is therefore the first item to focus, by sliding the eyepiece tube. All other focusing is affected by this setting, and follows a logical sequence from here right back to the light source.

Mount a neon pilot lamp (one watt or so) permanently alongside the entrance slit so that its light can be directed whenever needed into the slit by swinging the right-angled ' comparison prism '— which acts as a mirror—into the appropriate position. Neon gives a strong line at 5852 AU. Bring this into focus by means of the telescope control just beyond the eyepiece. Because a line is an image of the slit, you get a sharp image of the slit jaws, on which specks of dust and dirt (if any) show up in silhouette. Open the slit jaws to about 1 mm and remove the dirt with a match stick sharpened to a chisel shape. Nowadays slit jaws are made of stainless steel and have a safety stop to prevent their closing nearer than 0·002 mm. The slit control only opens the jaws; they are closed by a spring. Make sure the guides are not corroded and that the jaws move freely, but be sparing in lubrication. Many older slits are fairly soft and easily damaged, possibly by near-closure on large specks of hard dust. If they have at any time been damaged they are worth having trued up professionally. Damaged slit jaws, like dust-specks on them, result in horizontal lines along the spectrum at normal narrow slit-widths; unless damage or dust is equally distributed between the top and bottom halves of the field of view—an unlikely condition—you can't match the two halves of the field of view accurately. Clean slits are essential.

For photometrically analogous reasons, the slit jaws *must* be parallel. At small slit-widths, non-parallelism means that the light will be more restricted for one beam than for the other, an effect exaggerated by any diffraction that may occur when the jaws almost touch. The use of a photometric standard covers-up this defect, but it at least undesirably increases the zero error and the correction that has to be applied.

Powerful illumination is necessary unless you are going to work in a darkened room. I would advise at least 100 candle power. Two aptly named Pointolite lamps are available: 100 c.p. working off direct current; 150 c.p. off alternating current. In each, a small tungsten ball is heated to incandescence by direct electronic bombardment from a plate which is heated initially by an attached heating coil and which, when the coil is switched off, is thereafter kept hot enough for thermionic emission by the radiant heat from the adjacent incandescent ball itself. Radiative losses to the surroundings prevent too much temperature build-up on chain reaction lines. For quantitative photometric measurements, the d.c. version is preferred because the ' point ' is less liable to wander; but for the sort of confirmatory work I have in mind, the more powerful a.c. light is, I think, slightly preferable. A narrower slit can be used to advantage: in particular—and especially if the slit is unsymmetrical, i.e. with one jaw fixed—wavelength readings are more reliable, and the spectrum is inherently purer with a narrow slit.

ADJUSTMENT

The rest of the equipment can now be assembled on the Barfit bar: the photometer (probably a Hilger-Nutting); the stand carrying the cells; the light shield with two part-spherical lenses; and the light source. The photometer's own lenses demand that its position must be within a few mm of the slit. The light shield must be adjusted so that its centre is level with the source and the two beams are parallel and fall squarely on the entrance windows on the photometer. Tobacco smoke is a good indicator of light-beam location. Mount the cell holder so that the cells are at the same heights and in the same vertical plane as the two beams. They are insensitive as to lengthways position. The air-cooled lamp housing will probably not fit in the position shown in Plate 4, but may have to stick out vulnerably beyond the end of the bar. If so, increase the size of the grub-screw that prevents the housing from turning on its stand. Better, get a longer bar.

The Hilger-Nutting photometer works by a simple system of polarizing prisms (Fig. 5.1 and Plate 4). Two separate light beams

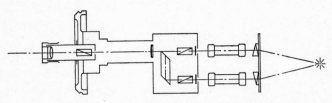

FIG. 5.1. Optical layout of the Hilger-Nutting photometer.

pass first through a pair of fixed Nicols orientated at right angles, then through a rhomb which directs them side by side through a third Nicol, and so into the entrance slit of the spectrometer. Rotation of this third Nicol from its balancing mid-position decreases the intensity of one beam and increases the intensity of the other. At an angle θ, $I_0/I = \tan^2 \theta$, and the absorbance of a specimen when the beams match is therefore $2 \log \tan \theta$. The scale is engraved with absorbances from 0 to infinity. If it is cleaned with a fine metal polish it is easy to read even at the closely packed but most useful calibrations just below 2.

Looking through the eyepiece when the photometer is in position, you see two sections of continuous visible spectrum, one above the other, just touching if everything is in correct adjust-ment. The horizontal width or wavelength range of the visual field is determined by how you have set two sliding shutters in the eyepiece. The vertical dimensions depend on the photometer, the diaphragm at the entrance slit, and another diaphragm just inside the eyepiece; adjustment of this last is obvious when you unscrew the eyepiece. How large you set the vertical dimension is mainly a matter of taste, unless you are seeking the utmost accuracy in photometric measurements. For our present purpose I like it as large as the photometer allows. To me, this is easier on the eyes, and I get better results that way.

If you withdraw the eyepiece completely you see a coloured image of the glowing tungsten ball, etc. Operate the photometer. If two slightly separated images appear and disappear alternately, slide the lamp housing and shield-cum-lenses simultaneously along the bar till the images coincide exactly. A wooden distance piece is useful to maintain the correct separation of lamp and shield while you do this. With suitable workshop facilities the shield and lenses can be fixed to the lamp-housing stand.

MEASUREMENT

For quantitative photometric measurements with the Hilger-Nutting, most people prefer to keep within the absorbance range $1 \cdot 6$–$2 \cdot 0$ ($2 \cdot 5$–$1 \cdot 0\% T$). The probable error of a single OD reading is about $0 \cdot 02$ over the whole range, so that at low readings it amounts to a considerable percentage. The eye soon tires, but the mean of 5 or 6 *quick* readings is reasonably reliable. Take your hand off the photometer control between readings, before looking at the scale. This avoids bias. I used to calibrate the instrument—and myself— during every 'session' by making 10 quick readings on an NPL-certificated glass standard to obtain a zero error (used as on page 32).

In 'qualitative' use, i.e. determining positions rather than intensities of absorption bands, the best set-up in my opinion is to have the test solution in a 'trombo-cuvette' (page 38) and to use the photometer as (1) a rough check on absorbance and (2) a means of obtaining optimum light intensity in the eyepiece for an accurate check on the wavelengths of absorption peaks. Absorption bands appear as patches darker than the rest of the spectrum. To my eyes, these regions of selective absorption superpose a brownish hue onto whatever colour is natural to that part of the visible spectrum. With the widest field of view available, gently oscillate the wavelength drum and adjust the ' Trombone' to give the narrowest easily seen brown patches. They will, of course, be seen only in the ' test' beam, so by means of the photometer adjust both beams to comparable and compatible intensities. This makes it even easier to see the shadows on one spectrum juxtaposed against the other, uniformly attenuated, spectrum. They are detectable even when they are too faint for photometry, so long as you keep them gently moving. Surprisingly, you may be able to detect the movement of the fainter shadows more easily if you turn your eye slightly away from them. The sensitive cones of the fovea centralis are less good than the surrounding retinal rods at detecting shadowy movements.

The narrowest shadows are the peaks of absorption bands. Judge their mid-points and bring them level with the pointer. If need be, alter the illumination of the pointer to the most nearly correct hue to decrease or eliminate parallax. Often the pointer is better left unilluminated, just a black silhouette making a little nick in the edge of the spectrum. With practice, the corresponding readings on the wavelength drum should be accurate to well within ± 1 mμ.

A visual check can be useful to confirm or contradict a ' visible' chart or corresponding results obtained on a manual instrument. Suppose, for instance, that a fairly broad band is suspected to comprise two nearly flat maxima with a shallow depression between them. Is this genuine? The practised eye will detect a light-dark-light-dark-light alternation in a genuine case, even when chart or other readings show the depression to be on the borderline of photometric experimental error. The eye tends (fortunately) to exaggerate such things. Maybe the same phenomenon (unfortunately) makes matching more difficult by introducing mental conflict.

CHAPTER 6

GENERAL WORKING INSTRUCTIONS

PHOTOELECTRIC SPECTROMETERS

Familiarity breeds expertise
MODERN INSTANCE

Until the late nineteen-twenties the photoelectric spectrophoto-meter was a collector's piece and, with a couple of notable exceptions from Hilger in the U.K. and General Electric in the U.S.A., usually home-made. A fortunate circumstance brought Professor Beckman and Dr Cary into collaboration, and with a far-sightedness rare even in America they designed and put into successful mass-production the original manually operated Beckman Model DU. Only superficial refinements have been necessary in over a quarter of a century.

After the 1939–45 War, two British firms showed what could be done by improving on, without departing far from, a basically good design. The Unicam SP.500, for instance, has a more solidly constructed chassis carrying virtually unchanged Beckman optics with improved electronics. The Hilger Uvispek understandably took longer to develop and went further with all-mains electronics and improved optics: instead of the entering and emerging light beams passing alongside the prism, thus producing a minor sideways fuzziness of the image across the exit slit, they pass above the prism, so that any fuzziness lies *along* the slit, with less impair-ment of spectral purity. Another pleasant refinement was to arrange a simple swivelling mirror to select light from either the hydrogen lamp or the tungsten filament, with a third intermediate position, between lamps, for use with an external source to provide wavelength calibration lines (Cd, Hg, etc.).

In practice all three instruments are broadly similar in perfor-mance and almost identical in operation. There are minor differences in ' feel ' and one major difference when the quartz prism of the Uvispek is interchanged (in the laboratory) for dense glass, which curtails the UV range and spreads the visible spectrum so that greater separation of visible absorption bands can be obtained.

I believe that at least a superficial knowledge of the inner workings of any device is necessary before one can use it intelligently and get the best results out of it, whether it is a car or a sewing machine or a spectrophotometer.   More than this is optional. If you do delve further you soon acquire a reputation as a pundit; but you get little credit for your work, and rarely have a chance to immobilize the instrument(s) for long enough to do anything interesting that the Man from the Works couldn't do in

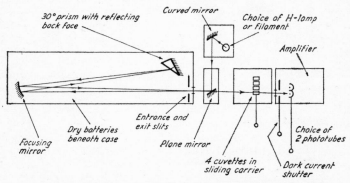

FIG. 6.1. Diagrammatic layout of the original Beckman DU. Compare with Figs. 6.2 and 6.3 for important differences in detail in nominally similar instruments. The emergent ray passes below the plane mirror.

a fraction of the time. So I skim lightly over the essentials, much as the Owner's Manuals issued by some car firms do, emphasizing only those items that don't need ' Special Equipment '.

Figures 6.1, 6.2, and 6.3 outline the original DU, SP.500 and Uvispek optical systems. Figure 6.4 further shows how visible dispersion increases when the silica prism is replaced by glass. In each of these spectrometers light from the source is mirror-focused on the entrance slit. A mirror is free from chromatic aberration: every wavelength that *is* reflected follows the same path. Since the spectrum is a continuous succession of images of the entrance slit, spectral purity depends in the first instance on a narrow entrance slit, and nothing can be done subsequently to

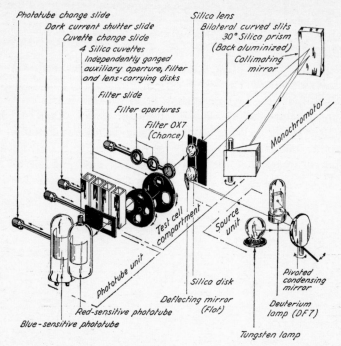

Fig. 6.2. Diagrammatic layout of the Unicam SP.500. (By courtesy of Unicam Instruments Ltd.)

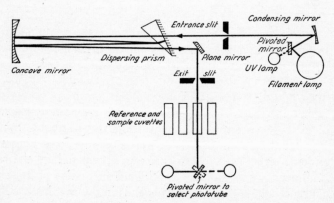

Fig. 6.3. Diagrammatic layout of the Uvispek.

remedy imperfections introduced at this stage: one can only add to them. Once past this primary hazard the ray falls on a concave mirror at the far end of the instrument, which sends it to a 30° prism back near the entrance. The first face of the prism refracts the ray into a small spectrum which is reflected internally from the opposite face, along almost the same path. As it emerges from the prism at a slight angle, the bunched-up spectrum is refracted a

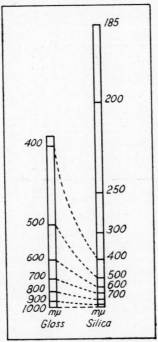

FIG. 6.4. How the dispersion of silica (Spectrosil) compares with the dispersion of glass.

second time, to fall again on the concave mirror and be focused as a long horizontal strip of spectrum across the vertical exit slit. The wavelength control fractionally rotates the prism and so moves the spectrum across the slit. The nominal wavelength as shown on the scale corresponds with the part of the spectrum which at that moment is opposite the centre of the slit. Being finite, the slit lets through a little of the spectrum on either side of this, a fraction of a mμ under favourable conditions, several mμ if the slit is wide in relation to the dispersion in that region. This ' spectral impurity ' is usually so small that it can be ignored. It becomes serious only when the peak of an absorption band is narrow relative to the spectral slit-width—a self-explanatory expression indicating the wavelength range emerging from the instrument at a given slit setting. Obviously, the slit must be substantially narrower than an absorption band or the whole band could escape detection. Not only, therefore, must the entrance slit be narrow to ensure a reasonably pure spectrum at the start, but the exit slit must also

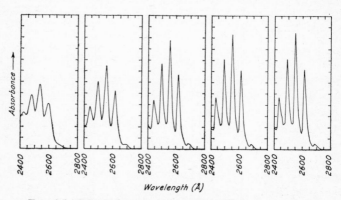

Wavelength (Å)

FIG. 6.5. Effect of spectral slit-width. The same sample of benzene in cyclohexane was scanned with different mechanical slit-widths on the same spectrometer. Both position and persistence of maxima are affected. Approximate spectral slit-widths at 2800 Å are 44, 15, 5, 1·8, and 1 Å. (Bauman, 1962; by courtesy of John Wiley & Sons Inc.) Compare the much smaller effect on a broad maximum (Fig. 17.1c).

be narrow to cope with the superimposed effects of selective absorption. Sometimes for this reason the two slits are mechanically coupled.

Use as narrow a slit-width as circumstances allow. Fig. 6.5 from Bauman's *Absorption Spectroscopy* (Wiley, 1962) shows how much effect the slit can have on an absorption spectrum. Admittedly this is a rather extreme case; but it does arouse the suspicion that many such published complex spectra have little quantitative significance. At least when the spectrum comprises a number of narrow bands, I think it good practice to specify the slit-width among the other relevant parameters. Manufacturers will usually supply a table or graph relating wavelength and spectral slit-width.

SLIT-WIDTHS

Slit-widths recommended by the makers for giving an effective spectral slit-width of 10 AU with the Uvispek

Wavelength (mμ)	Slit-width (mm) Silica prism	Glass prism
200	1·50	—
250	0·62	—
300	0·34	—
400	0·13	0·68
500	0·07	0·28
600	0·04	0·15
700	0·03	0·09
800	0·02	0·06

In a prism instrument the extreme visible spectrum becomes crowded, and a slit-width suitable for the UV would encompass perhaps 50 mμ in the red; but by correct choice of a brighter light source a much narrower slit is generally possible. That is one reason why you are recommended to change from the hydrogen or deuterium discharge lamp to the tungsten filament for wavelengths above 350–400 mμ (28600–25000 cm^{-1}). Conversely, the hydrogen lamp is much brighter in the UV, partly because the tungsten filament as usually supplied has a glass (not silica) envelope, partly because the hydrogen emission itself becomes much stronger towards 200 mμ, so much so that in some early hydrogen lamps a thin glass window was used fairly successfully. Fused silica is, of course, superior, especially the UV grade of Spectrosil which transmits well down to 180 mμ (55600 cm^{-1}) or lower. (The IR grade, designed for the other end of the spectrum, begins to absorb appreciably below 280 mμ, 35700 cm^{-1}. See Fig. 9.1.)

In order to use the smallest practicable slit-width you may have to compensate for the decreased light coming in through the entrance slit by increasing the 'sensitivity'. The control so marked varies the gain of the amplifier, and at very high gains there is often some instability and trembling of the galvanometer needle. If it won't keep still, you can't read it; but although irritating and tiring to the eyes, a slight tremor does not seem to affect reproducibility, and the shape of the spectrum you obtain is certainly nearer the truth. You have to choose between a steady needle that doesn't mean quite so much, and an annoying balancing act that, with patience, gives truer results. You can't always have a steady needle and the truth both at once (compare Heisenberg's Principle!) though with a modern instrument a good compromise is usually achieved. In some recording instruments the conflicting requirements can be reconciled by using a very narrow slit and recording very slowly. The problems of accuracy and reproducibility are discussed in Chapter 17.

INTERNAL ECONOMY OF MANUAL INSTRUMENTS

The total length of light-path in the DU, SP.500 and Uvispek is about the same as in a Medium Quartz Spectrograph: including light source, about a couple of metres. This doubling back upon itself of the light ray is common to all commercial photoelectric spectrometers. Without it you would never get enough dispersion in a compact instrument. The extra focal length that can thus be accommodated also allows greater freedom from optical aberration and the use of physically wider slits for the same spectral slit-width. In practice this also means that the numbers on the slit-width control can more closely represent the truth without the need for too much micro-machine-work and unnecessary cost. The length of spectrum—physical length, that is, not range of wavelengths— that can be accommodated in a photoelectric instrument, where the spectrum is moved across the slit, is not, of course, limited as in a spectrograph by the size of the photographic plate and carrier. The ends of the spectrum would in fact, but for the casing and various baffles, project well beyond the upright sides of the instrument and out into the laboratory. Unless the inside of the casing is well matt-blackened, reflection of the temporarily unused ends of the spectrum can be a powerful source of stray light.

These three spectrophotometers are neither true double-beam instruments, in the sense of the Spekker (Fig. 4.1) nor yet, despite the fact that only one light beam is used, properly single-beam. They are ' double-beam-in-time ' instruments: whereas in a true double-beam photometer the two beams are in simultaneous operation (' double-beam-in-space '), here the same beam is used alternately for blank and for test solution, with an appreciable time-interval between. With two beams simultaneously emanating from one light source, any fluctuations in source intensity occur identically in both, and so cancel out; here precautions must be taken to keep the single beam steady between checking the blank and testing the solution.

For a tungsten filament source this is not difficult. A large-capacity storage battery that has run for an hour or two since being fully charged will give a steady enough current for several hours. This condition is not always easy to fulfil in a hurry. An alternative is to insert a barretter between battery and lamp and have a trickle-charger ' on ' all the time while the lamp is in use. But the cleanest, most convenient, and in the long run cheapest, wherever a.c. mains are available, is a constant-output transformer, 6 or 12 volts according to lamp. The thermal inertia of the filament smooths out the a.c. ripple and the light remains steady within $\pm 0.1-0.2\%$ for hours. You should establish for each lamp how long it takes after switching on to attain a steady state. Some lamps are steady almost at once; others take several minutes to settle down.

The hydrogen or deuterium lamp, on the other hand, requires a far more complex stabilizer (Fig. 7.3) when it is used with a single-beam instrument. Much ingenuity has been shown in obtaining the required 60–80 volts d.c., kept steady within limits of around ± 0.01 volt. This can be, and has been, achieved in a variety of ways (Cannon, 1960), but all can be regarded as elaborate variants of the same sort of electronic feed-back that gives a roughly constant volume of sound on a radio set. A slight rise in output is fed back into an earlier part of the circuit in such a way as to decrease the output; a fall is similarly employed to increase it. The art lies apparently in so designing the apparatus that the resulting automatic adjustment between the imposed limits is well damped and does not show on the galvanometer. If it does, it takes the form of a slow rhythmic oscillation of the needle that makes photometric readings impossible, the spectroscopic equivalent of what we used to call ' motor boating ' in the early days of radio. The remedy will be found in the manufacturer's instructions. Otherwise maintenance is minimal—mainly a matter of reconciling the opposite requirements of good ventilation (for cooling) and dust-freedom. A copious supply of *clean* compressed air is handy in any laboratory, and can be used here to blow away dust periodically. Dust is inevitable in well-ventilated parts. But it must be clean air. Inadvertent sand-blasting with rust flakes from the pipe, or spraying with oil mist from the compressor, is to be avoided. More safely, a ' suction-brush ' can be used (Fig. 6.17).

The original Beckman DU and Unicam SP.500 amplifiers were

battery operated. The electrical circuit of a DU is shown in Fig. 6.6 and is fairly typical of the general idea, though easier to follow than

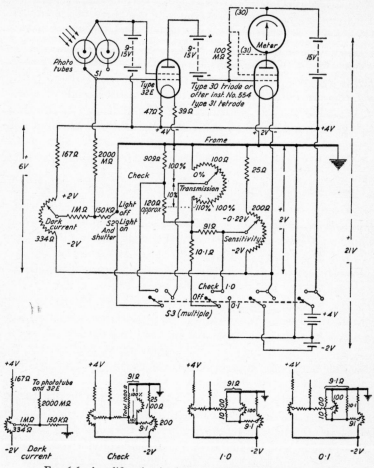

FIG. 6.6. Amplifier circuit of the early Beckman DU. Note the constancy of the total resistance (9·1 + 91 ohms) and the 10:1 ratio under all conditions. To achieve this, compound resistors are adjusted to less than their nominal values. The 'check' tapping and '100%' on the transmission potentiometer are adjusted to exactly equal potential.

most. It comprises a 2-valve d.c. amplifier which raises the initial current from either photocell (phototube), selected by switch S1, to a level sufficient to operate a moving-coil balance meter. A multi-turn potentiometer adjusts the external voltage applied to the phototube so as to balance exactly its slight electronic emission when not illuminated (' dark current '); the relevant light shutter is coupled to S2. A further potentiometer, appropriately calibrated, allows comparison of phototube potentials generated by the light transmitted by the blank and the test sample(s) when the relevant cuvettes are slid into the light beam. In other words, your scale reading simply compares two lengths of potentiometer wire, and tells you either their direct ratio (as $\%T$) or the logarithm of the reciprocal of this ratio [absorbance, extinction or $OD=\log(1/T)=2-\log\%T$; see first part of Chapter 3] on an adjacent calibration of the same dial.

OPERATION OF MANUAL INSTRUMENTS

A four-position switch S3 (' Off ', ' Check ', ' 1·0 ', ' 0·1 ') is ganged to operate four internal circuits simultaneously by being mounted on one spindle:

Position (1) applies the filament heating current to the valves;

Position (2) provides the correct condition for balancing the absorbance potentiometer circuit for the solvent (by definition $100\%T$) without the operator's having to reset the scale to zero OD ($100\%T$) for each reading. The ' 120-ohm approx' resistor shown in the ' Check ' circuit (middle of diagram) is adjusted to as much over 90·9 (i.e. one-tenth of 909) as is demanded by the unused part of the OD potentiometer beyond ' $110\%T$ ', with the ' Check ' tapping and the ' $100\%T$ ' point at equal potential;

Position (3), designated ' 1·0 ', provides a normal OD scale, which means just what the readings say, on which to re-balance the galvanometer when the sample is in the light beam; and

Position (4), marked ' 0·1 ', provides an extended scale, from 1·0 upwards. In this position, an effectively 91-ohm network is changed to 9·1 ohms without altering over-all resistance ($91+9·1=9·1+91$). The result is to lower the voltage across the absorbance potentiometer so that the entire scale now represents one-tenth of the previous radiant energy. This has the effect of dividing the normal $\%T$ figures by 10 or adding 1·0 (i.e. log 10) to each nominal OD reading—at the cost of some loss of responsiveness and the risk of stray-light hazards. The ' 0·1 ' position should therefore be used sparingly and with caution.

Four small circuit diagrams have been added at the bottom to show the circuit elements associated with the four S3 positions above, with all irrelevant circuitry eliminated (Beaven, 1950).

The original diagram (Cary and Beckman, 1941) was modified by Bainbridge-Bell, of Radar fame, to incorporate his favourite and very practical idea of showing zero (' earth ' or ' ground ') potential across about the middle of the circuit, with positive potentials above it and negative below. The circuit shown here is a development of his idea, with his permission and my thanks. A circuit is not a wiring diagram, and is designed to show the electrical rather than the spatial relationships of components. Bainbridge-Bell's ' central earth ' (or, to the juniors, ' geocentric ') idea brings out these relationships more clearly than most, and is worth copying more generally.

It will be noticed that one battery—in real life, a dry battery comprising two standard radio-type 9-volt grid-bias batteries—' floats ' in mid-air, electrically speaking, between the two valves. This makes replacement of the batteries by a mains supply a re-designing job. Proper kits are now available with a different internal set-up, specially suited for running off the mains. They are, however, expensive, more costly perhaps than the monetary value of an old DU. But a new lease of life can be given inexpensively by removing all the dry batteries from under the base to an accessible box outside the instrument. To save possible interaction between parallel leads the use of coaxial cables is a nice refinement and not over-costly.

The convenience of being able to move the wander plugs around to more appropriate battery sockets without having to turn the instrument over is well worth while. On the SP.500 the dry batteries are already accessible through the back of the instrument, and as they are easily reached they rarely give trouble (Joe's Law). The early multi-pin connectors to the amplifier did, however, give trouble and should be replaced by the latest positively locked type, in which the contacting surfaces are rigidly clamped together. Many a curious bout of galvanometer instability has been cured by attention to this matter. *Any* relative movement in a connection causes wavering of the galvanometer needle. In a very old, or less excusably, but still with regrettable frequency, in a very new instrument, defective soldering of circuit connections (' dry joints ') can cause hard-to-trace instability. Insulate a pair of strong eyebrow tweezers by wrapping adhesive PVC tape round them and test each join by giving the wire a sharp tug, taking due precautions against short-circuiting anything and/or giving yourself a shock. Most of the circuit is at a harmless potential, but in some instruments (particularly those involving photomultipliers, which go up to 10^3 volts or thereabouts) there are parts here and there that could give a heart-stopping shock. This is not a job for the unenlightened; you must know your circuit.

When the circuit is ' on ' and a connection is tweaked, a fault reveals itself by wild oscillations of the galvanometer needle. The insulation on the tweezers prevents any effects due to mere earthing by your own body. As solder has a tensile strength of a couple of tons per square inch, don't be afraid to tweak or tug hard. The join will give way only if it is already on the way out. Re-solder it with non-corrosive flux, making sure that the solder properly wets the wire and/or tab, and that it meets the metal at an acute angle, as the sea meets a shallow beach rather than a cliff. The extra mechanical strength that may or may not result from the use of good acid zinc chloride flux doesn't last long unless residual flux is washed off with hot water, and you can't do this in an amplifier. Even minor moisture is out of place: a fingerprint is enough to put a 2000-megohm resistor out of action. Hence the need for those packets or bags of dry silica gel, which must be renewed, or rejuvenated by heat, as soon as the contents begin to discolour. After heating them, let them cool in a good desiccator before replacing them in the instrument. It is a sound practice (but a council of perfection which can rarely be followed in a busy laboratory) to ' let things settle ' again for a few hours after re-assembly, overnight if possible.

NEVER put back the silica gel before it has cooled to room temperature. This applies with even more force to the optical part of the instrument than to the amplifier box, because thermal expansion of the metal parts controlling the wavelength temporarily upsets the adjustment considerably and might even, in extreme cases, have a slight permanent effect, calling for a readjustment. There is much to be said in favour of a thermostat. Some of the more advanced recording instruments are so fitted. Its presence can prevent many an elusive wavelength drift.

The next best thing is an air-conditioned laboratory. This is desirable even if the instrument has its own thermostat, but almost essential if it hasn't. Any box-like structure breathes with changes of temperature, exhaling air during the day, inhaling at night when the air is cooler, *unless* the temperature is kept constant; even then, if one wants to split hairs, changes in barometric pressure cause some slight exchange. To avoid this and at the same time keep the ' internals ' dry and provide a little extra range below 200 mμ (where atmospheric oxygen absorbs radiation strongly) a permanent slow stream of dry oxygen-free nitrogen through the instrument is to be recommended. A small exit should be arranged at a point remote from the point of entry; otherwise the flushing-out process is almost interminable. Progress can be followed by noting how far beyond 200 mμ (500oo cm^{-1}) the instrument will reach after various intervals of time. When stability is attained, the rate of flow can be decreased to a few bubbles a second. A large tube of coloured silica gel traps any airborne droplets that escape from a much smaller wash-bottle (with trap and provision for by-passing when a fast flush-through is needed) containing concentrated sulphuric acid which doubles as a precautionary dehydrator and flow-meter. Usually the nitrogen is already so dry that both acid and gel long outlast the lifetime of a cylinder, in which case the acid can be replaced by oil. Rapid rates of flow are often recommended; sometimes they are necessary; but obviously, for economy and convenience, keep the rate as low as practicable. When you do change to a fresh cylinder, try to arrange that it has already attained laboratory temperature before it is connected up. This saves work for the thermostat. And it is a waste of time to connect up at all unless you are sure the nitrogen is really oxygen-free.

SIMPLIFIED MANUAL INSTRUMENTS

There are several simpler instruments than the three ' classics ' with which I started this chapter. They cover the visible and only the near fringe of the UV, as far as a tungsten filament emits without stress and normal glass optics transmit, say from 750–800 mμ to 350–360 mμ (133oo–125oo to about 280oo cm^{-1}). This simplification roughly halves the purchase price. The same order of accuracy in performance can be expected, however, for they are precision-made. There is in fact much to be said for using such instruments for visible-spectrum work unless a good recording instrument is available, because their dispersion is usually much better than on an instrument that has to cover both UV and visible, and it saves having to change over the prism and

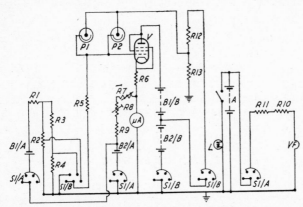

Fig. 6.7. Amplifier circuit of Unicam SP.600 for visible and near-UV.

P1, P2	Phototubes VS 50S and VA 50S
μA	Microammeter
V	Detector and amplifier valve ME 1400
VF	Valve cathode-heater filament, detached for clarity
S1/A, S1/B	Ganged two-deck selector switch, six-pole, four-way
B1/A, B2/A	Dry batteries, 1·5 volt
B1/B, B2/B	Dry batteries, 69 volt
A	12-volt accumulator
L	Light source, 12-volt, 36-watt, pre-focused

R1	100Ω
R2	5 kΩ %T and OD control
R3	875Ω (nominal)
R4	15 kΩ
R5	1000 MΩ
R6	10 kΩ
R7	1000Ω dark-current control
R8	5 kΩ
R9	1 kΩ
R10	10Ω
R11	33Ω
R12	3·3 MΩ
R13	2·2 MΩ

This circuit is readily amenable to all-mains working. (By courtesy of Unicam Instruments Ltd.)

scale on those more versatile instruments where this is possible. In a routine laboratory, even the short time necessary for this is in practice hard to spare.

Examples of full but simple spectrophotometric instruments intended solely for visible and only a little UV use that come to mind are the SP.600 Unicam, Model B Beckman and the Hilger Spectrochem. The first two are prism instruments; the third uses a grating (14600 lines per inch, 575/mm) which gives it

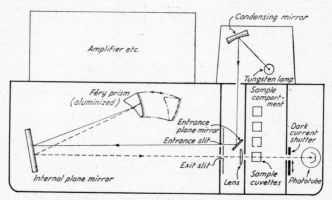

FIG. 6.8. Diagrammatic layout of the Beckman Model B. (By courtesy of Beckman Instruments Inc.)

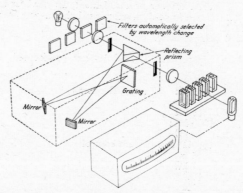

FIG. 6.9. Diagrammatic layout of the Spectrochem.

automatically rectilinear dispersion and therefore a more nearly constant spectral slit-width dependent on lamp intensity and photo-response at different wavelengths. This can be a considerable advantage in some circumstances, for instance in the far red where prism instruments have a decidedly overcrowded wavelength scale and tend towards unusably large spectral slit-widths, although the slit itself is nearly closed. Schematic drawings of these three instruments are shown in Figs. 6.7, 6.8 and 6.9. In each, the light path doubles on its tracks in the familiar manner to provide the desired focal length, etc., as mentioned earlier. And each has its own special ingenuities.

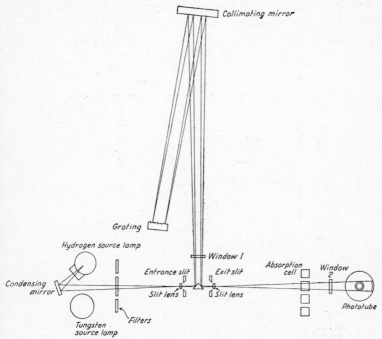

FIG. 6.10. Diagrammatic layout of the Perkin-Elmer Model 139.
(By courtesy of Perkin-Elmer Inc.)

Note for instance the slit mechanism and curved prism of the Beckman B; the efficient yet stable one-valve amplifier on the SP.600; and the novel incorporation of a series of built-in automatically selected filters to minimize stray light in the Spectrochem. The prism in this instrument is used purely as a double plane mirror to increase the light path. This system is also used on the Hitachi Perkin-Elmer 139, a more sophisticated instrument (Fig. 6.10) which normally covers a little on each side of 200–800 mμ and has a printed circuit with several transistors. A point of interest is that the output from the special phototube (with two sets of photo-sensitive surfaces, covering an unusually wide spectral range; see Chapter 8) is capacity-modulated from direct current to alternating current at mains frequency by a magnetically operated vibrating reed, which forms one plate of a condenser whose capacity thus varies synchronously with the mains. Fig. 6.11 shows the arrangement schematically. The a.c. input to this amplifier makes for good stability, as explained in *Electronics for Spectroscopists* (Cannon, 1960). In setting $100\% T$ (zero OD) on the Hitachi P-E 139, parallax due to the curved galvanometer face

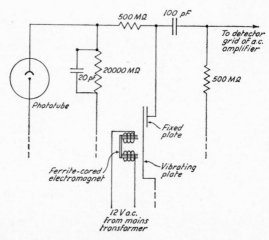

Fig. 6.11. Schematic diagram of vibrating-reed capacity modulator which changes the direct-current output of the photo-tube into alternating current of mains frequency for stable amplification, as used on the Hitachi Perkin-Elmer 139. (By courtesy of Perkin-Elmer Inc.)

can be eliminated by mounting a small reflecting prism at the end of the calibrations so that the operator can see the marks squarely without leaving his/her chair. This zero setting can be made still more exact if a potentiometrically extended scale is first selected (cf. Position 4, p. 57). On the ' 139 ' the extra accuracy persists over the other scales (Dr Beaven and Dr Johnson, private communication). The stability of an a.c. amplifier here justifies the procedure, but the idea is worth cautious trial on other instruments.

In manually operated instruments much the same routine applies, *mutatis mutandis*, to most of them. The main differences depend on the function of the galvanometer. In *null-point* instruments (e.g. DU, SP.500 and 600, Uvispek) only the centre of a short scale is used, and the pointer is returned to the same central position for each absorbance reading, which is shown on a dial or scale connected to, or integral with, the operating knob. A *full-scale* galvanometer, on the other hand, is graduated in absorbances (*OD*) from zero to infinity, and/or in light transmission from 100% to zero, often on adjacent scales. Such galvanometers are necessarily much larger. The longer pointer may be a lightweight metal or plastics needle or a weightless beam of light reflected off a little mirror attached to the moving coil of the galvanometer, which allows a still larger scale. This last system sacrifices some robustness for a gain in sensitivity and possibly accuracy.

(A) NULL-POINT INSTRUMENTS

(1) Switch on and prepare your sample(s) while the instrument is warming up.

(2) Fill the cuvette(s) to a suitable level (see Chapter 9). Some like to do this with the cuvettes already in their carrier; some don't, but prefer to stand them on a layer or two of filter paper where they can be seen better. The important thing is to avoid running any solution over the outside of the operative faces. The streaks thus left behind can be washed off by a judiciously applied stream of solvent from a wash-bottle, followed by wiping with lens tissue; but preferably no contamination at all should occur. Some cuvettes are fitted with lids. Use them, unless they are so badly designed that they encourage seepage.

(3) Place the loaded cuvette carrier *gently* in its movable cradle in the sample compartment, and replace or close the lid gently. There is no excuse whatever for any noise at any stage. Violent haste can waste time. The sudden mechanical shock of clapping the lid or cover back with a clatter can affect the stability of the amplifier (Chapter 17).

(4) Slide the carrier so that the solvent (or blank) cuvette is in the light beam, ready for (6) below. Again be gentle, if only to avoid spillage.

(5) With the ' Off-Check-1·0–0·1 ' switch or its equivalent in the ' check ' position, and the light shutter closed, select a wavelength and the appropriate phototube. Adjust the ' dark current ' control to centralize the galvanometer. Wait a few seconds. The pointer should not move. If it drifts appreciably away from zero in less than half a minute, the instrument either hasn't finished warming up or is unstable and in need of care and attention as indicated in the manufacturer's instruction book. Give it time; but if the pointer persistently drifts the readings won't mean much.

(6) Having balanced a stable dark current, switch-in the ' 1·0 ' condition or its equivalent on the range switch, open the light shutter (*gently*) and reset the galvanometer to its original mid-position (null-point or zero) by adjusting the slit-width. This provides the electrical and optical conditions corresponding by definition to 100% T.

(7) Slide the sample gently into the light beam, reset the galvanometer to mid-position by means of the Absorbance Control (OD, % T), close the dark current shutter as soon as is expedient, to prevent phototube fatigue. This gives you one point on your graph of the absorption spectrum.

For each point on the graph repeat the sequence from (4) to (7) inclusive. More often than not, the dark current will not need re-balancing, but it is better not to take a chance with more than a few readings between checking this. Just how many readings, only experience will tell.

Cover the ' interesting ' parts of the spectrum by taking readings at frequent wavelength intervals, 5 mμ or less around the peaks and troughs of bands, 10 mμ or more elsewhere. When the readings go above 1·0 OD (below 10% T) change the selector switch over to ' 0·1 ' and carry on, adding 1·0 to each OD reading (or divide each % T reading by 10). This takes you up to at least 2·0 (1% T), and even further on some instruments. Readings so obtained may or may not be quantitatively valid (see Stray Light, Chapter 12) but at worst they are useful guides to the extent of dilution required to bring things down to the normal scale. They also give you some idea of how closely Beer's law is being ' obeyed ' (Chapters 2 and 17), which is always useful information to have in case unsuspected fluorescence or micro-cloudiness effects (etc.) occur.

Cuvette holders have spaces to hold 2–5 cuvettes, according to size and design. When studying an unknown solution take advantage of this fact by preparing several dilutions in steps of $2\frac{1}{2}$ (e.g. 2 ml in 5, or 10 in 25) for testing. Two dilutions cover a range of about 6:1; three, 16:1; four, 40:1; and the 'valid-reading' overlap of the photometer itself (assuming a quantita-tively useful range of readings of 0·3–0·9) allows for the detection of ionization and fluorescence effects (etc.). Alternatively, use as many cuvettes of different path-lengths as can be accommodated. *If* the solvent is suitably transparent there is no practical loss of accuracy in using the same compensator for all thicknesses.

Obviously, a *completely* colourless solution does not need testing at any wavelength between 400 and 800 mμ; but be wary; some of the rare earths show intense, needle-sharp bands which, being narrow, absorb very little of the total visible light and so confer hardly any colour even when the readings go right off the map. The effect is almost entirely local and can easily be missed by the unaided eye.

(B) 'FULL-SCALE' GALVANOMETERS

By monitoring how far a calibrated control has to be rotated to restore the pointer to a standard position, the null-point galvano-meter shows the ratio between the respective lengths of potentio-meter wire needed to balance the phototube output under conditions of 'through solvent' (nominal $100\% T$) and 'through sample' illumination. This ratio is expressed either as a percentage ($\% T$) or logarithmically ($2 - \log \% T = OD$). The full-scale galvanometer directly indicates the relative electrical outputs themselves by the magnitude of the different deflections of the pointer away from the $100\% T$ position. The scale isn't calibrated in microamps, of course, but in OD (absorbance) and/or $\% T$ as usual. It is assumed for both systems that the output, before and after amplification, is exactly proportional to the intensity of the light incident on the photo-detector. Fortunately this is true under specified conditions below the light-saturation limit of the phototube, etc.

The sequence of operations is much the same as before, but simpler:

(1) Switch on and allow time for warming up, etc.

(2) Select the required wavelength.

(3) With cuvettes in position and the solvent (blank) in the beam,

set the galvanometer so that it reads zero transmission (absorbance=infinity) when the light shutter cuts off illumination from the detector, and zero absorbance ($100\%\,T$) when the shutter is open.

(4) Slide the sample(s) gently into the light beam and read the galvanometer.

(5) Repeat from (2) to (4) at various wavelengths.

This simpler sequence incurs the minor penalty that, on a usably compact galvanometer scale, the *OD* readings above about $0\cdot7$ (below $20\%\,T$) become overcrowded. In the Spectrochem, a simple electronic attenuation system, on similar lines to that used in null-point instruments, enables you to add $0\cdot5$, $1\cdot0$, $1\cdot5$, to the nominal scale readings. This gives the equivalent of a 20-inch (51-cm) scale as far as ease of reading is concerned. But the usual warning must be given about stray light at high readings, although admittedly it is less than customarily troublesome in the Spectrochem because of the automatic system of light filters.

' Adjustment ' of this type of galvanometer, as far as the normal operator is concerned, usually comprises no more than rotating the suspension of the moving coil through the small fraction of a turn required to bring the pointer, be it needle or light spot, exactly to the graduation marked zero transmission, or infinity on the absorbance scale, under conditions of no illumination of the photo-detector. This is best done initially with the rest of the instrument turned off, in case there is any interaction (there shouldn't be) with the main circuit(s) of the instrument: if all is well, the needle or spot should not move when the main instrument is turned on. As a further adjustment, the entire scale is sometimes made so that it can be moved lengthways a little after slightly loosening the securing screws. $0\%\,T$, infinite *OD*, is the true zero of the galvanometer; the other end of the scale, $100\%\,T$, zero *OD*, is a second fiduciary mark for providing a reference to base readings on, making the absorbance of the solvent or blank an arbitrary zero ($100T\%$) *whatever its real value is*. This second setting, of course, is made with everything switched on and the solvent cuvette in position. As one instruction manual says: ' It is assumed that the " blank " solution used is less dense than any of the sample solutions '. This is not as naive as it sounds. In differential absorption spectrometry some tests involve circumstances in which the blank and test solutions vary above and below each other along the spectrum (see Chapter 13) and the instruction merely warns the user that there is a possible snag here. The answer with simpler instruments like this one might lie in using the ' 0·5 ' setting (when available, as in the Spectrochem) for the so-called ' blank ', reverting to the normal range-setting for each reading on the sample, and then subtracting *OD*s.

(C) RECORDING SPECTROPHOTOMETERS

In an Age of Automation, the complete and rapid supersession of manually operated instruments would not seem surprising. Nevertheless, it is unlikely that this will happen for several years—at least not until further development allows easier and quicker and less costly recording of isolated stretches of 10 mμ or so of spectrum here and there around chosen maxima and minima, etc. At present this is definitely a job for the manual instrument. But I believe the time will come. Indeed on more than one recording instrument provision is made for repetitive scanning of selected portions, which seems to pave the way. Meanwhile, consider the problem of the automatic recording instrument:

A recording pen has to be moved two-dimensionally relative to a chart, the abscissae on which represent wavelengths and/or wavenumbers, and the ordinates percentage light transmission or ' absorbances ' (2—log %T).

The abscissae are fairly straightforward: either the pen can be moved along the chart, or the chart can be pulled past the pen, with all the force of a small electric motor geared-in to the same mechanical linkage that moves the prism or grating and so scans the spectrum across the exit slit. If a grating is used, each unit of pen movement along the abscissa corresponds to the same number of mμ at any point on the chart. The use of a prism adds a little complication in that it needs the intervention of an accurately ground cam to compress the wavelengths in the UV and spread them in the red in order to provide the convenient ' linear presentation ' that many users want; but this is not difficult.

The ordinates, however, tax the ingenuity. Somehow, the difference between the micro-currents generated by the different responses of the detector to illumination through the blank and through the sample must be translated quantitatively and without lag into movement of the pen along the ordinate. At first sight it

D

looks easy enough to amplify the current directly to a level sufficient to operate the pen, just like the pointer on a 0–100% T galvanometer. In practice this is not so: continuous provision must be made for the equivalent of re-setting a manual instrument to 100% T; too much power is needed to overcome pen/paper friction whilst maintaining quantitative amplification at an enormous level; and also many users prefer ordinate calibration in absorbances instead of % T. The answer is to use a servo mechanism.

A servo mechanism is a device for predictably multiplying a small effort and exactly reproducing any variations in it at the new higher level. As a simple example, imagine a rudimentary vehicle with a solid axle integral with the wheels, and brakes applied by a rope. If you wrap the rope loosely a few turns round the axle nothing happens until you pull; then it will grip the axle and apply the brakes harder than you can pull unaided—but only so long as the axle rotates or tries to. And it will cease to apply them as soon as you stop pulling. This immediate response (variously called ' absence of backlash ' or ' tightness in the servo ') is an essential feature of a good servomotor. In a recorder servomotor, special field coils are (*very* roughly!) the electrical analogue of the wrap-round turns of rope, except that the field coils are more versatile: they can not only stop but also start rotation of the armature and, by suitably controlled phasing, reverse its direction as required.

Commercial recording spectrometers operate on a double-beam system of one kind or another, usually ' in time ' rather than ' in space '. Although only the latter is strictly double-beam, the time interval between the incidence of the two beams on the photo-detector is so small that the effect is the same as if a true double-beam system were used. A typical arrangement lets the light beam emerging from the exit slit fall on a mirror device that directs it alternately, several times a second, through the blank (' reference beam ') and through the sample (' sample beam ') and thence to the photodetector. The reference beam can be attenuated in various ways: for instance, indirectly, by electrically shunting a known fraction of the reference signal generated in the detector; or directly, by the interposition of an optical attenuator which can be moved further or less far into the reference beam, thus inter-cepting a known fraction of it before it reaches the detector. A difference in the effective intensity of the alternate beams causes corresponding fluctuations in the output of the detector. These are amplified and fed in to the control coil(s) of the servomotor, which moves the attenuator one way or the other, or adjusts the potentiometer, until the beams are actually or effectively equal and there is no difference to amplify. Precautions are taken to damp any perceptible to-and-fro swing across the balance point where the conflicting requirements are met. The pen and the mechanical part of the attenuator are linked, so that movement of one exactly copies the other: the pen, in fact, merely records the position of the attenuator across the light beam, or the setting of the potentiometer at balance-point.

Operation of the pen and any form of attenuator is frequently by rack and pinion (as used on microscopes, but with minimal friction). To prevent relative motion, the pinions for both are often mounted on the same shaft. They are lightly spring-loaded against their racks to avoid backlash, and driven through an easily slipping clutch to save expensive noises if ever anything gets stuck or the pen tries to climb off the chart. With a logarithmically profiled attenuator, the position of the pen automatically and directly records absorbance. For a transmittance ordinate, a comb with straight-tapered teeth would similarly be suitable; or a moving vane with the edge that cuts across the slit forming part of a regular spiral; or a rectangular aperture with one side movable (as in the old Spekker photometer), moving along, not across, the slit; or a strictly linear potentiometer in an appropriate section of the post-detector amplifier circuit.

It is sometimes convenient to be able to change between absorbance and transmittance ordinates at the touch of a switch. This can be done electronically by using two potentiometers, one logarithmic, the other rectilinear, both (for simplicity) permanently linked mechanically to the pen drive but switched electrically in and out of the reference circuit at will. Less sophisticated is the use of a cam-controlled optical aperture, vane, comb, etc., in the reference light beam, with interchangeable cams; this involves much more than the touch of a switch for the changeover, but it makes up in ruggedness much of what it loses in convenience. In its carefully ground and hardened profile a cam can carry almost any programme, logarithmic or linear, plus minor idiosyncrasies if need be. Spring-loading is lavishly applied to avoid backlash when motion is reversed. Make sure that the springs, which are usually and preferably quite light, are not hampered by unnecessary friction. If there is any ' sticktion ' anywhere, the cam-follower may momentarily lose contact and then jump back with a little jerk that puts a spurious kink in the trace.

The time taken to scan the entire wavelength range on one chart can be anything from a couple of minutes to a couple of hours, depending whether you want a quick and qualitative spectral reconnaissance or a detailed and quantitative study. Lower speeds allow the use of narrower slits and—usually—a closer approximation to the truth (Fig. 6.5 and Chapter 17). The time taken by the pen to travel unimpeded from one end of the ordinate to the other is customarily of the order of one second—small, but significant in relation to the quickest rates of wavelength scan (up to about 30 mμ on the chart per second, though this is exceptional). There is a risk of imposing a false slope on the steeper parts of the spectrum, besides possibly missing finer details and taking ' short-cuts ' across the tips of maxima and minima. Like most cars, the pen is better on the straights than on corners. The magnitude of these effects should be assessed by experiment: do a run on the same stretch of spectrum at two extreme speeds, preferably on the same chart, and compare them.

The converse—overshooting—is less probable, even at sharp maxima and minima: the servo-force moving the pen along its ordinate is greatest when the pen is furthest from the relevant balance-point on the absorption curve, fading to nil at the balance-point itself. There is thus little chance of building up much momentum except when the true absorbance is substantially higher than the upper limit covered by the chart. Then the pen is apt to be brought up short against its stop, a mechanical barrier that it runs into at its full speed of $\frac{1}{2}$ mph or thereabouts. The crash sounds worse than it really is, and can be mitigated by the judicious use of thin padding.

A FEW TYPICAL EXAMPLES
OF RECORDING SPECTROPHOTOMETERS

This book is not a catalogue. I have therefore chosen only half a dozen out of the many available examples of recording spectrophotometers to show how various of the foregoing requirements have been met. The accompanying diagrams outline some of the inner workings in about enough detail to allow intelligent appraisal and comparisons with others you may encounter. Bauman (1962) gives other examples and a usefully candid list of the pros and cons of rival systems.

Despite the apparent complexity of Fig. 6.12, the optics of the 137 UV by Perkin-Elmer are basically simple. Instead of using a movable 30° prism, the P-E monochromator has a fixed 60° prism

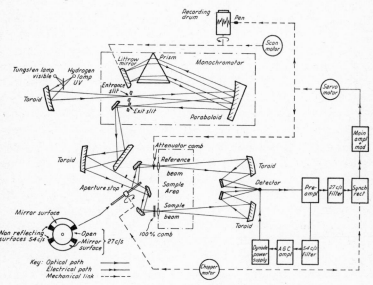

FIG. 6.12. Diagrammatic layout of the Perkin-Elmer Model 137 UV. (By courtesy of Perkin-Elmer Inc.)

with a Littrow mirror behind it to double-up the light-path and increase dispersion. Selection of wavelength is by slightly rotating this mirror around a vertical axis. Minor corrections can be made similarly: in fact, a bi-metal strip is permanently coupled to it to compensate for the dimensional effects of small temperature changes. Beyond the exit slit is a chopper-cum-mirror of unusual design with four additional, opaque, non-reflecting sectors as well as the customary pair of mirrors and gaps. Light is therefore completely obscured twice as often as it is either reflected along the reference path or transmitted directly into the sample. A synchronous motor rotates the chopper at 810 rpm, so that the photomultiplier receives two sets of light signals, one interrupted at 54 and the other at 27 cycles per second. The resulting electrical impulses are fed through a pre-amplifier to two bandpass filters. The 54 c/s filter is connected to an automatic gain control (AGC), which adjusts the sensitivity of the photomultiplier by varying the voltage on its dynodes, and so holds the over-all gain of the system constant at all wavelengths and extremes of absorbance of the sample; and the 27 c/s filter feeds the servo complex of synchronous rectifier, modulator, main amplifier and servomotor itself. Mounted on the shaft of the chopper motor, the synchronous rectifier converts the pre-amplified 27 c/s signal to direct current, *the polarity of which depends on whether the sample beam or the reference beam is the stronger*. This d.c. is now modulated to an alternating current (50 or 60 c/s to match the mains) *whose phase is determined by the polarity of the d.c.* In the servomotor the reference winding is permanently energized by the mains through a phase-shifting capacitor; the control winding is fed from the amplifier. The direction of rotation is governed by whether the reference or the control phase lags or leads the other by 90°. Through a lightly-loaded friction coupling, the motor partially rotates a shaft carrying a logarithmic attenuator at one end and a quadrant moving the recording pen on the other.

Two separate printed charts are used, one for the UV (190–360 mμ), the other for the visible (360–750 mμ), with wavelengths evenly spaced along the abscissa by the contours of the wavelength cam. Both charts cover absorbances from 0–1·5 evenly spaced along the ordinate by the logarithmic silhouette of the attenuator. The charts are mounted on a vertical drum which slowly rotates past the vertically traversing pen, and covers the full wavelength range of either chart in two minutes (fast, exploratory scan) or 8 minutes (slow scan for fine details). Rotation of the chart drum is cam-linked to a lever that swings the Littrow mirror through the necessary small angle to scan the appropriate wavelength range, and also, by another cam, to a lever that varies the slit-width so as to maintain the emergent light beam at as nearly as possible a constant energy level. The AGC smooths out minor variations. To suit exceptional conditions, the slit-width can be manually increased—but not decreased—from the setting automatically selected by the slit cam. Care is needed to avoid over-loading the photomultiplier when the slits are thus opened.

A ' 100% ' comb in the sample beam allows fine adjustment for equalizing the two beams without any sample in position, before recording. The attenuator in the reference beam, of course, con-tinuously restores this equality during recording.

With variations, much the same can be said of most recording instruments. The Hilger Ultrascan is, very roughly, a mechanized Uvispek (Fig. 6.3) but without interchangeable prisms. Emergent light from the 30°-prism monochromator is mirror-chopped as in the Perkin-Elmer instrument, but at a higher rate of rotation and omitting the four non-reflecting sectors. The resulting 67 c/s pulses from the photomultiplier are amplified, with due benefit of automatic gain control, 100% correction, etc., and fed to the control windings of the servomotor. A small lamp, under-run for long life, shines through the chopper, *at a point circumferentially midway between reference and sample beams*, on a germanium phototransistor, which sends another set of 67 c/s pulses through a separate amplifier to the quadrature phase windings of the two-phase servomotor. Thus, from the start, the two sets of signals differ in phase by 90°. The direction of rotation of the motor depends on which set leads or lags the other, as determined by which beam is the more intense. A tacho-generator, coupled to the servomotor, provides a velocity feedback that prevents the pen from overshooting at the ends of long ' excursions ', as when recording narrow bands of high persistence. The pen can cover the full ordinate of 8 inches (20 cm) in 1 second.

The normal direction of traverse is from lower to higher wave-lengths. The pen automatically lifts off the flat-bed chart during the return traverse, as when ' re-cycling ', i.e. repetitive scanning between chosen limits of wavelength. Three scanning speeds are available: 4, 8 and 16 minutes from 200 to 750 mμ (50000–13300 cm^{-1}), from one end of the chart to the other. This is about the same speed as the Perkin-Elmer, which covers half the spectrum in two sections taking 2 or 8 minutes. While the pen traverses the abscissa, a cam on the same shaft as the wavelength cam adjusts the coupled slits to an average optimum bandwidth between 3 and 10 AU. This can be doubled or halved at will, to suit the circumstances. By switching-in an alternative potentio-metric network the ordinate can be ' expanded ' (as on the

Uvispek, DU, SP.500, etc., at the '0·1' setting of the selector switch) so that '0–2·0' becomes '1–3' absorbance, and '0–100% T' becomes '0–10% T'.

Many older spectroscopists, myself included, obstinately think in terms of wavelengths rather than in wavenumbers: to me, cm^{-1} still has an air of unreality, and I mentally translate into the equivalent wavelength to bring things back to earth. The Ultra-scan wavelength cam is thoughtfully profiled to give equal spacing of wavenumbers, but the charts are ruled and marked in wavelengths. This makes the best of both worlds: ease of reading for

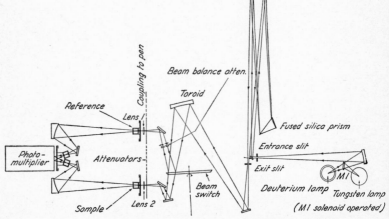

FIG. 6.13. Diagrammatic optical layout of the Unicam SP.800.
(By courtesy of Unicam Instruments Ltd.)

the old (or obstinate), plus the substantial advantages of rectilinear frequency presentation when you want to compare band-spacing or widths in different parts of the spectrum. This can be done simply with a ruler and/or dividers without calculation of reciprocals. (See Chapter 19.)

In the Unicam SP.800 (Fig. 6.13) the optical system is fairly conventional apart from a few refinements such as unusually generous separation of the sample and reference light-paths and the provision of a thermostatically controlled monochromator (35°C). Marked 'Beam switch' in the diagram is the beam chopper. It will be noticed that the initial manual beam-balancing is by optical attenuators in the reference beam, instead of in the sample beam. In addition to their normal trimming function, the beam-balance attenuator can be employed to move the zero-absorbance line up to 0·5, allowing difference spectra (Chapter 13) to be recorded on the scale −0·5 to +1·5, with the lower-absorbance sample in the reference beam. The complete wavelength range is covered by two flat-bed charts, 190–450 mμ and 315–700 mμ (5260o–2220o and 3170o–1430o cm^{-1}), a useful overlap, the normal scanning time for either being 2 or 8 minutes. Other times can be arranged by the makers to order. The charts are calibrated in 0–2·0 absorbance linearly along one edge, with the corresponding %T along the other. Alternative abscissae are linear wavelength or linear wavenumber, ordered at the time of purchase and not interchangeable by the normal user. The pen is mounted on what amounts to a stationary gantry with the chart traversing beneath it: this simplifies the linkage between the servomotor and the pen and enhances lasting accuracy of absorbance recording.

The SP.700, at about twice the price of the SP.800, incorporates many further refinements and includes a grating as well as a prism for extending the spectrum into the near infra-red. The over-all range is 186 mμ–3·6 μ (5400o–2800 cm^{-1}). A photomultiplier is used for UV and visible, a lead sulphide cell for the IR. Recording is again by a moving chart beneath a laterally stationary pen, but the chart is a continuous strip on rollers which engage perforations along the edges. The slits are servo-operated to maintain constant energy in the emergent beam. On the latest models a single nine-position switch allows selection of any of the following modes of operation:

Linear transmittance: 0–220, 0–110, 0–22, 0–11 and 80–102% T

Linear absorbance: 0–1·1, 0·9–2·0 and −0·3–+0·8

And of course, energy recording, for wavelength calibration, etc.

The scales extending above 100% T (or below zero absorbance) can be used for recording difference spectra, with the lower-absorbing sample in the reference beam (Chapter 13). The 80–102% T scale can also be used for scale expansion at low extinctions. The 0–11% and 0–22% T scales (like the 0·1 setting on the SP.500, etc.) enable higher absorbances to be measured and so provide a quicker alternative to varying the concentration or pathlength of the sample. The diagram (Fig. 6.14) shows the general

D*

arrangement of the optical system and a schematic presentation of the ' machinery '.

A typical member of the Beckman DK series (Figs. 6.15 and 6.16) uses two beam choppers: the first (480 c/s) to give an alternating current for easy, drift-free amplification; the second (15 c/s), a mirror-chopper, to provide a double-beam-in-time. On the same shaft as the 15 c/s chopper are (1) another rotating mirror that collects light alternately from reference and sample and passes it on to the 1P28 photomultiplier; and (2) a commutator that sends the amplified pulses alternately to two demodulators, one to

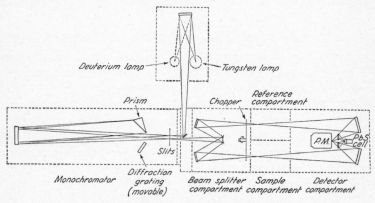

FIG. 6.14. Diagrammatic optical layout of the Unicam SP.700.
(By courtesy of Unicam Instruments Ltd.)

maintain, with the slit servo amplifier, a constant 100% direct-current reference voltage for the recorder, the other to energize the pen servomotor, which records the ratio between the two beams. The ratio is expressed as transmittance or absorbance, at will, through two appropriate potentiometer slide wires. Eleven modes of ratio presentation can be selected by the range switch through potentiometric networks, five of them suitable for differential recording. By changing the gearing between cam-drive and recorder-drive, the wavelength scale can also be expanded at will for recording fine details. The mirror drive can be disconnected for single-beam operation. Slit height is adjustable to 1·3, 3·0 and 13 mm—an unusual refinement, useful with cuvettes of unorthodox sizes. Continuous strip or flat-bed recorders are available, with scanning speeds between 1·5 and 1800 mμ/minute. Repetitive scanning is possible only with the flat-bed chart(s).

With double monochromation we enter a new world. Unlike the foregoing, which are all high-quality single monochromators,

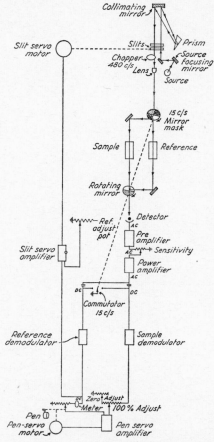

FIG. 6.15. Diagrammatic layout of the Beckman DK 2.

Cary has favoured double monochromation* from the start. The first Cary was simply two DU Beckmans mounted physically side-by-side and optically in series. The emergent beam from number one was reflected into the entrance slit of number two. In some

---

* Examined critically by Hales (1953) and Tarrant (1953)

later versions, the second monochromator was available as a grating instrument, giving linear wavelength presentation (if required) without intervention of cams. Problems of alignment, multiple slit operation, etc., were immense, but successfully solved.

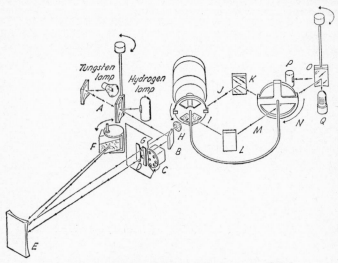

FIG. 6.16. Optical arrangement of the Beckman DK 2.

A   Source condensing mirror
B   Entrance mirror
C   Entrance-beam chopper
D   Entrance slit
E   Collimating mirror
F   Quartz prism
G   Exit slit
H   Exit-beam condensing lens
I   Rotating mirror
J   Reference beam
K   Reference stationary mirror
L   Sample stationary mirror
M   Sample beam
N   Rotating mirror, driven from I through flexible shaft
O   Detector selector mirror
P   Lead sulphide cell
Q   Photomultiplier

The major advantage lies in the practical elimination of stray light. Even if both monochromators are bad enough to include 1% of stray radiation in their emergent beams, the result of combining them in a double monochromator is to reduce it to 1% of 1%, that is, 0·01%—a very satisfactory level after an unusually unpromising start. Few instruments would get into such poor condition as that. A realistic value for a single monochromator in fair condition is about 0·2% over the ' usable ' part of the spectrum: 0·01% made the possibility of recording absorbances above 3·0 practicable for the first time. Stray light below 0·0002% at 210 mμ is now claimed for the Perkin-Elmer 350 double monochromator, which uses a horizontal drum chart, 11×17 inches $(28 \times 43$ cm) with reversible direction of scan. An example of its performance is shown in Fig. 19.7.

GENERAL COMMENTS
ON PHOTOELECTRIC SPECTROMETERS OF ALL TYPES

A deuterium lamp gives about three times the radiant output of the hydrogen lamp, and seems to be superseding it. In a double monochromator the inevitable loss of energy in traversing each half leaves two small fractions whose product gives the very small resultant energy of the emergent beam. For this reason some instruments use a water-cooled hydrogen or deuterium lamp with a considerably higher output than is possible with the small air-cooled 30-watt lamps. One seldom-mentioned precaution is worth emphasizing here: take special care that the water flow and lamp on-off switch are interlinked. An easy way to do this is to let the outflow from the water-jacket run into a plastics vessel with a small drain hole which empties it in say 10–15 seconds, so that the vessel continuously overflows into a large funnel beneath it. The weight of the vessel plus the water must be enough to hold the switch on against a spring. Without water, the weight must be low enough for the spring to turn the switch off. A tilting mercury switch is probably best for this fail-safe gadget. A momentary interruption in the water supply will have no effect on the circuit—this could be inconvenient—nor will it harm the lamp; but anything over a quarter-minute's delay is decidedly risky. The lamp then overheats and when the water comes on again a cracked lamp is the result. In some water-cooled lamps the silica window is held in position by wax. This is a great convenience for servicing, but will not stand the heat for long without a brisk water flow.

A continuous flow of dry nitrogen through an entire monochromator—optics and electronics—discharging through the cuvette compartment, ensures not only absence of moisture and unwanted absorption due to atmospheric oxygen, etc., but also maintains in the monochromator a very slight positive pressure of a few mm, which discourages the entry of noxious vapours from the sample compartment. The laboratory is assumed to be air-conditioned. As an added refinement, I suggest that a tube be led into the sample compartment and attached to a laboratory water pump, or a small enclosed extractor fan, or mechanically operated suction bellows (each with trap) continuously drawing away vapours as soon as they appear. There shouldn't be any, of course; but such things do happen and it is well to be prepared. At least one manufacturer is far-sighted, or pessimistic, enough to leave the sample compartment open at the bottom, with precautions against entry of light, so that spilt solutions will go through to the bench rather than mess up the instrument. A wad of blotting or filter paper underneath will save the bench.

Talking of benches, I prefer a wooden bench every time. They are kinder to fragile apparatus (cuvettes in particular) and easy to drill for extra ' facilities ' such as water, compressed air, nitrogen, suction, drainage, etc. Besides its practical advantages, well-polished wood with natural grain has an aesthetic appeal unequalled by any imitation-stone slab. Aesthetics does have its place in science.

The importance of having a completely light-tight sample compartment is obvious. You should from time to time test the light-tightness of the the whole instrument, while it is switched on, by shining a really powerful electric torch at close range on every part that shows any sort of seam or joint. There should be no movement whatever of the galvanometer or recording pen. If there is, restore light-tightness by replacing any gasket (etc.) or, if the light is entering past a fixed but damaged joint, rub a little black flexible adhesive into the crack, and paint over it. Anything that ' dries brittle ' is only temporarily effective.

With a tuned a.c. amplifier, the steady daylight of the laboratory should (on paper) not affect the photometer. In practice it often does, by over-loading the photo-surface if the instrument is ' on '. With the photomultiplier, this can, in fact, be ruinous, and manufacturers make provision to link the lid of the sample compartment with a shutter that shields the photomultiplier from daylight when the lid is opened for access to the cuvettes. Short of traumatic fracture, a photomultiplier should last almost indefinitely if it is never exposed while the high-tension is on, and it needs no attention except occasional dusting of the base and cleaning of the light window with lens tissue dipped in alcohol. Redistilled alcohol is one of the few solvents that will run off a clean surface and dry without leaving streaks.

A photo-surface of any kind emits electrons not only by reason of photons falling on it but also if it gets hot. Thermal electrons are, in fact, the cause of much ' amplifier noise ', tremors in the galvanometer needle, spurious waviness in the chart record. Photomultipliers are more sensitive to heat than the simpler phototubes, and respond favourably to being kept cool as well as completely dark apart from the beams from the monochromator. Coolness *and* darkness are two conflicting requirements. I suggest that, in the absence of any special provision by the manufacturers, the point of entry for ventilating nitrogen should be as near as possible to the photomultiplier. That, at least, will prevent heat from leaking through to the photomultiplier from any other part of the instrument (e.g. a thermostatted monochromator). In some circumstances, cooling jackets are fitted, but I doubt whether this is often necessary in normal spectrophotometry.

You will sometimes see the recommendation to use only amplifying valves, phototubes or photomultipliers specially chosen by the manufacturers. This is true, for instance, of the old DAF 91 valves for the SP.500, and the 1P28 photomultiplier for the Ultrascan. For many purposes, such as a radio set or talkie soundhead, the published characteristics of such components, which are correct within only fairly broad limits, are uncritical. In a delicately balanced amplifier for stable photometry, there is often enough variation between nominally identical valves (etc.) to make some of the batch unsuitable. Whether you can buy a suitable replacement locally is entirely a matter of luck: you might have to try several. The manufacturers are obviously in a better position to do this, e.g. by arrangement with the makers of the valves (etc.), and usually it is cheaper in the end to obtain the slightly more costly ' manufacturer's selection '.

Always replace the various covers of the instrument as soon as possible after any maintenance work, even if the laboratory is air-conditioned. If they have to be left off for any reason while parts are being obtained, cover everything with a polythene or similar dust-free sheet. This will save time and trouble later. Many of the optical parts are not properly cleanable by the user—the mirrors of the beam chopper, for instance. Mirror surfaces of any kind are very delicate indeed, and unless the instruction manual sanctions it, don't touch them, even with a suction-brush (Fig. 6.17). If they have been aluminized and then flash-protected with silica, a gentle wash with cotton-wool dipped in detergent followed by distilled water usually restores 'works performance'; but even this calls for extreme delicacy and must be avoided with fluoride-bloomed surfaces. The same can be said of the operative face of

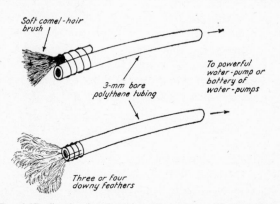

Soft camel-hair brush

3-mm bore polythene tubing

To powerful water-pump or battery of water-pumps

Three or four downy feathers

FIG. 6.17. Suction brush and suction duster. The brush is of the type used for dusting laboratory weights, with its handle cut short to 2–3 cm and bound to the end of a polyethylene tube. The suction duster has three or four curly down feathers similarly secured with thread plus a little rubber-based adhesive, such as Bostik 1. Dry dust is very mobile. (See pp. 55, 162)

the 30° prism common to many monochromators, recording and manual. The shortest face never needs touching, since it does not take part in the dispersing process. The back face, where light is reflected internally, is usually completely shielded from everything and is a job for the Man from the Works *if* it ever does need attention.

In most instruments, little silica windows over the slits protect the internal optical parts. These windows are not always as easy to get at as they should be; but at least dislodge any dust from them and if possible clean them occasionally with lens tissue+alcohol and/or detergent and distilled water, judiciously applied with due regard for adjacent electronics. In conjunction with a *very* soft brush (to avoid scratching optical surfaces) suction can be effective in removing dust and is sometimes preferable to blowing with compressed air; but again be careful to follow the manufacturer's advice in avoiding vulnerable parts. One precaution I have not seen mentioned, perhaps because of the ribald comments that are almost certain to be evoked, is to wear a simple operating-theatre mask when you have to peer really closely into the inner workings. Even moisture from the breath must be excluded.

When you are studying explanatory diagrams of optical systems, a good deal of innocent fun can be had from the treatment of prisms. The prism seems to be an unnatural hazard for some draughtsmen. Note how, if the light rays are allowed to enter the prism—which they just bounce off in some diagrams—they reflect internally at the oddest unequal angles. No manufacturer is immune. Catalogue editors, Beware! The light-paths outside the prism are usually reasonably realistic, though not always strictly quantitative; in a diagrammatic representation they don't have to be. That is why the sample is often shown in a very divergent light beam: the angle is exaggerated for clarity. In practice the light rays form a nearly parallel pencil, diverging only enough to throw a reasonable-sized image on the photo-surface. They must never diverge enough to reflect off the sides of the cuvette. This would lengthen the true light-path (see Chapters 9 and 17), besides displacing its ' landing ground ' on the photo-surface and so possibly making nonsense of the zero setting.

CHAPTER 7

LIGHT SOURCES

Many hands don't always make the light work

In routine spectrometry by photoelectric response there is no call for the old type of arc or spark line sources except as standards of wavelength, to be used solely for purposes of calibration. A strong continuous emission spectrum with as little as possible variation along its length, and as small as possible fluctuations in intensity with time, simplifies both design and operation. Existing commercial sources are therefore contrived to achieve these ends.

Two types of lamp dominate the present scene: the tungsten filament lamp depending on the black-body radiation of incandescent tungsten; and the gas discharge lamp, nowadays almost exclusively hydrogen or deuterium. [Use of the rare gases—xenon as a powerful visible and near-UV source, helium for the remote UV beyond 200 mμ (500oo cm^{-1})—has so far been confined to specialized instruments.] The two types supplement each other admirably: the tungsten filament's emission straddles the entire visible spectrum and covers useful portions of the near UV and infra-red; the hydrogen lamp goes well down into the far UV with usefully increasing intensity that does much to compensate for any falling-off in the response by the photo-detector and transparency of the optical system. Its continuity is, however, broken by a few lines in the near UV and the visible, and its intensity falls off badly as the wavelength increases. This is fairly obvious from the appearance of the light, which looks a pale inoffensive blue; but don't look too long or too closely if you value your corneas. Some manufacturers advise the use of the tungsten lamp for all wavelengths above 350 mμ, and in some instruments an automatic changeover between sources is arranged at or near this point. In practice, it is sometimes more expedient with a manual instrument to use the hydrogen lamp up to well into the visible, despite instrusive lines and weakening emission. Try for yourself. If you take care to avoid the vicinity of the lines (*vide infra*) you have nothing to lose but your narrowness of slit-width; and so long as this remains moderate and in keeping with the work in hand (e.g. absorption bands not too sharp) there is no objection to the use of whatever source gives adequate photoelectric response.

INCANDESCENT TUNGSTEN

Incandescent tungsten comes in a variety of forms. The form most used in commercial instruments is a coiled filament mounted vertically and consuming some 20 or 30 watts. It is almost a point source in its horizontal cross-section and therefore easily focused. Pre-focused lamps are useful and a great convenience when replacement is necessary. A ribbon filament, also mounted vertically (parallel to the slit), gives a slightly more uniform field of illumination at a greater intensity commensurate with the higher consumption (maybe 100 watts or more) and is standardized on some instruments. This is not a suitable subject for experiment by the average user: filament and ribbon lamps are not usually interchangeable, as focusing problems differ. This is also true of the Pointolite (Chapter 5) which has its own special applications and seems *in its present form* to offer little or no obvious advantages in existing photoelectric instruments.

If a tungsten lamp (coiled filament or ribbon) is under-run by $\frac{1}{2}$–1 volt it lasts much longer than at the nominal voltage; but it does not ' go down ' so far into the UV. As this limit is already pretty well dictated by the transmission cut-off of the glass envelope of the lamp, the only sacrifice is of some illuminating power, with the consequent need for a fractionally wider slit. Unfortunately little is gained by over-running, and the life of the lamp is shortened disastrously. During an emergency in the 1939 War, when our spark light source transformer packed-in and was being replaced, I successfully ran a dozen urgent E.528 spectrograms on vitamin-A assay in Lease-Lend fish-liver oils by using an over-run 36-watt car headlamp bulb to measure absorptivity at 325 mμ *and* get an idea of the shape of the maximum. The plates looked odd—vastly over-exposed above 340 mμ, nothing at all below 300—but despite what must have been an abundance of stray light (among other misdemeanours) results were both consistent and in gratifying concordance with the vendor's quotations.

I got through four bulbs. I wished then that I could fit the glass envelope with a silica window so as to extend the lower limit of wavelength of the lamp without increasing the already severe thermal stress on the filament. Lipsett (1959) and Smith (1943) have successfully done just that; but although adequate for their purpose and a marked improvement on standard performance, the results disappoint me. A more promising development is the so-called Quartz-Iodine lamp, recently made available for car headlamps and projectors, and, as I see it, adaptable (by the manufacturers) for use in spectrophotometry.

Under comparable conditions, the Quartz-Iodine lamps ' go down ' some 30 mμ further than their glass counterparts, although the ' quartz ' used is chosen more for its thermal qualities than for its far-UV transparency, which is not needed in either headlamps or projectors. With an envelope of, say, Spectrosil UV grade, I imagine a still better performance would be obtained. This seems to me a potentially rewarding line of research, only the fringe of which has so far been touched. The action of the iodine seems to be to intercept flying particles of tungsten from the filament and combine with them to form volatile tungsten iodide. When the circulating iodide encounters the hot filament, it decomposes into free iodine, so re-starting the cycle, and metallic tungsten, which deposits on the filament instead of being wasted on the inside of the bulb. The filament is thus conserved and an obscuring ' mirror ' avoided. Filament temperature is about 3000°C (some 500° higher than is conventional) and the small bulb attains 600°C.

The black-body radiation of tungsten could probably never rival the hydrogen arc in the far UV—there are limits to the temperature which even tungsten, with or without iodine, will stand—but already such instruments as the Spectrochem and SP.600 could have their lower limit usefully extended by a few mμ without over-running the lamp, and without encroaching on the wider domain of all-silica instruments.

A Pointolite plus iodine plus a small Spectrosil envelope instead of glass offers considerable research possibilities. And there are, surely, other combinations besides iodine vapour and tungsten in its normal forms . . . But enough of speculation.

Tungsten lamps can be run off storage batteries or, through a transformer, off the mains. If circumstances demand that batteries *must* be used, choose a heavy-duty high-capacity type, preferably two of 80–100 ampere-hours, used and trickle-charged alternately. I do not recommend using the same large battery for both the amplifier and the lamp, though it can be, and often is, done. At the very least, amplifier stability is apt to be impaired. Where a.c. mains are available, use a constant-output transformer. This is often less costly initially than two adequate batteries, and it lasts indefinitely.

A sliding light-filter is incorporated in many spectrophotometers to cut out most of the intense visible spectrum of the tungsten filament and to transmit only the extreme blue and near-UV whenever readings are required below about 450 mμ (2220o cm^{-1}). Although this necessarily and understandably involves the use of larger-than-usual slit-widths, the consequent

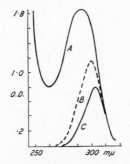

FIG. 7.1. Spectrum of tyrosine in alcohol (pH$>$10). (*A*) Hydrogen lamp, (*B*) tungsten lamp with filter, and (*C*) tungsten lamp without filter. The illustration shows the effect of using a tungsten lamp outside its useful range. (By courtesy of Dr F. D. Collins, 1951.)

slight loss of resolution and possible small increase in photometric uncertainty at narrow maxima are more than compensated by the elimination of stray light, which has a far more serious effect. Unless the filter is moved automatically in and out of the beam, as in the Spectrochem, be careful to remove it before attempting measurements at wavelengths above its cut-off point. You won't do any harm by leaving the filter in position; but you won't get any readings either.

As a minor check, it is a good idea to make a tungsten lamp reading or two with and without the filter, well inside its range limit. There should not, of course, be any significant difference (compare Fig. 7.1 with the results on Wood's glass, p. 191).

The same applies to the change-over point between blue/UV-sensitive and red-sensitive phototubes, near 625 mμ. Over a range of several mμ, where the detectors overlap in sensitivity, there should again be no difference that cannot be accounted for by changes in slit-width. If there *is* a substantial difference, suspect one of the phototubes of non-linearity, or uneven response over the operative area of photosensitive surface, or ' tiredness ' of the photo-surface, or possible electrical leakage along the outside of the envelope due to dust, damp or fingerprints.

When handling a lamp, hold it by the base and clean the outside surface with alcohol to remove possible latent fingerprints before the lamp gets hot enough to bake them onto the surface. They can still be removed even then, but probably not without taking the lamp out of its housing.

The useful life of a normal tungsten lamp (the ' Q-I ' above may be an exception) is not necessarily as long as the filament lasts. There comes a stage when the inside of the bulb becomes coated with a thin layer of metallic tungsten from the hot filament. Sometimes this can be seen without removing the lamp from its housing, for instance by using a dental mirror or (SP.600) taking off the light-shield and looking through the lamp while it is switched off. Sometimes it is necessary to remove the lamp and hold it against a white background. The deposit will be more easily seen if you rotate the lamp so as to bring the part ' behind ' the filament support into view; where the support has shielded the surface from bombardment, it shows as a clear ' shadow ' or silhouette surrounded by the slightly darker metal film. If you can see any film at all, change the lamp. It has gone too far for good spectrophotometry.

THE HYDROGEN (OR DEUTERIUM) LAMP

The UV/visible lines emitted by a gas discharge arise from quantized transitions between pairs of fixed electronic energy levels which, in a line-of-sight stationary source, uniquely determine the positions of emission lines. Under the conditions of excitation in the hydrogen lamp, the spectrum contains very few such lines above 200 mμ, the emitted energy being satisfactorily concentrated in a continuum due, if the pundits will pardon my over-simplification, to a semi-infinite number of overlapping random transitions between indefinite levels. The few lines that are shown are useful for quick wavelength checking. They should, however, be avoided when an absorption spectrum is being recorded or manually plotted; most recording instruments do this automatically by switching over to the incandescent filament source at a convenient point in the near UV. Even in a high-resolution instrument the immediate neighbourhood of a bright line constitutes a needless stray-light hazard, practically impossible to filter out. Besides this, sudden brighter bits of spectrum give unnecessary work to whatever balancing mechanism is used, whether it is an automatic gain control or servo-operated slit on a recording spectrophotometer, or the human operator of a manual instrument.

Several versions of the hydrogen lamp have been produced experimentally and are irrelevant here. Two broad types are commercially available: the extra-high-tension type (EHT), very intense and requiring water-cooling; and the now more popular small air-cooled type, used almost universally in various forms. More often than not, it now contains deuterium ('heavy hydrogen') instead of normal hydrogen.

The EHT hydrogen lamp could profitably be used in conjunction with the photographic equipment mentioned in Chapter 4, but is unnecessarily powerful for most photoelectric use. It provides an exceptionally intense UV continuum which is viewed endways through a silica window on the end of the tube. In at least one make, this was originally held on by high-melting wax; Thermal Syndicate fuse theirs in position; you take your choice between accessibility and rugged durability. The T/M5/528 lamp is water-cooled and designed for horizontal mounting. Having a cold cathode, it starts instantly as soon as the necessary 4000 volts a.c. is applied, and runs thereafter at 2500 volts with a consumption of 300 milliamps (i.e. some 750 watts, which accounts for the need for water-cooling). An appropriate circuit is shown in Fig. 7.2. The whole tube is 16 in. (400 mm) long, and the end-viewed arc itself is about $4\frac{3}{4} \times \frac{1}{3}$ in. (120×8 mm). Its size and lethal possibilities are not in its favour, but it could be fun to play with. A 'fail-safe' switch in the primary circuit (page 81) is a wise precaution against accidental prolonged interruption of the cooling water.

The air-cooled hydrogen lamp with a hot cathode is much smaller, typically about $1\frac{1}{4}$–$1\frac{3}{4}$ in. (30–45 mm) diameter, and about twice this height. It can be mounted in any position as long as cool air circulates freely round it. It works off direct current (about 80–200 volts at 300–500 mA) and because the intensity of emission depends critically on the potential difference between anode and cathode a stabilized power supply is needed in most spectrophotometers. For a manual instrument, stability to $\pm 0\cdot01$ volt is desirable, and is claimed to be maintained despite mains fluctuations of 10%. This degree of control is not necessary in instruments of the true double-beam type, or in the double-beam-in-time type where the interval between successive flashes on the photodetector is a small fraction of a second, during which fairly

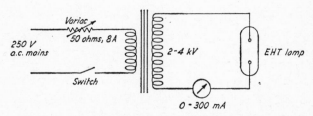

FIG. 7.2. Circuit recommended by Thermal Syndicate Ltd for the EHT cold-cathode water-cooled hydrogen lamp, which is normally adjusted by Variac to run at about 2·5 kV, 300 mA.

elementary stabilization is adequate: there just isn't time for the source intensity to change significantly between reference and sample beams. But a fair degree of constancy makes for simpler working generally, and allows the use of predictable slit-widths, etc.

The working of one of the more refined power units can be followed from the diagram (Fig. 7.3) which shows the stabilizing circuit used with the SP.500, a manual instrument. Tappings are taken for various purposes from the secondary of the mains transformer. One of these tappings is used for heating the cathode; the current from another is rectified and amplified to 80 volts for the anode. This latter output is held constant by a system of feedbacks which decrease the amplification (or ' gain ') whenever the input increases because of mains fluctuations, and increase the gain when the input falls. Other refinements are included to automate the starting cycle. Fig. 7.4 shows a much simpler circuit, suitable wherever such extreme stabilization is not needed, as when photographic use is contemplated, or in a double-beam recording instrument. Whatever voltage-control system is used, all commercial

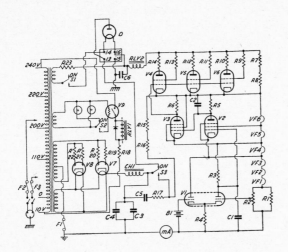

FIG. 7.3. Stabilizer for the deuterium lamp of the Unicam SP.500.

RLY1	3000 Ω relay coil	V4–6	KT33C valves
RLY2	30 Ω relay hold-on coil	V7–8	5R4GY valves
F1	1-amp fuse	V9	DLS10 valve
F2	5-amp fuse	R1	14 Ω
F3	5-amp fuse	R2	1 kΩ
S1–3	contacts on relays	R3	2·2 MΩ
mA	milliammeter, 500 mA	R4	150 kΩ
	full-scale deflection	R5	2·2 MΩ
CH1	1·8 H, 300-mA choke	R6	47 kΩ
B1	3-volt dry battery	R7	450 Ω
C1	0·1 μF	R8	450 Ω
C2	0·001 μF	R9–14	47 Ω each
C3	8 μF	R15	450 Ω
C4	8 μF	R16	450 Ω
C5	0·05 μF	R17	220 Ω
C6	0·25 μF	R18	6·8 kΩ
VF1–6	valve filaments	R19–22	47 Ω each
V1	6SL7GT valve	R23	0·050 Ω
V2–3	6J7 valves	D	deuterium lamp

hot-cathode hydrogen lamps call for much the same general routine:

First, switch on the cathode-heater filament; this glows dull red and takes some 6–8 amps at 4–5 volts for anything from a few seconds to a minute to heat the cathode enough to start copious emission of electrons. Then switch-in the anode circuit and either (according to lamp) decrease or switch off the current to the heater, which in some designs is kept sufficiently hot by the discharge itself. The arc should now strike, and the milliammeter register 300 mA (500 mA with some lamps). If it is *substantially* less— maybe by 30–50 mA—the arc has not struck properly and a 'pin-hole glow' starts eroding the metal parts of the lamp. In these

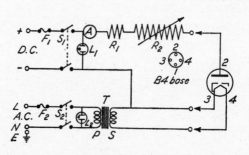

FIG. 7.4. A simple unstabilized control unit for a hydrogen-arc lamp.
(G. H. Beaven, 1954.)

F_1 and F_2	2-amp fuses
S_1 and S_2	double-pole single-throw switches
R_1	fixed resistor, 120 ohms, 90 watts
R_2	variable resistor, 327 ohms, 200 watts
T	filament-heating transformer, 8 amp at 5-volt output
L_1 and L_2	neon indicator lamps
A	anode current meter, 0·1 amp

circumstances, the arc can usually be correctly struck by bringing the electrode of an induction coil up to the side of the lamp. If the milliammeter reading is only a few percent lower than nominal, adjustment of the supply is generally possible; but this is often a sign that the lamp will soon need replacing. Alternatively, if the arc does not strike, momentarily increase the anode voltage to about double *while the heater is on* and the cathode is thoroughly hot. In the P-E 137 UV this is done automatically, circuits being provided to limit the voltage to 170 during the warm-up (when anything much higher would probably cause incorrect striking) and to give a transient boost to over 300 volts if the arc has not struck within a quarter-minute after warm-up. For laboratories with both a.c. and d.c., Beaven (1954) recommends a simple system for Hilger-Flood hydrogen lamps, nominally unstabilized but stable enough for many purposes, in which the heater filament is given all it can take from a 4–5 volt transformer (giving reputedly a 2-second start) and the anode is rheostatted through a barretter to a 230-volt d.c. main. In place of the d.c. main, a simple silicon rectifier could be used with the a.c. main.

As I see it, manual instruments need all the stabilization of the lamp that they can get; but recording spectrophotometers, with either true (static) or chopped double-beam optical systems, could well be simplified and given so much less to go wrong by the use of a rugged semi-stabilized device like Dr Beaven's, shown on p. 94. The extra effort of manually operating a couple of switches during

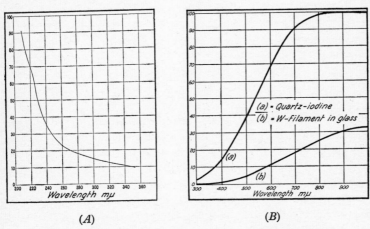

(*A*)   (*B*)

FIG. 7.5. Spectral energy distribution of (*A*) Flood deuterium lamps, as given by the makers, and (*B*) typical tungsten filament lamps. The ordinates are arbitrary.

the warm-up period is a small price to pay for elimination of a 'proper' electronic stabilizer, even a reliable one. I would, however, retain any automatic change-over of light sources (which only involves swivelling a mirror).

The early commercial hydrogen lamps used on the first Beckmans were made of glass, with a very thin window for the radiation to emerge through. This, being curved like the dam of a reservoir, was stronger than it looked, and its thinness made it serviceably transparent down to about 220 mμ. Later silica lamps are, of course, far superior (Fig. 7.5). With a Spectrosil (UV grade) envelope it is said to be possible to ' go down ' to 160 mμ (625oo cm^{-1}). The problems concern the spectrophotometer, not the lamp.

The discharge occurs inside a little metal open-box-shaped structure in the lamp, and radiation shines out through an aperture in one side of the box. This aperture is either round (about 1 mm diameter), or rectangular ($\frac{1}{2} \times 3$ mm) and parallel to the slit (i.e. usually vertical). There does not seem much to choose from the user's point of view; but from the designer's, the rectangular aperture simplifies the production of that little banana-shaped image which goes so well with a slightly curved slit. It also allows more latitude (or should I say longitude?) in vertical adjustment, and more closely simulates the usual vertical filament of the tungsten lamp. The two types are not always interchangeable, and the manufacturers should be consulted if you have reason to want to change.

LAMP ADJUSTMENT IN COMFORT

In early instruments at least, vertical adjustment of the H-lamp was quite a major and sometimes thermally painful operation. Nowadays, a proper screw adjustment is often provided. I have a notion that Sanders and I (1954, 1955) started the trend, after suffering burnt fingers for a year or two.

Any light source needs, at some stage, adjustment along three axes at right angles. The tungsten lamp is customarily pre-focused at the works, and has already been correctly orientated relative to its fixed mounting. At most, its image needs lateral fine adjustment, typically provided by one of the adjustable stops limiting the partial rotation of the mirror that serves to select which of the two lamps is in use. The H-lamp is not so amenable. It is usually held in spring clips gently but firmly gripping the lamp envelope, one above and one below the aperture. When cold, the lamp can be slid up-and-down fairly easily, though not so freely that it slips spontaneously. Adjustment to-and-from the mirror (focusing adjustment) is not fussily critical. The slot and lock-screw often provided at the foot of the mounting (as on the SP.500) seems quite adequate, though not always easy to reach; use a cranked screwdriver or spanner, preferably insulated. Lateral adjustment, though highly critical, as for the tungsten lamp, is easily done by means of the relevant mirror-stop screw. Neither of these adjustments involves touching the H-lamp. Remember that all adjustments must be done with lamp ' on ', and that it gets untouchably hot in a few moments. Vertical adjustment used to be a matter of trying to slide the lamp up-and-down into its best position before it got too hot to hold. Bits of skin are apt to burn into the lamp surface and obscure the light. So does the rubber of typists' finger-stalls. And a vertical fine adjustment is essential every time a hydrogen lamp is replaced, which, though infrequent, is almost always in an urgent

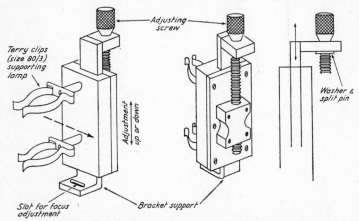

FIG. 7.6. Screw adjustment for the Unicam hydrogen lamp (Edisbury and Sanders, 1954). The broken arrow between the two Terry clips shows the direction of the light towards the pivoted mirror. The focus adjustment is usually satisfactory as set by the makers.

hurry. Figs. 7.6 and 7.7 show how the problem was solved on a very early Unicam SP.500 and an even earlier Beckman DU.

One immediate result was the ability to use, on both instruments, markedly narrower slits because of the increased radiation intensity delivered squarely into the monochromator. Another was a reduction in stray light. The performance of the Beckman became in fact rather better than new, and the Unicam was restored to as good as new. If there had been room in the lamp-house, I should have liked to try whether a fine-focusing adjustment could improve on the original Unicam works setting (Dr Campbell later found it did on one instrument); but I couldn't expect much improvement on near-perfection.

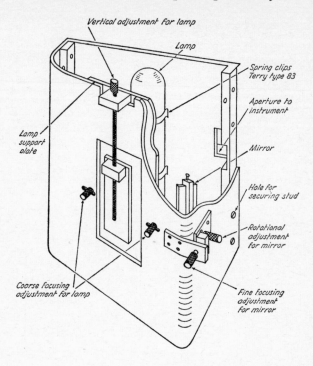

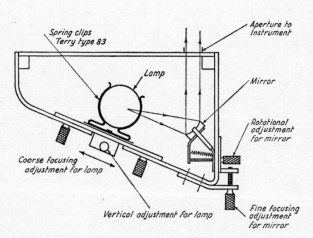

Fig. 7.7. Screw adjustment for the hydrogen lamp of an early Beckman DU (Sanders and Edisbury, 1955).

If anyone feels inclined to make a vertical H-lamp adjuster for an early SP.500 I advise allowing for a more generous range of movement than we did, so that the base of the lamp (where the wires are connected) can be lifted well clear of the hole in the floor of the lamp-house (through which the external leads enter) while they are being soldered. And whatever fine adjustments you incorporate anywhere, always make sure that you are able to adjust right *through* the optimum setting, so that you can over-shoot. If the optimum does happen to coincide with a limit of adjustment, you can never be certain of the fact; if you are able to pass right through it, you can.

After a few hundred hours' use, a hydrogen lamp understandably begins to fall off in performance. This deterioration will probably not be perceptible on a recording instrument (with servo-slits, etc.) until replacement is urgently needed. That is one reason why routine inspection is so desirable. On a manual instrument, deterioration can be followed easily if a control chart is intelligently used (Chapter 18). This reveals any drift in slit-width as time passes. Without a control chart, defects creep up on one unexpectedly.

To inspect the H- or D-lamp, remove the lamp-house cover and look at the aperture of the cold lamp with the aid of a dental mirror. If the lamp is approaching the stage of replacement, the metal around the aperture will be discoloured for a distance of maybe a mm, and the aperture enlarged. It may even be obscured by a reflecting film of sputtered metal on the inside of the envelope in line with the aperture. This film will transmit a fair proportion of light and may not be easily detected when the lamp is ' on '; but it is obvious enough when looked at squarely by external illumination with the lamp ' off '. You can't usually see it from above or from the side; you must look straight in through the area opposite the aperture whence the trouble came. Experiments now said to be proceeding with a modified direction of discharge should substantially prolong the useful life of the lamp.

THE UNDER-WATER SPARK

In the history of spectrophotometry, the under-water spark holds somewhat the same position as the Cornish Beam Engine does in the history of engineering. In their day, both were majestically supreme: yet neither is remotely likely to be revived for general use. Few people seem to know about the under-water spark, surely the noisiest Ancient Monument of all time, so I round-off this chapter with a brief outline.

In its first form (Konen, 1909; V. Henri, 1913, 1924) it was no more than a discharge of several kV through distilled water, noisy, temperamental, dangerous, and not particularly powerful as a light source, but at least giving a UV continuum then otherwise unobtainable. Brode and McNicholas at NBS, and Morton and Rosney at Liverpool University, added a new dimension by amplifying the

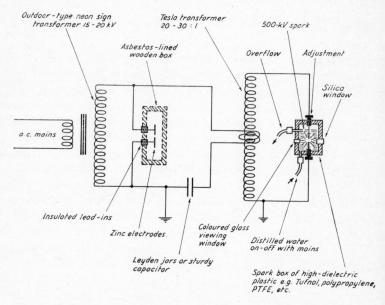

Fig. 7.8. Diagrammatic circuit of the under-water spark.

already high voltage with Tesla coil about a metre high and $\frac{1}{2}$-metre wide, plus auxiliary spark gap and condenser, and then passing the final spark between tungsten or nichrome electrodes under *running* distilled water. [See McNicholas, 1928; Brode, 1943; Mellon (K.S. Gibson's contribution), 1950.] If the water ceased to flow for more than a few seconds it rapidly became contaminated with colloidal metal which provided too easy an alternative path to earth: remember the dielectric constant of good distilled water is 80. Interference with local radio and telephones and, later, radar was considerable but was cured by enclosing the whole set-up, including the operator, in a grounded chicken-wire cage.

The only minor improvements I was able to introduce when I made my own under-water spark source (Fig. 7.8) was to use a more rugged outdoor neon-sign transformer to energize the primary of the Tesla; to replace the unreliable and unneccessarily noisy rotating auxiliary spark gap by a simple stationary pair of boxed-in Leclanché battery zincs; and to replace the original mains on-off switch (which, to conserve distilled water, turned a tap through a pulley mechanism) by a monel metal water tap with an extended arm that also doubled as a knife switch. A plastic shield guarded against mains shock, which can be fatal; so can the output from the neon sign transformer; whereas the half-million or more volts from the Tesla secondary is almost a static discharge of only a microamp or two—wildly startling when encountered unexpectedly, briskly tingling when deliberately approached, but harmless anyway. In darkness, the brush discharge from everything, especially from the down-lead to the light-box, profoundly impressed feminine visitors.

Looking back nostalgically over thirty years at the under-water spark, I feel that its manifest drawbacks were at least partly counterbalanced by such occasional moments of charm. With what other light source can you *safely* ignite a bunsen burner with a 5 cm spark from your finger tip?

E

CHAPTER 8

PHOTO-DETECTORS

Optics sharp it needs, I ween,
To see what is not to be seen

JOHN TRUMBULL, *McFingal* i 67

Apart from the trained eye and the photographic plate, which have been briefly dealt with in Chapters 5 and 4, there are three methods of light detection commonly used in the UV and visible:
(1) Photo-conductive; (2) Photo-voltaic; (3) Photo-emissive.

(1) PHOTO-CONDUCTIVE

The electrical resistance of a photo-conductor is lowered when it is illuminated. Several variants are available. All work on the same principle: unilluminated and cold, they are practically electrical insulators, $\sim10^{10}$ ohms. Incident photons of appropriate wavelength raise the energy level of some of the electrons bound to individual atoms up to the point where they become mobile and susceptible to the influence of an impressed voltage, typically 5–10 volts. The material then becomes in a limited sense a conductor, and over a small range of low illumination the response is rectilinear. Heat has much the same result: to decrease as far as possible all extraneous effects ('noise') and make full use of the relevant light signal, the photo-conductor must be kept cool. The same applies to most photo-detectors.

Lead sulphide has been successfully used for the 'upper' end of the visible region and into the near infra-red. Some spectrophotometers are fitted with a PbS cell as a built-in alternative to the photomultiplier, selected by means of a swivelling mirror for use whenever the wavelength exceeds about 700 mμ, where normal photomultiplier sensitivity begins to fall off.

Another notable photo-conductive material is cadmium selenide. This has a sharp response-maximum at 710 mμ (141oo cm^{-1}) though it shows some sensitivity from the X-ray region right through to the near infra-red. Again, at low levels of illumination, response is rectilinear; but it is better to use the cell as an unusually sensitive and compact qualitative detector rather than to attempt serious quantitative work with it, at least in its present stage of development. Response is such that, even under quite low illumination, there is sufficient current for the direct operation of some relays, and the time constant is of the order of $\frac{1}{2}$–1 millisecond.

(2) PHOTO-VOLTAIC

The simplest photo-detector is the barrier-layer, 'sandwich' or 'rectifier' cell, which responds to light by generating a current strong enough to be registered directly on a galvanometer,

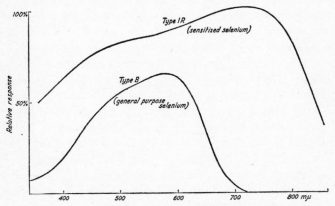

FIG. 8.1. The spectral response of a barrier layer. (By courtesy of Megatron Ltd.) See also Fig. 1.1.

without further amplification or the use of any external source of potential. Hence the name ' photo-voltaic '. It is understandably popular for the less costly photometric instruments, and is ruggedly reliable in rough handling; being the basis of most exposure meters used by amateur photographers in all manner of circumstances and climates, indoors and out, it needs to be. It is, in fact, especially suited to photography because the response curve (Fig. 8.1) is inherently fairly similar to that of the human eye, and can, by interposition of a pale khaki-green light filter, be made almost exactly so. Of more interest in spectroscopy, the useful range without a filter is normally from about 350/400 mμ up to

650 mμ (2900o/2500o–1540o cm^{-1}) or, after special sensitizing treatment, to the near infra-red, beyond 850 mμ (1180o cm^{-1}). There has not yet been enough development work with trace additives to extent UV response appreciably. But I hear rumours . . .

The barrier-layer cell consists essentially of two dissimilar materials in contact: one a metal or material of n-type that behaves electrically in some ways like a metal (that is, it conducts electricity by means of mobile electrons); and the other, supported on a metal base and so forming the middle component of the sandwich, a photo-sensitive semi-conductor of p-type (a reluctant conductor in which the current carriers are mobile centres of electron deficiency, or 'positive holes'). (Veszi, 1953. See also Preston, several papers.) The 'barrier-layer' or interface between the two acts as a source of electrons when it is illuminated, and also as a rectifier in that the electrical resistance through the layer is a few hundred times higher in one direction than in the other (see below). Sargrove (1947), I think rightly, distinguishes between the effects of two barrier-layers: one, the 'front wall', which is the normally recognized layer receiving light; and the electrically opposing 'rear wall', which is a second hypothetical barrier-layer between the selenium and the metal base, normally in permanent darkness but affected by infra-red radiations to which the light-opaque selenium is relatively transparent. This is a complication worth noting, but not to worry about, as it is part of a background that remains constant so long as the temperature does not vary significantly and genuine infra-red radiation is avoided. Here we are concerned with the 'front wall' barrier-layer only.

It seems (roughly) that, under illumination of this layer or interface, electrons prised loose from the selenium by the incident light are further urged to pass through the barrier in the 'difficult' direction from the p-type material to the n-type; simultaneously, owing to the build-up of electrical back-pressure, an electronic internal fall-back occurs which, at equilibrium and on open circuit, exactly equals the 'up hill' flow (Fig. 8.2). Connecting a galvanometer in the external circuit upsets this equilibrium, and the charge is drawn off quickly as it forms in the n-type layer. The galvanometer reading is a measure of the electron output and hence of the light energy being received. With a low external resistance, the flow is proportional to the light intensity over a wide range (short, of course, of saturation); with a high resistance, response becomes more nearly related to the logarithm of the light intensity.

Selenium is the most-used, best-known and most photo-active semi-conductor used in barrier-layer cells, and has been developed to a high degree of electrical performance. A layer of purified molten or glassy selenium, a few thousandths of an inch thick (one or two tenths of a mm), is applied to the chemically clean roughened surface of a sturdy steel or aluminium base plate—one extreme of the sandwich—which forms the positive electrode of the cell,

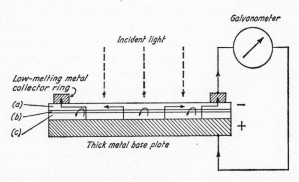

Fig. 8.2. Diagrammatic section through a barrier-layer photocell.

    (*a*) Transparent conductive layer
    (*b*) Theoretical barrier layer at interface between (*a*) and (*c*)
    (*c*) Selenium layer

The solid arrows show the direction of the electron flow, including internal 'fall-back' (see text) and sideways flow along the transparent layer to the collector ring. (Adapted from Veszi, 1953, *inter alia*.)

possibly carrying a terminal. Under pressure and heat-treatment at about 200°C the selenium layer is converted from whatever form it was in, to the β-form, which is the photo-sensitive allotrope required, so-called grey selenium. Onto the sensitive surface a thin film of suitable transparent *n*-type conductor—the other extreme of the sandwich—is applied by cathodic sputtering, plus a substantial peripheral strip, 2–3 mm wide, of low-melting alloy (e.g. Wood's metal) sprayed or run on to reinforce, and to provide electrical contact with, the delicate film. This is the negative pole. The favoured mode of external contact is through gentle spring pressure against this strip, to avoid damage to the underlying film. Never try to ' solder ' on a connection, even with the lowest-melting Wood's metal; although a connecting wire is sometimes imbedded in the strip, this is done under carefully controlled conditions during manufacture. The exposed area of n-type surface is protected by lacquer, leaving the strip itself bright and bare for good electrical contact. The completed photo-cell is matured by short-circuiting the electrodes and strongly illuminating the surface for a couple of days, followed by storage in darkness for three months. Finally it is checked for performance.

The lacquered surface must never be touched. Removal of a fingerprint is likely to remove the lacquer and maybe the film itself. At most, a soft dry brush (Fig. 6.17) and gentle stream of dry air, or suction, can be used to remove dust, but if this is not sufficient the makers should be consulted. Work in the visible is not likely to be affected by a light fingerprint, anyway, though it could interfere with attempts to penetrate the UV. If a perspex cover is fitted, it can be cleaned with tissue dipped in distilled water containing a little detergent, if care is taken to prevent moisture from getting behind the perspex. Similarly with thin glass or silica, which will stand alcohol. Some cells are completely encapsulated (' potted ') in araldite, thin enough at the appropriate portion to admit whatever radiation is in use. This should avoid embarrassments such as the mercurial ' poisoning ' of a photocell described by Cannon and Butterworth (1953). Encapsulation seems to me worth pursuing further, in conjunction with a glass or silica window over the light-sensitive part, with the protective plastic coming right up to the edge to complete the seal.

Many materials have been used for the thin n-type film. Cuprous oxide (as in the rectifiers used in trickle-chargers), gold, a whole host of base metals including copper, some in double films with gold on the outside, and various oxides. The best results to date seem to have been with cadmium cathodically sputtered on under controlled conditions of oxygen and inert gas admission which ensure that the active interface in contact with the selenium is CdO. This is indefinitely stable and of low electrical resistance because of the presence of metallic Cd atoms in the crystal lattice, making it a good n-type semi-conductor. Too much Cd makes for opacity; too little for poor conductivity. One of the major problems is, of course, to achieve a working compromise between these two incompatibles: transparency and conductivity. The film has to transmit as much light as possible to the interface between itself and the underlying selenium, and it also has to pass currents of up to about a milliampere ' sideways ' along the film. Often the film is so thin that it shows interference colours; yet the conductivity remains satisfactory. In this almost two-dimensional world, strange-sounding expressions are used: thus, electrical resistance is logically described as so many ' ohms per square ', meaning ' ohms between two electrodes separated by a distance equal to their own length '.

In the dark, the effective internal resistance of a small photo-voltaic cell some 5 or 6 cm^2 in area is of the order of 10^2–10^3 ohms one way, 10^5 the other, and in inverse proportion for larger and smaller areas. This provides the basis for a rough but quick test of a suspect cell. Connect longish insulated wires to the two poles and cover the cell generously with a black cloth or enclose it in a light-proof box. With a microammeter in series, apply 1·5 volts d.c. (one cell of a dry battery), negative to the base, positive to the light-sensitive face, i.e. the ' wrong ' way round. The current through a 25 mm diameter cell should not much exceed 15–35 microamps. If it exceeds 50–100 microamps, there is something very wrong (Veszi, 1941). On the other hand, a milliammeter should be needed to cope with the current when the cell is re-connected in the normal working direction.

This is why a photo-voltaic cell gives its best rectilinear response (essential in transmittance measurements) when it is used with a low-resistance galvanometer, 100–200 ohms, even though this limits its performance. The sensitivity of a galvanometer depends *inter alia* on the number of turns in its coil, and each turn adds to the resistance. The potential generated by a photo-voltaic cell is governed by the intensity of illumination and by the composition of the components of the sandwich, and it is largely independent of the area of the photo-active surface, which governs the maximum current obtainable on short circuit. The current actually flowing, however, depends on the potential *and* on the sundry resistances it encounters on its way round, including the resistance of the galvanometer, which must ' harmonize with ' the rest of the circuit. A nice balance is needed between the conflicting factors, and little can be worked out quantitatively on first principles. But it is not difficult to rationalize *post hoc* why, for instance, rectilinear response can be assured only by using the smallest (i.e. with highest resistance) light-sensitive area compatible with other requirements.

Because the photo-cell and galvanometer are ' matched ' or harmonized into the circuit, they cannot be replaced at random without probably impairing the designed performance. A low-resistance external load also complicates the problem of fitting an amplifier, though this rarely arises because most people are understandably reluctant to spoil the essential simplicity of the amplifier-less set-up. As one who has struggled all too often with the wayward thermionic valve, I sympathize. Nevertheless, I feel that the advent of the minimum-battery, transistor-based, amplifier does rather alter the picture.

By the use of vastly improved cathode-sputtered films of good conductivity and transparency, and by judiciously doping the selenium with trace impurities, photo-voltaic response in the 800–1000 mμ region has already been enhanced up to a usable level. This increase has had milder, but hitherto accidental, favourable repercussions right along into the mid-UV. So far, there do not seem to have been any deliberate efforts to boost UV response, beyond half-hearted attempts to prevent too much of the incident light from being absorbed by the top layer. But it is at least conceivable that deliberate UV-sensitizing may be possible some day. I can visualize a simple ' Model T ' type of spectrophotometer with a 200–800 mμ photo-voltaic detector coupled to a transistorized amplifier (sealed in plastic and discarded for another to be plugged in when anything goes wrong), the resistance of which would provide enough external load to shift the response curve away from the rectilinear to the logarithmic, or near-logarithmic, and so allow an almost linear photometer scale . . . A crazy idea? Maybe. ' The best way to get a good idea ', says Professor Linus Pauling, ' is to have lots of ideas '.

(3) PHOTO-EMISSIVE

Photo-emissive cells within the scope of this book comprise two related, but in practice distinct, types: phototubes and photomultipliers, or, more correctly, electron-multipliers. Phototubes are used on most manual instruments of the type started by the Beckman DU, e.g. SP.500 and 600, Uvispek, etc. Photomultipliers are customary on recording spectrophotometers, but have also been fitted with marked success to manual instruments where they allow the use of much narrower slit-widths. Kits are available for conversion of some instruments.

PHOTOTUBES

Also called ' photocells ', a term preferably reserved for the photo-voltaic type to avoid ambiguity, phototubes consist of transparent cylinders of glass or silica, according to purpose, evacuated to a near-vacuum, containing two electrodes: the cathode is uniformly coated with a layer of photo-emissive metal or alloy and connected to the negative input of the amplifier; the anode is a well-spaced grid of fine wire, fairly close to the cathode, standing squarely in the light beam but too fine to obstruct it significantly, and maintained at a steady positive potential by the other side of the amplifier input.

Most metals emit electrons when heated; many emit them when they are illuminated. The alkali metals are notable for their copious photo-emission, and each has its advantages over a limited range (see Lothian, 1958). Caesium in various guises maintains a good average performance over most of the spectrum, and practically monopolizes commercial UV and visible spectrophotometry: an antimony–caesium alloy for the near-visible and the entire UV down to about 180 mμ (55500 cm^{-1}); and caesium oxide, or caesium on caesium oxide on silver (to name only one combination), for 600–650 mμ upwards (16700–15400 cm^{-1}). In popular language the Sb-Cs surface is called ' blue-sensitive ' and the caesium oxide surface ' red-sensitive ' from their original use in colorimetry. These expressions make up in convenience much of what they lack in exactness. Given vigorous illumination, the Sb-Cs surface is *usably* sensitive up to the fringe of the infra-red, though Ag-O-Cs is theoretically preferable if the changeover is not inconvenient. Practice usually wins over theory. An important practical requirement is that over-all response (photo-surface + light source) should remain reasonably uniform over the spectral range in use. As much as possible, light intensity and detector sensitivity should therefore vary in opposite directions. From 180 mμ to the near-visible, the hydrogen lamp and blue-sensitive surface complement each other well, and where the hydrogen lamp's performance falls off, the tungsten filament takes over adequately (Fig. 7.5).

E*

After traversing the sample the light beam enters the phototube through the side opposite to the cathode—practically unimpeded by the positively charged grid—and liberates electrons from the photo-surface. These are attracted to and caught by the anode, delivered as a micro-current to the amplifier, and duly registered on a milliammeter. (See Chapter 6.) The ' dark current ', which flows even in the complete absence of light, is of the order of 10^{-11} amp, lower if the cathode is cool, much higher if it is allowed to get hot, when thermionic emission occurs. Deliberate cooling is not needed, except perhaps in an uncomfortably hot laboratory; but it is a sensible precaution to shield photo-surfaces from the heat of nearby amplifier filaments, and to keep the amplifier casing itself cool. This is another argument for laboratory air-conditioning and judiciously placed fans, particularly in a hot climate. An over-large dark current and its usually attendant random ' electronic noises ' partially obscure the genuine photo-current, which you want as free as possible from inconstant background effects. Any current that gets into the amplifier is amplified indiscriminately. Unwanted effects are most noticeable at those hard-to-get readings where a low noise-to-signal ratio is particularly important, because the signal has already been attenuated by the light absorption of the sample. Sensitivity of photo-response can be increased by the presence of a trace of ionizable gas, but much over $5 \times$ improvement tends to induce instability.

Some photo-surfaces fatigue rather quickly and give lower response and drifting readings. If you are ready for this effect it need not trouble you. Just release the absorbance/transmittance control as soon as you have balanced the meter, and close the light shutter *immediately*; then, but not till then, write down the reading. That prevents your accidentally moving the control again, and about halves the period of photo-surface illumination. Not all photo-surfaces are thus afflicted. The Sb-Cs surface, for instance, seems largely immune, besides being more usefully sensitive over a wider range than most and usually emitting a much smaller dark current than Cs-O-Cs. Hence its extensive use in photomultipliers, which work well despite the very prolonged spells of rapidly intermittent illumination they receive in recording spectrophotometers. A special phototube employed in the Hitachi P-E 139 makes the best of both worlds by including two photosurfaces in one tube: Ag-Cs for sensitivity from 600 mμ up;

Sb-Cs, 600 mμ down. Both dark current and drift can be kept low if the temperature is well controlled.

There is no need for the envelope of a red-sensitive phototube to be made of anything but glass; but be very careful to verify that the envelope of a blue-sensitive phototube is made of good quality silica if you intend to study the UV below about 350 mμ. Not every blue-sensitive phototube is made with UV spectrometry in mind.

Not much can go wrong with a phototube if it is not dropped or heated above 70–75°C, when the photo-surface is apt to vaporize, at least partially; but the outer surface and (often overlooked) the base and socket must be kept free from dust, damp and smears. Unless an amplifier housing—which usually also accommodates the phototubes—is sealed by silica windows, it ' breathes ' gently with every change in temperature, diurnal, nocturnal, or casual, due to cloud movements or doors left open, and can accumulate an astonishing amount of dust over a period of months. Some of it will provide a much easier alternative electrical path than, say, a 2000-megohm resistor, even if it does happen to be dry; and the biggest surfaces are the envelopes of the phototubes. It is wise to remove the phototubes from time to time (perhaps quarterly) and clean the outer surfaces with alcohol, not forgetting the base and sockets, and taking the usual care not to leave any fingerprints.

PHOTOMULTIPLIERS

The photomultiplier is (roughly) an electronic extension of the phototube. Near one end of an only slightly longer tube, and for UV work ' viewed ' by the light beam through a silica window (if the whole tube is not already of silica), is a photo-emissive surface, usually Sb-Cs alloy. This first electrode (the ' photo-cathode ') emits electrons as usual when illuminated. These are directed along curved paths by fixed electrostatic fields to a nearby electrode (the first ' dynode ') which is held at a controlled potential some 60–120 volts higher. Each electron impinging thereon releases a further four or five electrons (' secondary emission ') to be similarly directed towards and caught by the next dynode, which is held at a still higher potential. So the miniature controlled chain-reaction cascade proceeds for eight to a dozen or more dynodes, with a cumulative potential difference of upwards of 10^3 volts and an internal amplification of some $10^6 \times$. This is a useful start for any amplifying circuit.

Each dynode is both a cathode and an anode—a cathode in the sense that it emits electrons to be caught by the next dynode; an anode, in that it receives electrons from the dynode before. There is no theoretical limit to the number of dynodes; in practice, the crowding together of a dozen or more dynodes in one compact envelope—often under 10 cm long—and trying to connect each of them to a graduated high-tension supply through an insulated 11–15-pin base about 2 cm diameter, sets acute mechanical and

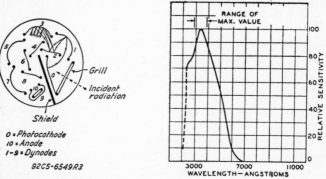

FIG. 8.3. Schematic internal arrangement and response curve of the 1P28 photomultiplier. (By courtesy of the Radio Corporation of America.)

electrical problems. Commercial photomultipliers with more than nine dynodes are understandably rare, though not unknown in spectrophotometry. The 1P28 as used in the Ultrascan is typical of current practice (Fig. 8.3).

This has nine dynodes and an 11-pin base, itself quite a problem in electro-topology. The base is non-hygroscopic, so it is a waste of time to use anything else for the socket; PTFE can be recommended. Spectral response of the Sb-Cs photo-cathode is useful from below 200 to above 800 mμ (500oo–125oo cm^{-1}). Interstage potential, between adjacent dynodes, is designedly 80–100 volts, which can be supplied by (literally) a pile of radio high-tension batteries, but is far better achieved by tappings from a potentiometer fed from the rectified output of a stabilized mains transformer (Fig. 8.4). The average gain per stage is about $4 \cdot 7 \times$, giving an over-all amplification of 1 250 000 at the designed voltage. Response is rectilinear under normal conditions of illumination, and almost instantaneous—at over 100 megacycles/sec the minor variations in electron transit times are said to be the limiting factor, so chopping frequencies of a few hundred per second cause no difficulties.

The final dynode (ninth) of the 1P28 partially encloses the anode and acts as a shield which prevents the fluctuations in anode potential from interfering with the electron focusing between the dynode pairs. At the other end, the electrode structure is further electrostatically shielded by an inter-connected assembly comprising (1) a metal grille through which the incident light illuminates the photo-cathode, (2) the photo-cathode itself, and (3)

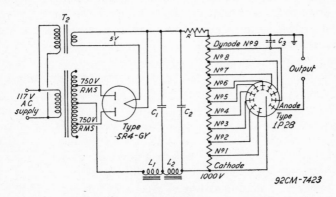

FIG. 8.4. Typical circuit for the 1P28 photomultiplier before full stabilization.

another shield isolating the first couple of dynodes from the rest. As a refinement, not always necessary, an external electrostatic shield, held at a negative potential about equal to that of the photo-cathode, reduces unwanted ' noise '. This shield is at a dangerous d.c. potential, and should be so labelled. Magnetic shielding is rarely needed; a field strength of 4 or 5 gauss, however, decreases the anode current by about 10%. Obviously, a fluctuating magnetic field of even one tenth of this would distort many absorption curves unacceptably. Ideally, the successive dynodes are operated at voltages increasing in equal steps of 75–95 volts, except that at the last stage, between Dynode 9 and the anode, a lower voltage—as low as will only just allow current saturation—is recommended. Depending on the output required, this voltage could be as low as

50. This improves stability without sacrificing sensitivity. For maximum stability the anode current should not normally exceed 10 microamperes, with at least a ½-hour warm-up period. There is much to be said for leaving the circuit switched on continuously unless the rest period is more than a week. Here, photomultipliers differ between themselves, and one can only seek advice from the makers.

In some photomultipliers the dark current starts at a high level when the photomultiplier is first installed, gradually falling back to an acceptable value during several hours' rest in darkness. Exposure to full daylight (*with the voltage supply ' off '*) raises the dark current to a temporary high level again, calling for another period of rest. Sensitivity is also apt to fall during such exposure, and to recover slowly in the dark. The moral is, of course, to refrain from attempting serious quantitative use of a photomultiplier immediately after replacement or cleaning, or even after routine inspection of the ' works ', until the photomultiplier has had a night's rest to get over it. Again, the makers will advise.

One rule applies to all photomultipliers now on the market: NEVER, IN ANY CIRCUMSTANCES, EXPOSE ANY WORKING PHOTO-MULTIPLIER TO DAYLIGHT OR EVEN TO ARTIFICIAL LABORATORY LIGHTING. This links up with the manufacturer's usual injunction to switch off before removing the main cover from the spectrophotometer. The combination of excessive light plus high tension will probably ruin the photomultiplier with an uncontrollable cascade of electrons. The HT itself could kill you. Damage to other components during adjustment can be guarded against by using a protective resistor of at least 10 000 ohms in the output circuit.

Less sophisticated light detectors are neither so vulnerable nor so dangerous; but, at best, any photo-surface is not benefited by uncontrolled exposure under working conditions, and individual photo-surfaces can be damaged, at least temporarily.

The cleaning of the outside of a photomultiplier is even more important than it is with a phototube, because of the higher potentials involved. The envelope is easy; the base, difficult. Choose—if you have a choice—a non-hygroscopic base and socket, like PTFE (polytetrafluoroethylene, in case you have forgotten). Remember that high tension attracts dust, and dust builds up in, and bridges over, the insulating gaps between the close-set pins and sockets. A suction tube, clipped to a small brush (Fig. 6.17) is a useful accessory; but it is easier to prevent dust from entering than to remove it completely afterwards.

An operational temperature of not more than 25°C is recommended, preferably much lower. Some users have gone so far as to cool their photomultipliers deliberately in order to minimize dark current and random ' electron noise '. This has been found worth while in a few instances. Only the ' open ' end of the tube need be cooled (by a jacket surrounding that part, a window being left for ingress of the light beam), because by the time the fourth dynode is reached the cascade of electrons has already multiplied a hundred-fold, or more, and ' noise ' forms a correspondingly smaller proportion of the total flow. The cold spot created within the instrument by the presence of a jacket containing cooled brine, or the gas from liquid nitrogen or solid carbon dioxide, can cause complications with the thermostat (if any), so it is wise to surround the jacket with heat-insulating material, leaving the rest of the photomultiplier exposed. Beware of leaks; brine, because of danger of short-circuits; CO_2, because of its opacity in some parts of the spectrum. In a properly dry instrument, there should be no risk of the photomultiplier frosting over. But if it did, there would be cause for minor panic and prompt action.

Turk (1952) gives a monumental exposition of the theory and practice of photomultiplication which is still not wholly out-of-date; it forms a good introduction to the subject, more easily understandable than most. As he points out: ' The process of photo-activation still defies the scientific approach and largely boils down to a cookery problem. Most processes capable of yielding high photo-sensitivity involve the use of caesium, which is also used to produce high secondary emission, *but* the same proportion is not always required. . . . The multiplier should add no new noise, but, as with the photo-cathode, this is impossible since secondary emission is also a random phenomenon.' Which is only one of the reasons why I dedicated this book to the Goddess of Chance.

The normal photomultiplier is designed to give as nearly as possible a rectilinear relationship between light input and electrical output. For transmittance measurements, therefore, little is needed (in principle) beyond a strictly straight-line amplifier and—in recording instruments—an adequately responsive servo-motor to move the pen along its ordinate. Absorbance (optical density, extinction) recording in equally-graded steps, which is more generally useful, requires a logarithmic mode of operation: Absorbance=1/(log transmittance). This can be provided (cf. Chapter 6) by a suitably contoured cam that varies the position of an optical wedge, comb, or shutter in the ' reference ' or ' blank ' beam, or by potentiometric attenuation of the electrical output derived from this beam, the potentiometer being graduated logarithmically, like a slide-rule. It is a matter of compromise. Changing-over of cams is at the best of times irksome to the operator; switching-in a logarithmic network is operationally easy, but technically fairly difficult, though usually successful and more reliable than one would expect. Davey (1963) describes an alternative method patented by Gilford Instrument Laboratories Inc., Ohio, whereby a logarithmic ordinate can be obtained more directly. Over a fair range, the gain of a photomultiplier is proportional to the logarithm of the voltage applied across the dynodes. In Gilford's patent, the output of a 1P28 is kept constant by deliberately varying the dynode voltage. A reading or recording of this required voltage is proportional to the absorbance of the sample, and the meter or chart can be calibrated accordingly in units of absorbance instead of in volts. By the introduction of very minor trimming corrections, rectilinearity of better than 1% is claimed up to about 3·0 absorbance (0·1% T).

To me, the main interest of this idea is the promise it holds of simplifying the direct recording of *log absorbance* by using a logarithmic attenuator somewhere else in the same set-up. I leave the details to be worked out by the experts.

CHAPTER 9

ABSORPTION CELLS OR CUVETTES

... O'er brimmed their clammy cells
KEATS *To Autumn: Canto* i

Just as ' capsule ' can nowadays mean several things from soft-shelled pills to space-craft, so the word ' cell ' means any one of a variety of containers from the unit mass of living matter to a small room in a monastery or prison, as well as, in a metaphorical sense, isolated and usually subversive minor political groups. Exactly which meaning happens to be appropriate is revealed only by the context or descriptive adjective (battery-, photo-, etc.). In spectrophotometry, to avoid possible confusion, the transparent container designed to hold the test solution or compensating solvent is often called a ' cuvette ', which (among other things) is French for a small tub, bucket, or cistern, i.e. temporary liquid-container. Very apt, I think, and a suitable name for any shape or size of absorption cell.

Cuvettes come in a large variety of shapes, sometimes merely for user-convenience, sometimes because a particular shape genuinely suits a particular purpose. Plates 4 and 5 show an assortment. The physical requirements are that a sample of liquid or gas shall be contained without contamination or leakage between two parallel transparent end-plates a known distance apart. The rest of the outfit is merely a means of holding the end-plates at their appointed separation and confining the sample between them. Sideways dimensions are dictated only by the space in the cuvette holder; by the available volume of liquid; and by the need to keep the light beam clear of the bottom and side-walls of the cuvette and the top surface of the solution. From any of these surfaces, internal reflection can occur, deflecting an indeterminate fraction of the beam away from its proper path. Theoretically, a minimal clearance is all that is necessary; in practice, it is well to allow at least a mm all round, and perhaps a little more at the top. Parallelism of the end-plates, through which the light beam enters and leaves, is important less because of any minor uncertainty in the exact length of light-path within the solution than because the wedge effect of an inclined end-plate deflects the whole beam away from that part of the photo-surface ' calibrated ' by the light through the compensator or blank. Some photo-surfaces are not perfectly uniform in response over their whole sensitive area. (See Chapter 17.)

Nowadays the most popular cuvette is the square or rectangular type, open at the top. Early examples were beautifully but fragilely made from five separate pieces of glass or silica cemented together along eight double edges—four upright for the ends and sides, four horizontal round the bottom—the end-plates alone being of optical quality. Later examples were cautiously fused along the edges, more durable but not always free from distortion. Another development was the use of a process called ' adhesing ', in which the edges were polished flat and the whole assembly clamped together and heated to a temperature, just short of fusion and distortion, at which enough surface-softening occurs for the parts in contact under slight pressure to diffuse into each other on a micro-scale. Only areas with an optical, interference-fit, finish will do this, and—with luck—the result is a weld as strong as the material itself. This was more successful with the later (and now almost universal) three-piece construction, in which a U-shaped distance piece is sandwiched between two end-plates (I have often wondered how *five* pieces were ever held satisfactorily in an assembly jig). But despite its initial promise, and its undoubted aesthetic appeal, adhesing lacks permanence. Even after annealing, unexpected stresses develop slowly and local separation occurs here and there, spreading sometimes until the whole join comes adrift, usually not *in*, but closely parallel to, the plane of junction. In this, they lived up to the manufacturer's claim that the joint was stronger than the original material; but that was small comfort to the user of a cuvette that fell to pieces. Unless or until a new breakthrough occurs in the technique of adhesing, edge-fusion is far to be preferred, and is now standard practice except for a few special-purpose cuvettes which are cemented; much cheaper—and more fragile.

Early examples of fused-edge cuvettes got a bad reputation for distortion—understandably, when you think of the problems involved. These have now been overcome to the point that a

British Standard (B.S. 3875: 1965) has been issued to the effect that there must be a minimum optically flat, polished, area in the middle of each end-plate, large enough for its limits to clear the light beam by a good margin. To ensure complete absence of central distortion, despite local fusion of the contacting edges barely a couple of mm away, needs considerable expertise in manufacture, and high cost is only to be expected. All things considered, including permanence and robustness as well as accuracy, the cost is not excessive.

At least one maker engraves his trade mark on an inoperative part of the incident face so that the cuvette can always be oriented the same way round in the light beam. This is a wise precaution. If any of your cuvettes is not so marked, I strongly advise you to etch an arrow with hydrofluoric acid on the outside of a side wall to show the preferred direction of the light. (See Chapter 17.)

To prevent evaporation of solvent and/or contamination of the interior of the cuvette compartment with vapour of any kind, noxious or not, most cuvettes are provided with a lid. You need seldom use it but it is worth having. The lid should fit *inside* the filling aperture; a lid that merely rests on top, or fits over—or even projects over—the outside, can allow any splashed liquid that touches it to seep down the outside of the cuvette. If this happens to be over an end-plate there is little hope of a quantitative result unless you can wipe the surface with alcohol without spilling any more contents. Spillage over a side does not matter so long as the spilled liquid does not creep onto an end-plate or dirty the cuvette carrier, which contaminates the next cuvette. If the compartment is large enough to allow it, place the lid on after the cuvette and carrier are in the beam. An exceptionally steady hand is needed to move a full cuvette without at least some liquid coming into contact with the lid, even though surface tension will normally prevent spillage from an open cuvette unless it is absurdly full. Experience will show the best level. Incidentally, if the lids are of plastic, even nominally inert plastic, it is a sensible precaution to extract them in a Sohxlet with an assortment of solvents to remove any possible traces of plasticizer which could otherwise contaminate a solution. But if a lid won't stand up to boiling, I don't trust it. And I would never trust a solvent out of a plastic ' squash-bottle ' for work in the UV. Dr E. M. F. Roe often tells of her experiences with UV spectra ruined by butyl phthalate; and that is not the only UV-opaque plasticizer.

I prefer to fill most cuvettes while they are standing on a couple of layers of thick filter paper, as if on a tablecloth. If, as sometimes does happen, the cuvette falls over, the paper prevents its breaking and protects the bench from much of the mess. (It has not been unknown for most of a scarce sample to be recovered from a filter paper by solvent extraction; which *could* be used as an additional argument for the use of clean paper . . .) If you have to ' make do ' with a stone bench, real or imitation, instead of a proper wooden one, three layers of paper might be a good precaution against breakage. Whether they are being filled or drained, *always* stand the cuvettes so that they miss each other when they fall over. They crack easily if they knock together.

While it is being filled, hold the cuvette gently by the sides to avoid the trouble of cleaning fingerprints from the end-plates. A large flat cork with grooves to hold the cuvettes upright is convenient, and prevents heating through over-long contact with the fingers. The use of a set of home-made pipettes, with or without inert plastic bulbs to draw up the liquid, and a second glass bulb above the rough calibration as a safety measure for noxious liquids, simplifies filling without spilling, and makes it practicable to fill cuvettes after they have been loaded into the holder. This is usually impossible by mouth; it is well worth the trouble of making a set of manual pipettes. For very small cuvettes, a fountain-pen filler with a fine-drawn nozzle is suitable if the bulb is kept clean. Contamination of its inner surface by the more volatile solvent vapours is hard to avoid, but need not cause trouble. Remove the bulb after use to allow free access of warm air and easy evaporation.

The modern cuvette of any size or shape usually has integral, leak-proof ends. There are, however, probably some surviving examples of the old demountable type of cuvette with detachable end-plates. The main—perhaps the only—advantage of this type is ease of cleaning. In one form, a sandwich comprising ' end-plate|glass ring or tube with optically flat ends|end-plate ', is held together by spring pressure in a frame or holder which is later clamped in position in the light beam; in another, threaded metal rings are cemented onto the ends of a tube, and the end-plates are pressed squarely against the optically flat ends by hollow threaded end-caps containing rubber rings to provide necessary resilience, without which there is risk of breakage and certainty of leakage. Sometimes a side-arm filler tube is thoughtfully provided, as is often used in polarimetry. A third type is shaped like a small Petri dish, with one permanent end-plate and an optically true rim against which the second end-plate is held. This is an excellent compromise, rarely leaking and easy to clean. It is particularly good for very short path-lengths of 1 mm or less, though a proper micrometer cuvette is even better if laboratory funds allow it. Here, side-arm filling and a micrometer thread, close-fitting enough to prevent leakage, combine to make what I consider the nearest approach to perfection in cuvettes. At the price, it ought to be. Its bigger and cruder brother, the Baly Tube or ' Trombo-cuvette ' (Fig. 4.6), deserves wider use wherever it can be accommodated, which unfortunately is not everywhere. I still have a nostalgic affection for it, and can vouch for the accuracy with which its length can be read off—something well under $\pm \frac{1}{2}$ mm at all lengths from 1 to 100 mm. In both the micrometer cuvette and the ' Trombo-cuvette ' the filling-arm doubles as a reservoir and the orifice is large enough to take a small cork to discourage evaporation. *Good* cork is preferred to a plastic or glass stopper. There is no danger of contamination once the cork has been thoroughly solvent-extracted, and its resilience saves breakages.

GLASS OR SILICA?

For working in the visible and near UV there is no need to use silica. In fact, in the old days when natural quartz was generally used for the UV, the optical properties of quartz other than transparency were quite a detriment—polarization (which could affect readings on a Nutting or König-Martens photometer), double refraction, fluorescence, etc., had to be allowed for. Nowadays, quartz has been practically ousted by refined synthetic silica with no asymmetric centres to cause optical rotation, and (generally) higher transparency, without loss of thermal advantages. And the cost is not very much higher than that of good quality, bubble-free, striation-free glass.

Most laboratories do not for long restrict themselves to one spectrophotometer. Starting with, perhaps, a simple visible + near-UV instrument, the attractions of the further UV beckon, and a more versatile instrument is demanded, extending the spectral range to about 200 mμ. (Later, the infra-red becomes interesting, but here the techniques and instrumental vagaries are so different that they call not only for a separate book, but also a separate laboratory. Visible and UV can live together; infra-red needs a laboratory to itself.) As soon as a 'proper' UV instrument is installed, the value of all-silica equipment becomes obvious. Silica and good glass look much the same at first glance, and can cause minor consternation if they get mixed. It is unfortunately only too easy to attempt to compensate a silica cuvette with a glass one of exactly the same shape. Until some convention is introduced

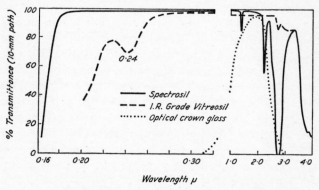

FIG. 9.1. Transmission curves of two varieties of fused silica compared with an average grade of optical crown glass.

whereby one material is clearly marked on the side-walls with (say) coloured dots, I think it an economy to use all-silica; time is money, and an awful lot of time can be wasted in chasing after UV spectra through a visibly transparent, UV-opaque cuvette. When the shapes are vastly different, trouble does not arise; for home-made cuvettes (see page 126) boro-silicate (e.g. Pyrex) glass is the obvious answer. This is transparent down to 350 mμ (2800o–2900o cm^{-1}) and sometimes a little further, which serves many purposes. Test-tubes are also used as cuvettes for certain specialized purposes. Here, breakages are of minor consequence and little respect is engendered among the younger members of the staff. But results can be very good indeed, especially if the instrument is deliberately designed with 'test-tube optics'. The Hilger Biochem is one such instrument (Fig. 9.2). The light-path through the cuvette is measurable accurately as the actual diameter of the test-tube, instead of a function of it, because the light rays are focused to enter and leave radially, i.e. normal to the surface, as in a 'proper' cuvette. Any other arrangement introduces an arbitrary factor due to the focusing effect of the test-tube and its contents, which act as a cylindrical lens. The effective path-length within the tube is then determinable only by directly comparing its performance with that of a normal cuvette, unless you want to get involved in some fairly high flights of mathematics. When used with light filters some such standardization against a spectrophotometer is in any case necessary for 'absolute' results even

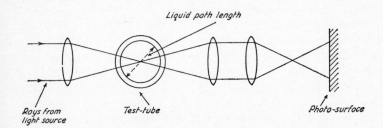

FIG. 9.2. Quantitative use of test-tubes as cuvettes in the Hilger Biochem. Parallel rays are focused so that they enter and leave the test-tube radially and are then re-focused on the photo-surface. The test-tube does not here act as a cylindrical lens. The liquid path-length is therefore the exact diameter of the tube, which can be measured directly.

with normal cuvettes, because filtered light is far from monochromatic, covering maybe 10^2 mμ, which will decrease the apparent extinction of the sample by an (almost) unpredictable amount. Whatever the cuvette shape, I think it is more practically useful to construct a calibration curve for each test substance against arbitrary readings whenever light filters are used. These readings will be simple direct functions of extinction, and what the exact relationship is between readings and true extinctions does not matter so long as it is known and remains constant, i.e. so long as the filter and test-tube characteristics do not change.

I see no reason, however, why the above radial light-path idea should not be extended to monochromators, for quantitative 'absolute' use when otherwise a large number of cuvettes would be required (for instance, in testing a series of solutions at intervals, as in fading tests, etc.). Cuvettes are costly; test-tubes are not. In one boxful of test-tubes a dozen or so can be picked out with indistinguishable internal dimensions. The remainder can be returned to store—for use as test-tubes. Silica, even UV Spectrosil, test-tubes are also available. The cuvette carrier would need modifying, of course, to slide between two lenses, as shown in Fig. 9.2, and the lid (at least) of the cuvette compartment would have to be raised, though remaining light-tight. But accuracy need not suffer seriously if care is taken.

Not all silica is adequately transparent in the further UV. Any old equipment, which might have originated as natural quartz, should be specially tested. With air as the blank, run a spectrum from 300 mμ downwards. Morton (1949) reports a cuvette which showed an absorption maximum at 240 mμ (41700 cm^{-1}) with an absorbance of 0·137 when it was compared with a nominally identical cuvette, both cuvettes being filled with distilled water. This seems to have been due to a trace of iron oxide dissolved in the quartz. Compare Fig. 9.1 (IR). Insist when buying new cuvettes that their transparent range covers, and if possible more than covers, the range you want. Spectrosil (made by Thermal Syndicate Ltd, Wallsend, U.K.) is noted for its quality; but be sure you get the correct grade. The IR grade is excellent in the near infra-red, but poor from the mid-UV down; the UV grade is transparent to below 190 mμ (52600 cm^{-1}) or even better, but shows massive bands in the near infra-red, where it would be useless. Always test for yourself.

FILLING DEMOUNTABLE CUVETTES

Cuvettes of the modern type, with both end-plates fused on, present no problems. Detachable end-plates do. And there are probably examples still to be found in the older laboratories. If possible, fix one end-plate on first, while the centre tube is empty. The retaining cap should be screwed on only just tightly enough to take up some of the resilience of the rubber or plastic pressure-ring. If the end-plate is squarely in position, surface tension will provide its own seal. Stand the tube upright on the filter paper. Hold it gently, or through cloth, so that the heat of the hand does not warm the tube. Fill with solution until the liquid bulges about $\frac{1}{2}$ mm above the top. Slide the other end-plate gently across the end, ' shaving-off ' the meniscus, which will run down the outside of the tube and be absorbed by the cloth; this prevents possible wetting of the end-plate already attached at the other end. If it does get wet, either (1) wait until the second end-cap is on and then wash the outside of the first with alcohol, or (2) refill, using clean end-plates. The choice is governed largely by the volatility of the solvent, and whether the rubber rings are at all soluble in it. The fashion is, or was, to use fairly hard rubber; I prefer it to be fairly, but not very, soft. Hold the filled cuvette up to the eye and look along the bore. Experience will tell you how big a bubble can be tolerated; there should theoretically be no bubble at all in a freshly filled cuvette. A side-arm-filled cuvette, even one with two detachable end-plates, should give no trouble. If there is a small bubble, tilt the cuvette slightly so that the bubble comes into the filling arm, and top-up as necessary.

If both end-plates are detachable and not held on by screwed end-caps, the process is more tricky. Place one end-plate in its recess in the holder, and stand the dry tube squarely on it. Hold it steady, and fill. Slide the other end-plate on rather more gently than in the previous paragraph because both end-plates can now leak. Bring down the spring clamp squarely and firmly. Inspect for bubbles and finger-marks. With the more volatile solvents it is almost impossible to avoid a bubble. Water is easy; diethyl ether or low-boiling petroleum are not for this sort of cuvette, even with unchipped end-plates and tube ends.

A well-assembled cuvette should not develop an obstructive bubble for an hour, but don't expect miracles. Nothing can beat sealed-on ends, especially on a warm day.

The Petri dish type of cuvette (Hilger Type J), with one end fixed, is easy both to clean and to fill. Use the same technique of shaving off the meniscus, and don't worry too much about wetting either or both end-plates. The whole cuvette is easy to wipe clean with a cloth moistened with alcohol, followed by a polish with a dry cloth or lens tissue, without spilling the contents. You save time, however, if you don't let the end-plates get wet in the first place.

The same applies to the shorter type of cuvette with a fairly squat detachable ring separating the end-plates. With practice, the whole assembly can usually be picked up and wiped, the ends being held on by the solvent; but make sure that this isn't due to some evaporation having cooled and contracted the liquid, and incidentally altered its concentration from what you intended. What seems good luck may be misfortune. Unless you really must, or you are looking for a simple way to do penance, don't use this type of cuvette in anything less than 2–3 mm liquid thickness, except with viscous liquids, which are easier to clean off the parts of a demountable cuvette than from out of a very narrow one-piece cuvette.

Volatility is not the only cause of bubbles developing in a demountable cuvette. Surface tension (or rather its virtual absence) and viscosity are both at least as important. Water and n-heptane have almost the same boiling points (100° and 98°C) but they behave very differently in demountable cuvettes. Water is amenable; heptane is almost as bad as hexane, boiling at 30° lower. I haven't heard the word 'fugacity' bandied about since the nineteen-twenties, but whether it is strictly right or wrong semantically it certainly seems appropriate here.

HOME-MADE CUVETTES

Although it is not to be recommended as a regular practice, it is possible to make special-purpose cuvettes in the laboratory. Unless you have the proper equipment, don't attempt to grind end-plates; they have to be plane and polished, and are better bought separately, ready for use, in Spectrosil or glass according to needs.

For small path-lengths and viscous solutions (don't try to get solvent-tightness with hexane, ether, etc., but you might be successful with isopropanol and will be quite happy with oils or glycerol) grind the ends of a Pyrex tube or ring of appropriate length and diameter, first with coarse, then with fine, carborundum powder on a small piece of plate glass, to a good plane finish, unpolished. Measure the path-length with an engineer's micrometer at at least two opposite points on the circumference. This checks parallelism as well as telling you the size of cuvette. Incidentally, if the faces are *exactly* parallel and exactly perpendicular to an exactly parallel light beam, internal multiple reflection is theoretically possible, with optical interference effects; but as $\frac{1}{2}$° out of truth is more than enough to prevent this, and not nearly enough to affect the proper working of the cuvette, just aim at getting parallelism. For a small demountable cuvette, end-plates of exactly the same diameter as the separator ring are easiest to handle. If they are larger than the tube, they hamper picking up by the edges with the thumb and forefinger; if they are smaller, they leave too little margin for solvent-tightness.

For anything above a few cm path-length up to the largest that the cuvette compartment will accommodate, attach a side-arm mid-way along the tube before grinding the ends. The cuvette can then be used with one or both end-plates fixed on permanently with Araldite (etc.). So long as the adhesive really does not dissolve in the solvent(s) that you intend to use—make very sure of this— almost any strong adhesive is suitable; Le Page's Glue, for instance, is suitable for alcohol, carbon tetrachloride or oil, and has the advantage that the end-plates can be removed for easier internal cleaning by soaking in hot water. Sounds crude, but it works well in the right context. I used a pair of 10-cm tubular cuvettes this way for some years. They didn't match exactly, but by interchanging and averaging (page 203) good results were obtained.

CLEANING CUVETTES

It is impossible to over-stress the importance of cleanliness, but if a solution is *never* allowed to dry in a cuvette, cleanliness is no problem. A lot depends, of course, on the volatility of the solvent, and to a lesser degree on its viscosity.

(*a*) *Open-top type*
Immediately after use, empty the cuvette and drain it by letting it stand inverted on filter paper for half a minute. Rinse with a quarter cuvette-full of solvent (e.g. from the compensator), drain again, repeat three times, finish with alcohol (ethanol), which drains off better than anything else I know without leaving streaks. Blow dry with low-pressure air from an air line (filtered), or foot bellows. Rinse the compensator with alcohol. Blow dry. Polish the outside optical surfaces with grit-free lens tissue.

If the solvent is not miscible with alcohol, use some other solvent miscible with both the original solvent and alcohol, and then finish with alcohol.

Isopropanol is one of the more viscous common solvents, and it takes rather longer than usual to drain; half a minute may not be enough. It washes out easily, however, with ethyl alcohol.

If, as sometimes (but rarely) happens, a precipitate forms when the solution is diluted, it is usually diffuse enough at first to swill out. As a precaution with any unfamiliar solute always try out its dilution and/or washing-out behaviour in a test-tube before consigning it to one of the less-easy-to-clean types of cuvette. All that may be needed is a change of pH or the use of some other solvent, undesirable during the test but harmless for cleaning afterwards.

(*b*) *Side-arm filling types*

Some cuvettes have filling ' horns ' attached. They can usually be stood on these horns for draining, as for the open type. It is quicker to swill them out with solvent from a wash-bottle (glass, not a flexible plastic ' squash ' bottle), but be careful that the nozzle is small enough to fit loosely into the side arm. Otherwise breakage is likely. A filling funnel with a fine-drawn stem is useful with single side arms. Fill about half-full, and shake well before emptying. Allow to drain for rather longer than with the open type of cuvette. It is worth while to make a fine nozzle for blowing dry after the final rinse.

(*c*) *Demountable Cuvettes*

The completely dismantleable type is straightforward. Clean the end-plates with a soft rag wet with alcohol, and finish by polishing with lens tissue. Treatment of the centre section depends on its size and shape. The tubular type with screwed end-caps is best dismantled first at one end, emptied and drained, rinsed, then dismantled at the other end only if it is not going to be used immediately for a similar test. The ' ring ' type of centre is released as soon as the clamp (etc.) is loosened; take care it doesn't drop, and be careful when you wipe it. Thin rings are fragile when they are of glass and bendable when they are of metal; I don't like either. Petri dish cuvettes (Type J): both halves are treated as if they were both end-plates; just wipe them with an alcohol-damp cloth and polish with lens tissue.

(*d*) *Variable-path* (*Micrometer*) *Cuvettes*

Only general instructions can be given here. The manufacturers probably issue advice in individual detail. If the assembly *can* be dismantled, it certainly should be. Otherwise solute can get to the first few threads of the micrometer part and be difficult to remove until some solvent or solution that you particularly don't want to get contaminated does it for you. The thread is close-fitting to prevent leakage, and for that reason it is not always easy to screw back the parts of a dismantled variable cuvette. Brute force causes damage that only the makers, or an unusually expert and well-equipped instrument-man, can repair. Practise assiduously until you get the knack. The thread is generally of large diameter, which makes things more difficult; but by gently rotating the movable member anti-clockwise until a slight click is felt you can find the start of the thread, and go on from there in the correct clockwise direction.

Between runs on similar solutions it usually suffices to drain the cuvette and rinse once with the new solution; sometimes even this rinse may not be necessary. Try for yourself.

(e) Dirty Cuvettes of all kinds

If, through negligence (someone else's, of course, not yours), a solution has dried out in a cuvette, first consider its construction. If it can be dismantled, dismantle it. If it cannot, find out whether the parts are cemented or fused together. Cemented cuvettes are not necessarily inferior or fragile, but they will not always stand up to certain cleaning processes that are permissible with fused cuvettes, and they might not survive some boiling solvents. If in doubt, ask the makers. Unless some accident breaks the separate pieces, however, the worst that can happen through failure of the cement is for the cuvette to come apart at the seams; the separate unbroken pieces can then be thoroughly and drastically cleaned, and the whole thing reassembled with Araldite, applied thinly enough to simulate the original cement and restore the cuvette to its precise nominal path-length and parallelism. The major problem here is to keep the optical faces perfectly clean during reassembly and baking. The reconstituted cuvette should last long enough to make history.

To clean dismantled parts (glass or silica), reflux them with the solvent last used, or a mixture of likely solvents, for an hour. If a Sohxlet is used, allow longer to compensate for the lower temperature. An effective cleaning method attributed to Professor Hilditch (who was at Liverpool University for many years), but not to my knowledge ever openly recommended by him because of its potential danger, is to wet the object(s) superficially with ethyl alcohol (recovered), drain briefly, place in a porcelain dish in the fume cupboard, add a ml or two of concentrated nitric acid, and cover with a large beaker. Too much alcohol either inhibits the reaction or, if enough nitric acid is then added to make it work, makes it explosively dangerous. Fuming nitric acid is too violent for use on any but a one- or two-drop scale. After a short induction period of perhaps a minute (surely a merciful dispensation, giving enough time to cover the dish) close the fume cupboard and retreat to a safe distance. Nitric fumes, plus sometimes nitrogen pentoxide, can be seen, and a small-scale eruption cleanses the glassware. If the protective large beaker stands in water, some of the water is later sucked into the partial vacuum. After the reaction has subsided, rinse the clean parts with distilled water.

This method is usable with fused silica cuvettes if it is suitably scaled down; but fused *glass* cuvettes are unlikely to stand the local thermal shock which silica, with its low coefficient of expansion, is able to cope with. And it would probably be quickly fatal to cemented cuvettes. I can recommend the idea for any tough, inexpensive and uncalibrated glassware, NOT for pipettes and standard flasks, which can take on a semi-permanent set for a week or two after heating, nor for thick pieces of any form of glass; but for thin end-plates and test-tubes, especially of Pyrex, where local fairly intense heat does no harm, it is unexelled. *I do, however, advise great caution.* The graduate will appreciate the dangers; the student may not.

Less dramatic, but effective if time is not important, is overnight soaking in concentrated sulphuric acid containing a few crystals of dichromate or permanganate. The principal problem here is to fish the things out of the acid and wash them with water. A sensible evasion is to drain off the liquor into another beaker, holding back the glassware with a glass rod or fork, and then flooding the well-drained articles with water to take away the evolved heat. Otherwise local heat might cause cracking—less likely with silica than with glass, of course.

A mild process, suitable with most cemented cuvettes, is to boil with distilled water containing a little detergent (Teepol or Decon 75 are suitable) and ease away the dirt (IF you can get at it) with a wooden ice-cream ' spoon ' sharpened to a screwdriver shape. But of course none of this should be necessary. NEVER let a solution dry out in a cuvette, even an open one.

To free a stuck ' Trombone ' (Fig. 4.6) which has dried with a solution in it, first fill it with the last-used solvent (if known) or a likely mixture of solvents, and allow to soak for an hour or so. Then, with the sliding member uppermost, spray ether into the

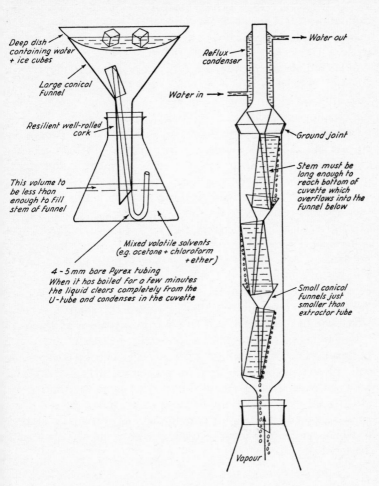

FIG. 9.3. Simple cleaning of neglected cuvettes by prolonged reflux.

hollow of the sliding member to cool it, and warm the outside of the stationary member with a flannel wet with hot water. The resulting combined expansion and contraction acting in opposite directions should free the stuck members in a few minutes. Twist gently to help the process. Once free, they can be cleaned as below. The outer member is apt to crack fairly readily, usually in a partial spiral formation; it will then last for years if it is wrapped round with PVC tape, which being transparent does not obscure the calibrations. If it cracks right round, of course, probably only the makers can do anything about it, and the cost may not be worth while.

What of the permanently sealed (horn or side-arm filling) type of cuvette? Sohxlet extraction may not allow full access to the inside nor full drainage afterwards. An idea by Fripp and Powell (1960) for cleaning open cuvettes could be useful generally. Invert a cuvette over a gentle jet of solvent vapour, which condenses in the cuvette and runs back into the 'boiler' below. Protection of the cuvette from hard contact with the 'jets' by interposition of soft plastic does not contradict anything I have said (Chapter 10) about obnoxious plasticizers finding their way into your purified solvents: they are well removed by the first couple of runs. Glass is, however, softer than silica, and scratching does not occur unless contact is forcible. Figure 9.3 shows how condensed vapour cleaning can be done in two ways: one demanding a little inexpert glass-blowing, the other—cruder, but if left to itself for a few hours equally effective—demanding none. As it should never be necessary to clean cuvettes thus, I regard the simpler version, which can be made up in half an hour by anyone, as adequate.

Self-filling and self-emptying cuvettes are useful for many purposes. They won't suffer if they are neglected, but the operator will. Flush them out with clean solvent immediately after use, and try to provide efficient drainage in preference to, but not necessarily to the entire exclusion of, blowing-out with clean air. This applies especially to complex flow-through or 'dynamic' cuvettes in which transient colour reactions can be studied (Gibson and Taylor, 1945).

PLATE 4

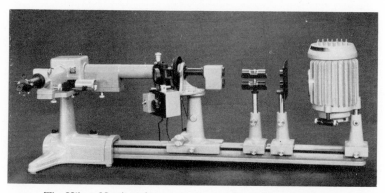

The Hilger-Nutting photometer in use with a Hilger Barfit wavelength spectrometer. The lamp housing usually has to be mounted farther from the photometer by means of an alternative locating hole, or by using a longer bar.

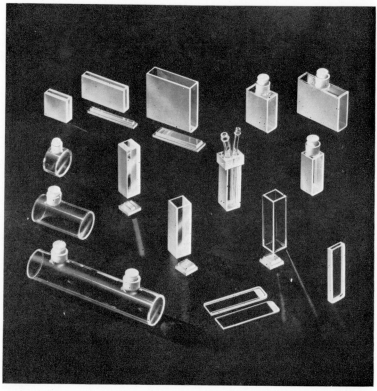

Representative Spectrosil cuvettes.
(Thermal Syndicate Ltd)

PLATE 5

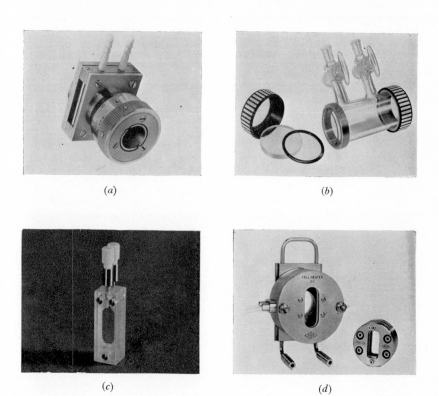

(a)

(b)

(c)

(d)

Some cuvettes for special purposes.
(Research and Industrial Instruments Company)

(a) Micrometer cuvette with two filling arms for easy filling and flushing out, or for flow-through use.

(b) Demountable cuvette for gases and/or flow-through.

(c) Short-path cuvette; a non-adjustable version of (a)

(d) Jacketed cuvette for use at selected temperatures, and a smaller un-jacketed type, both demountable with appropriate tools.

CHAPTER 10

SOLVENTS

*It seemed that the next minute they would discover a solution.
Yet the hardest and most complicated part was only just beginning*
ANTON CHEKOV *The Lady with the Dog*

A sample can be solid, liquid, or gas. A solid sample needs special preparation: if quantitative absorbance measurements are needed, the faces through which light enters and leaves must be polished optically plane and parallel (which is more than can be expected of most laboratories) and reflection losses at these faces must be compensated by using a single silica plate, similarly prepared, in the reference beam. Except for qualitative work, therefore, such as the assessment of *whereabouts* in the spectrum light is absorbed by a solid, without any attempt at measuring *how much*, solid specimens are limited to such items as photometric standards or wavelength standards, already prepared and ready for use without compensation (unless specified). Sometimes a useful qualitative assessment can be made of a solid, insoluble, and apparently opaque powder by filling a cuvette with it and then adding a clear liquid to occupy the empty spaces and endow the mass with some transparency by damping inter-particle light scattering.

Dr A. J. Everett, of the Wellcome Research Foundation, is trying out a neat variant of an infra-red technique: compressed KBr disks are UV-opaque, but disks of finely powdered KCl pressed at 70–80 tons/in² are giving promising results.

Gaseous samples require special cuvettes and are rather beyond the scope of this book. Quantitative work calls for careful control of gas pressure, which is the counterpart of solute concentration. At atmospheric pressure, some work can be done in normal cuvettes with close-fitting lids. It is as well, however, before experimenting with such charmingly picturesque subjects as the spectrum of sulphur dioxide (Fig. 10.1) to make sure that the internals of your instrument are under slight positive pressure (nitrogen) and the cuvette compartment under continuous suction

133

(Chapter 6) to prevent contamination and/or corrosion of vital components. Even benzene vapour is bad enough. Such spectra are largely qualitative on the absorbance scale, although, within the limits imposed by finite slit-width, wavelength values can be read with some precision.

In everyday work, solutions of one kind or another are the main basis of absorption spectrometry. ' The choice of a solvent ', says Lothian (1958), 'must depend primarily on its being transparent over the range of wavelengths to be covered, and on its giving

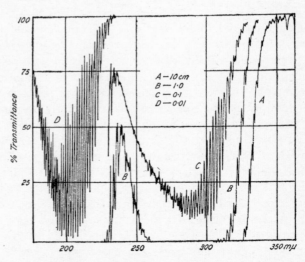

FIG. 10.1. The transmission spectrum of gaseous sulphur dioxide as recorded with different path-lengths. (By courtesy of Beckman Instruments Inc.)

adequate solubility.' Without fulfilling at least those two conditions nothing can be done. Other desirable qualities include what we may term ' spectrometric neutrality ', or non-interaction between solvent and solute; limited flammability and volatility; ease of purification; absence of toxicity or corrosive properties; stability to light and to prolonged storage. Further generalization is unprofitable: you must take each solvent on its own merits in relation to the job in hand. With so many requirements, some restriction in the range of suitable solvents available on the shelves is obviously desirable, if only to cut down on preparative work. I would also advise that the chosen few bottles be distinctly labelled FOR SPECTRO USE ONLY. This will not entirely prevent unauthorized use, but it will at least morally discourage it. Having carefully purified a Winchesterful of solvent to ' spec ' quality, it is depressing to see it frittered away on something less worthy, even worse if someone ' economically ' pours solvent back into its bottle after use or replaces a glass stopper, or a *cleaned* and solvent-extracted cork, with a rubber bung, which is part-soluble in most organic solvents.

PURIFICATION

As a preliminary, distil at reduced pressure when possible. It is only too easy to ruin (temporarily) a good commercial product by distillation in unsuitable apparatus. Condensers, flasks, receivers, should all be in glass or, preferably, in Pyrex (for ease of repair) with standard ground joints. Spherical joints are easier to handle than tapered joints. If corks have to be used, reflux them repeatedly with the same pure solvent for a few hours before use. After distillation, try for transparency in the largest cuvette you can. Maybe the result will be satisfactory. If so, bottle the solvent in a clean stoppered Winchester or large flask. If not, re-purify.

Water is best purified by repeated distillation. Make it alkaline for the first run, and (if you like) add a little permanganate. The alkali holds back any dissolved carbon dioxide. Keep the distillate in a glass container with precautions (usually unnecessary, but wise on occasion) to exclude atmospheric carbon dioxide. As a means of dispensing, use the same sort of apparatus as you would for a standard caustic solution, adding precautions against contamination by plasticizers (etc.) in any flexible tubing. Such tubing, if it must be used, should first be boiled in several changes of distilled water. The same applies to flexible 'squash' bottles— convenient, but spectrometrically deadly. If all-glass wash bottles are used, don't blow into them: use a well-washed bulb-pump, or similar device, to produce air pressure by hand.

With organic solvents, use the usual text-book methods for the first stages. Some materials can be made into salts with an inorganic acid or base, recrystallized *ad lib* (often conveniently from recovered alcohol), freed, and then distilled. Dimethylform-amide is an example. Some, like cyclohexane, melt at not much above 0°C and can be purified by distillation followed by repeated recrystallization, or by that rather more efficient mode of recrystallization, zone refining. Try all variants: freeze the whole column and expose a small slowly moving section to room temperature, making sure it has time to melt; or, with a small close-fitting brine-cooled ring of metal tube, make several slow freezing ' passes ' up or down a liquid column of impure cyclohexane. Alternatively, run overnight (i.e. very slowly dripping) a long chromatographic column with silica gel or activated alumina (trihydrate heated for 4–5 hours at 400°C). This is generally better than trying to remove the main contaminant, benzene, by sulphonation. Commercially purified cyclohexane is expensive but cheaper as a rule than laboratory purification. But always test it before acceptance, even if it has a certificate. Beautiful childlike faith is out of place in spectrometry.

Light petroleum (low-boiling petroleum, Skellysolve) is a useful solvent. Usually it can be bought in a state pure enough for most work above the 240–250 mμ region (40000 cm^{-1}). If not, try first a long all-glass silica gel column; then, if this is insufficient, sulphonate with fuming sulphuric acid. Your initial purification will have removed most of the aromatics, so a few treatments with very small amounts of acid, a few ml at a time, will be enough. A convenient set-up is a large globe-shaped separator mounted at an angle like a concrete mixer, rotating at 25–30 rpm. (Caution: Make the tap very secure.) Periodically drain off the blackened acid and replace with fresh. Wash the top layer cautiously with water. Filter slowly through powdered caustic. Benzene bands should not be detectable in a 10-cm thickness, even with a Holiday cam or echelon cell technique (pp. 36–40). At all times, avoid tap grease.

A generally applicable but laborious method for purifying hydrocarbons is by repeated catalytic hydrogenation, with distillation as the final stage. Decahydronaphthalene (' dekalin ') is a useful solvent and should theoretically be as transparent as cyclohexane. When pure, it is; but it is rarely pure. Until 1934 (Morton and Gouveia), published spectra of dekalin showed traces—sometimes more than traces—of di-, tetra-, hexa-, octahydronaphthalene, and even naphthalene itself, despite normal evidence of purity. The fact that no two spectra were more than vaguely similar should have provided a hint, but few people noticed. Moral: If a spectrum shows bands that from first principles ' shouldn't ' be there, suspect it, and try for yourself on a sample purified by another method, GLC for instance.

Chloroform, for certain limited purposes, has its uses, even though its transparency stops short at about 240 mμ. It is worth noting, therefore, that it needs the presence of about 2% ethanol to stabilize it, and that it keeps best in the dark. Brown-glass Winchesters are popular but ill-advised: the chloroform leaches

Lower usable wavelength limits of some of
the commoner purified solvents
(give or take a few mμ, according to thickness)

	mμ
Acetone	330
Pyridine	305
Glycerol	290
Toluene	285
Benzene	280
Carbon tetrachloride	265
Butyl acetate	260
Ethyl acetate	260
Chloroform	240
p-Dioxane	220
Methanol	215
n-Hexane	215
Acetonitrile	210
Ethanol	205
Cyclohexane	205
Distilled water	180–190

Intensive purification can sometimes extend the limit a little, but beyond this is ' built-in ' opacity that nothing will remedy except decrease in thickness.

out some of the iron salts in the glass and contaminates itself with a few ppm of iron, which can ruin the solvent for some reactions. Distillation and repeated water-washing, followed by further distillation, seems to be the remedy. As chloroform is slightly soluble in water, this wastes a lot of solvent; but it's worth it.

Ethanol is sometimes required to be transparent down to the far-UV. If so, there are various methods available. One of the more reliable is as follows: Set up a reflux condenser and a distillation flask which can later be connected to a normal condenser and receiver. Add 2% by weight of benzene-free sodium (cut into dice and washed with benzene-free light petroleum) and reflux for at least 8 hours, or maybe overnight. Distil, rejecting the first and last 10–15% (which can be recovered for cleaning). Test for transparency. If unsuitable, try another supplier. Only aldehydes and suchlike are removed by this method. Aromatics are not. And removal of aromatics from alcohol is no job for a busy laboratory.

There used to be what was commercially called ' lime-process ' ethanol, which was expensive but invarably excellent. This has been superseded by a very much more reasonably priced product made by azeotropic distillation (' benzene process ') which is as good for most purposes as ' lime-process ', and often is transparent well into the far-UV; but not always. Each Winchester should be tested. If, as often happens, the ethanol is supplied in carboys, test the carboy. Maybe you'll be lucky enough to have one whole carboy not contaminated already with a previous solvent. Mark it and set it aside—FOR SPECTRO USE ONLY. Amazingly (to me) the alcohol itself is usually free enough from benzene. A simple and quick non-spectroscopic test is to pour a drop or two into that little depression which appears on the back of the hand when the fingers are outstretched and the thumb raised, and sniff at the small pool: if it smells drinkable (no ' methylated ' odour, for instance, though what that has to do with it, I don't know) it will *probably* be transparent; if not, it *certainly* won't. This unscientific test has the advantage that it can be applied anywhere, immediately, and is comfortably ' fail-safe '.

Now that gas/liquid chromatography can be used on a preparative scale, instead of being limited as it was at first to microgram quantities, it offers great possibilities with more ' difficult ' solvents like dioxan. GLC and zone-refining between them should in fact be able to provide all the purity necessary in most spectroscopic solvents. A general process that sometimes works and sometimes doesn't, but is nevertheless usually worth trying because it can be left unattended, is very slow, overnight or longer, dripping of a solvent through a two-metre column of silica gel.

SOLVENT EFFECTS

Much has already been written on solvent effects in easily accessible publications. I refer you to the indexes of the more popular journals, and give only a few comments here.

In water solutions ionization can be a cause of trouble. Ions and undissociated molecules often show the same absorption spectra, but often they differ dramatically. That is why pH is so important in many spectroanalyses, and is specified in detail, together with temperature, which can affect ionization substantially. At the low concentrations customary in much absorption spectrometry it is rashly assumed that ionization will be sensibly complete. Often it is, but you can't depend on it. It is usually worth while to exercise some control where possible. One of the more striking common examples is chromate/dichromate (Chapters 15, 16). Fortunately, the goulash of ions resulting from attempted control seems to be reproducible, non-interfering, and, except for the ions containing chromium, transparent in the regions of interest. As a precaution against embarrassment, it is wise to try variations of pH on any aqueous solutions you regularly use. If nothing else, you will probably encounter some interesting isosbestic points where they were not expected. Any solution that changes colour with changes in pH is likely to show one or more.

The wavelength (and sometimes the absorptivity) of some absorption maxima is liable to be affected by the type of solvent. This effect is somehow related to refractive index, but not (as far as I can see) consistently. The carotenoids as a class are profoundly affected by solvents. All show a complex series of maxima and sub-maxima. These progress from (relatively) low wavelength, high absorptivity, to higher wavelength, lower absorptivity, as the solvent is changed from hydrocarbon, through chloroform, to carbon disulphide, while the dilute solutions grade from pale yellow, through orange, to vivid red, all at the same concentration. It is important, therefore, to specify the solvent exactly when you publish an absorption spectrum. And because of this, mixed solvents are generally to be discouraged. They are not as a rule so precisely specifiable. (There are exceptions: Skellysolve, for instance.)

Sometimes the solute interacts (reacts is too strong a word) with the solvent, forming loose complexes. This is more likely, and less predictable in its outcome, with mixed solvents. In a sense, of course, every solvent is a mixed solvent, because absolute purity is an idealistic figment; but practically it is possible to free a solvent entirely from some specific contaminant which interacts undesirably. A case in point is moisture in nominally dry organic solvents.

Hexane, heptane, cyclohexane, are not notably miscible with water; yet, unless they are rigorously dried far beyond what is normally considered to be usual and reasonable, their water content makes nonsense of the absorption spectrum of pyridine. Published spectra of pyridine show something similar to benzene, give or take a mμ or two and a few orders of absorptivity. This is understandable, and happens to be true of pyridine in the presence of anything that interacts with the –N– atom in the aromatic ring, such as acid, hydroxy-compounds like alcohol, water, etc. If, however, the pyridine is dried and dissolved in a dry non-polar hydrocarbon, the narrow benzenoid bands smooth out progressively as the drying proceeds; the peak of the curve falls a little as it becomes smoother and a set of even narrower bands appears lower down on the long-wave side of the main absorption curve. These seem to have been first reported by Fischer and Steiner (1922) but did not attract much attention. [For still earlier work see Hartley (1885), Hantzsh (1911), Baly and Tryhorn (1915), Herrmann (1919); there have been many papers since.]

In six weeks of progressive dehydration of both pyridine and hexane, I did not manage to smooth the peak of the curve completely; but the trend was obvious, and strongly indicated that if ' Bakerian dryness ' had been achieved the curve would have been completely smooth over most of its periphery, except for those sharp little bands tacked on the long-wave side. Morton and I never got round to publishing this (see however Ph.D. Thesis, Liverpool, 1933). Other things kept continually cropping up which seemed more important. It might be worth while to re-open the study now with more modern methods and equipment, extending it to cover quinoline, isoquinoline, and derivatives. The converse could also be interesting: the effect of intensively dried pyridine (etc.) on the spectra of solutes in it.

After a while, you get used to the smell of pyridine, and find fresh air distinctly odd, almost oppressive, and people give you plenty of room in public transport. . . . There are compensations in most things. One that will probably occur to you is the possible use of pyridine as a water-detector. I don't see much future in that. The spectrum is so sensitive to water that it will detect the moisture in sodium-dried hexane after a couple of minutes' exposure to air; you can't make up a solution quickly enough for the ' water effect ' not to be detectable photographically with a continuous light source properly used (Chapter 4). The faintly wavy spectrum might even show up on a recording, if you knew what to look for.

If there is a moral to be drawn from all this, it is that you should be wary of published absorption spectra unless you know what precautions were taken, and are familiar with the consequences of neglecting to take them. Which doesn't leave much to trust blindly, but also doesn't mean you should entirely ignore published spectra; just take them *cum grano salis* but without too much prejudice. They might be right.

RECOVERED SOLVENTS

Set aside two containers for solvent residues. Into one of them pour all the drainings from the cuvettes, etc., that have not been used for solutions containing volatile aromatics in any form, particularly benzene or pyridine. Keep the other for 'contaminated' solvents, to be used in preparative chemical work, perhaps, but NOT in any phase of spectrometry. Benzene, pyridine, etc., *can* be eliminated from apparatus by intensive washing, but they are distressingly persistent and need repeated flushing with uncontaminated solvent to remove them. Even the apparatus in Fig. 9.3 may not be sufficient unless the process is repeated. My advice, if benzene or pyridine have been used, is to drain the cuvette thoroughly; wash a couple of times with a 'throw-away' solvent; then dry it in a steam oven to evaporate any residual volatile aromatic; then apply the Fig. 9.3 apparatus, using only uncontaminated solvent in the flask; finally rinse with the pure solvent you are next using, and drain.

Recover solvent for cleaning only from the 'uncontaminated' container, distilling slowly and rejecting anything that does not distil freely below 100°C. That way, the recovered solvent can be depended on to evaporate completely in a gentle air stream, even without heat. And of course it simplifies the use of the Fig. 9.3 apparatus.

Although it savours rather of a counsel of perfection, I would advise against using any recovered solvent(s), even if 'uncontaminated', for making up solutions for spectrometry. They are, after all, very mixed solvents (see *Solvent Effects*, page 138). The uncertainty of possible solvent effects and the virtual impossibility of reproducing test conditions make it unwise even for 'qualitative' (i.e. wavelength only) work. Keep the recovered solvents exclusively for cleaning. Granted you can use them, *if adequately transparent*, in a 'blank' cuvette for compensating for reflection losses (though this is mathematically wrong in a hair-splitting sort of way); but it is a wise precaution to instruct all staff members to avoid using recovered solvents for any photometric measurements at all; and for you to set them a good example.

CHAPTER 11

PREVENTIVE MAINTENANCE

... when 'tis done, then 'twere well
It were done quickly
MACBETH I vii 1

The basic idea here is no newer than ' An apple a day keeps the doctor away ' or ' A stitch in time . . . '; but credit for first committing Routine Inspection and Preventive Maintenance of spectrophotometers to the immortality of published print belongs I think to Dale (1957), who was at that time servicing the Unicam SP.500. Spruit and Keuker (1965) extended the scheme to the Beckman DK recording instrument. The following notes embody my own experiences as well as drawing freely on the foregoing. They are intended more for the novice and/or non-specialist than for the expert spectrometrist, who is likely to have worked out a suitable scheme already.

Dale's scheme can be applied with minor modifications to almost any manual instrument. It takes about half an hour, or at most an hour, once a week, at a suggested time of either Monday morning or Friday afternoon. I prefer Friday afternoon, because all the machinery is nicely warmed up, even though the staff are cooling down; personnel generally, though possibly tired, haven't got that post-weekend syndrome; and there is time to telephone an order for urgent spares or expert help IF they are needed. They shouldn't be, of course: the whole idea is that urgent need for expert attention can be almost eliminated if frequent *regular* routine checks are made and acted on by the less expert but intelligent user who has been told what to look for. Work out your own scheme of preventive maintenance for your own instrument on the basis of the following paragraphs.

MANUAL INSTRUMENTS

Unless the instrument is powered entirely from the mains, check the accumulator(s) for voltage and specific gravity. Clean and

143

top-up as necessary. Look particularly for signs of corrosion. All connections should be soldered onto the lugs and liberally smeared with silicone grease. Connections by clips to a trickle charger should be made at some distance along the wire, not near the battery. Dale makes the important point, which applies equally to the Beckman DU and Unicam SP.500, that the unused lead strap between cells 2 and 3 should be ' effectively and permanently ' insulated to prevent possible misconnection of 4 volts to the frame/ earth, which *must* be connected to the 2-volt tapping.

Test the sensitivity. With this control set midway, movement of the transmittance control from 100 to 99% T should move the galvanometer needle $1\frac{1}{2}$–2 divisions on the SP.500, or about 3–4 on the DU. Adjust the tappings of the dry batteries in the phototube/ galvanometer circuit to suit. Test for drift. If the sensitivity is too high, the amplifier tends to be unstable, but any instability (tested with the dark-current shutter both open and closed) could be due to a mobile trace of moisture. Replace desiccants if necessary, though they should last much more than a week in a dry laboratory. If the desiccants have to be replaced, regenerate them by heat, and cool them to laboratory temperature in a desiccator before replacing them in the instrument. Better, keep a supply of regenerated desiccant in an air-tight container which you can trust. Fully drying out an amplifier (etc.) is a long process, and the galvanometer needle will slowly drift for quite a while. This does not make the instrument inoperative, but it does make it harder to operate. I used to change the desiccants routinely, whether necessary or not, every Thursday evening, so that everything was dry before the Friday.

While you are checking stability, make a note of the slit-width needed to balance the meter: at 625 mμ (16000 cm^{-1}) with the filament lamp, anything much more than 0·07 mm with the ' blue ' (i.e. blue- and UV-sensitive) phototube, or 0·5 mm with the ' red ' calls for inquiry within the next few days, but is not necessarily urgent (see Chapters 17 and 18). Check the wavelength scale against the 4861 AU hydrogen line (' blue ' phototube) with nearly full sensitivity. Scan this region very slowly, keeping the galvanometer needle near mid-scale by continuous simultaneous adjustment of the slit, and watch the needle for a sudden kick as the line crosses the exit slit and illuminates the photo-surface with a momentary intensity well above the background level of the hydrogen (or deuterium) continuum. Ideally, the same wavelength reading should be obtained from whichever side it is approached; but expect this only with very slow scanning. If the reading differs from 4861 AU by much more than 1 mμ (10 AU) check the 3799 and (with ' red ' phototube) 6563 AU lines. If these also are incorrect—probably much more so at 6563 than at 3799—adjust the collimating mirror: insert a box spanner through the hole in the end of the casing remote from the amplifier, and ease a long screwdriver down the bore of the spanner. Before loosening the lock-nut, press gently with the screwdriver: if the galvanometer needle moves to the left, the screw should be turned clockwise; and *vice versa*. Over-correction is the main danger, with consequent confusion of lines; for instance, a spurious ' line ' is often detected at 4700 AU. This, however, always needs a wider slit than 4861. When adjustments are complete, do a final check on a standard wavelength glass (Chapter 15). In normal weeks, only the half-minute 4861 AU check will be needed. Mirror adjustment can be quite a lengthy business, though well within the capabilities of the painstaking non-specialist. A realistic tolerance is 0·5 mμ in the far UV, rising to perhaps 2–4 mμ in the red. You may often do better than this. If so, be thankful. A lot depends on the instrument.

Check the reality of the inscription around the selector switch. With the transmittance scale set at exactly 100% T the meter reading should not change when the selector is moved from ' Check ' to ' 1·0 ' (or ' Measure ' etc.). Success here partly depends, of course, on the preciseness with which you set 100% T manually; but, if nothing else, this test does emphasize the convenience of the ' Check ' switching-in of a 100% T-equivalent network, and the thoughtfulness of Beckman and Cary who introduced the idea (Chapter 6).

A useful test is for what Spruit and Keuker call ' Workable Limit ': at 200 mμ (50000 cm^{-1}) with full sensitivity and an empty light-path, the slit-width should not much exceed 0·2 mm. A width of 0·4 mm shouldn't cause any panic *unless* it has increased since the previous test (which could indicate looseness somewhere, or incipient lamp failure). Remember that on a DU or SP.500 a physical slit-width of 0·4 mm at 200 mμ represents a spectral slit-width (or bandwidth) of only about 0·2 mμ, whereas 0·1 mm at 625 mμ covers about $4\frac{1}{2}$ mμ.

Together with the daily check on a solid photometric standard (Chapters 15 and 18), which I most strongly recommend, this completes the weekly routine of *preventive* maintenance. Regular overhauls, preferably by a service engineer and at intervals of several months, are another matter altogether and will be cheaper and easier if you spend a weekly $\frac{1}{2}$–1 hour as above, plus a stray-light check every fourth week or so.

Once a month is sufficiently often to check for stray light. This is not a defect that develops suddenly, but slowly and insidiously. It is important therefore to follow the progress of the malady by noting any changes in the position of the nearly vertical cut-off of the standard test-substance, and in the estimated value of $\% T$ at any point of spurious maximum absorption (Chapters 12 and 17). Half a dozen points will be enough to plot the curve after the first time. Saturated lithium carbonate or 4% KCl in distilled water are suitable solutions for use in a 1-cm thickness. A single specimen of glass with a sharply rising curve (e.g. Corex) is a good alternative, if it is kept clean and used every month to preserve continuity. It is convenient to use transparent graph paper, dated, and to superpose the curves over the light of a viewing stand (Chapter 4, Fig. 4.4). This in fact is an extension of the control chart idea.

RECORDING INSTRUMENTS

The weekly routine for checking a recording spectrophotometer varies in detail too much, according to type of instrument, for an adequate general account to be given here. A few pointers may, however, be useful. For instance, a brief scan of one or two peaks on a rare-earth spectrum (holmium or didymium glass; see Chapter 15) will check whether any drift has occurred in the wavelength adjustment; and another scan of an appropriate part of the photometric standard will confirm whether the ordinate on the chart really means what it says. A nice further check recommended by Spruit and Keuker for the DK2 (and, or course, similar instruments in which the change between absorbance and transmittance presentation is merely a matter of switching) is to scan a region of spectrum where the absorbance is about 0·35–0·45, and repeat it as a transmittance curve (or *vice versa*). On both curves, the same wavelength should be shown for 0.399 *OD* as for 39.9% *T*, i.e. the traces should intersect at this point or very close to it.

In those recording instruments where the change-over in ordinate presentation is not by switch but by substitution of a different cam, this test is best done immediately after changing cams, as a comforting verification that despite the disturbance everything is still in good order. I would not recommend it as part of the weekly routine, which should be kept short to discourage evasion. In any case, there is much to be said for a policy of ' leave well alone ', and the weekly check is intended to *test* performance rather than to modify it unless obviously necessary. Lack of agreement between 0.399 *OD* and 39.9% *T* by more than about 0.01 *OD* is something for the service engineer to rectify on his next visit. I do not advise tampering beyond what is laid down in the maker's instruction book.

(The equivalent test on a manual instrument is the identity of the 100% *T* setting and ' Check ' network, already mentioned. It is neither necessary nor possible on a manual instrument to verify 0.399 *OD* $= 39.9\%$ *T* because both calibrations move round together on the one dial and represent a single point on the same potentiometer.)

A weekly check on the 100% *T* (or zero absorbance) recording is worth while. This is, after all, the ' base-line ' for all ordinate readings. Deviation should not exceed 1% *T* or its equivalent along the entire length of the line. If it does, maybe the mirrors on the beam-chopper need cleaning. Inspect them, but don't touch them. This is a job for the expert. After a couple of cleanings (with weak detergent on cotton wool) any mirrors usually need replacement or re-aluminizing. Spruit and Keuker recommend keeping one or two re-aluminized mirrors in stock; they report that the ' matured ' surface is more robust. If this is generally true, it is worth remembering in connection with the aluminized mirrors in other parts of other instruments.

To decrease reflection losses, some optical parts are bloomed with magnesium fluoride. These, and diffraction gratings, must *never* be touched. A fingerprint is irremovable without damage, and needs factory attention. Here, even gentle use of the suction-duster is to be discouraged. Blow away any dust with clean air (air syringe, for instance) taking care not to touch any optical part with the solid tip of the syringe. There shouldn't be any dust to remove if the instrument is well made and well maintained.

Monthly, record a stray-light standard (Chapter 12), making a point of always using the same strength of solution, or the same glass, and a transparent chart for easy superposition to detect drift. With some instruments the same chart can be used several times. Sedulously date all records. I favour the astronomers' notation for the date: year, month, day . . . This allows *inter alia* for orderly multiple entries on one day, if need be.

GENERAL

During a check-over of any instrument keep an ever-watchful eye open for signs of wear, particularly *uneven* brightness of potentiometer wires (Tarrant, 1965), fraying of cable ends, etc. Slightly more-than-usual looseness anywhere might need the attention of a screwdriver or spanner, applied with caution to avoid overtightening and thread-stripping. Most of the controls are finger-light to operate, and many would be improved by backlash-free slow-motion knobs. But some—for instance, the multi-contact selector switch—need a fair effort and tend to work loose. Here, if they can't afford to use proper splines, manufacturers would do well to fit man-sized grub-screws and provide grooves, flats, or dimples on the spindles for the screws to bite into. A few minutes work with a sharp file will suitably modify a spindle, but there might not be enough thickness of material to warrant drilling-out and tapping a larger thread for the screw in the existing knob. If there is room, fit a larger knob, or (better) a permanent lever or double tommy-bar.

Incidentally, am I alone in preferring finely milled or knurled controls where possible? Although admirable for the regulation of water mains, coarsely fluted knobs seem to me incongruous on a refined and sensitive instrument. The incongruity is heightened by the wrist-watch complex that afflicts so many designers, who—wherever there is room—should rather emulate the grandfather clock. I have nothing against miniaturization, semiminiaturization, or microminiaturization (apart from the nomenclature) if they are intelligently applied and take full advantage of easy plugging-in of whole throw-away printed circuits. That is the most convenient form of accessibility. And at present the most costly.

As a check on the wavelength performance of any instrument—much slower than the hydrogen-line check, but on the whole better because the instrumental behaviour is more ' natural '—scan a short section of the didymium spectrum (Chance ON 12 glass) covering the double peak at 573 and 586 mμ (1750o and 171oo cm^{-1}) and/or the two sharp bands at 741 and 803 mμ (1350o and 124oo cm^{-1}). For various reasons this glass is unsuitable for use in the UV in the same thickness that gives good results in the higher reaches of the visible, where other glasses are apt to lapse. For the spectrum region below 550 mμ, holmium oxide in silica (Corning 3130) transmits well down into the UV and shows eight useful bands (there are others) at 241·5, 279, 287·5, 361, 446, 453 and 536 mμ (414oo, 358oo, 348oo, 277oo, 224oo, 221oo, 186oo cm^{-1}). In 2-mm thickness, the 446 mμ band tends to run off the map, and 536 is a shade low in intensity; but the rest are all within easy reach and not easily confused with each other. Ideally, use both ON 12 and 3130, but if you are restricted to one, choose 3130 (2 mm). Realistic tolerances, on which you should be able to improve, are about 0·3 mμ at 241·5 mμ; 1 mμ at 361 mμ; and 3–6 mμ for the didymium bands above-mentioned. Unless divergences exceed these by a substantial margin, adjustment is, in practice, not worth while. Wait for the service engineer's routine visit.

A check on photometric performance should rarely be left for as long as a week. On a manual instrument, a daily check (taking no more than a couple of minutes every morning) has proved its worth: see Chapter 18. On a recording spectrophotometer, more is involved; 10 minutes and a chart may be ' wasted '. But I think it well worth the cost. A Chance ON 10 glass is suitable; or a piece of rhodium-coated silica: either should have been calibrated by some official body of high standing, such as the NPL of Teddington or the NBS of Washington, nothing less. (I have often wondered what would happen if one got a few such august bodies all to calibrate the same standard: a sort of collaborative test of Official Testing Centres without any of them knowing what the others were doing. ... But perhaps that's an improper thought.) How much tolerance to allow depends on the work of your laboratory. I suggest that $\pm$0·01 *OD* on the absorbance scale is a little lenient; $\pm$0·005, a little optimistic for a single reading, even after due propitiation of Tyche.

On instruments that take individual (drum or flat-bed) rather than strip charts, economy and extra information are the rewards of re-using the same chart several times, each duly dated. This is an excellent way to detect any drift in adjustment. For the same reason transparent, or at least generously translucent, charts are an advantage in being superposable. Also for the same reason, an essential feature of the weekly check is to register the results in a notebook, and to plot some of them—notably slit-width and absorbance checks—as a control chart (Figs. 18.1 and 18.2). The extra cost in time, effort and money is negligible; the usefulness, immense.

When the instrument is powered entirely from the mains, ask the manufacturer whether it is better to switch it off at night or to leave it permanently on. Spruit and Keuker recommend that the DK2 be left switched on (apart from the chopper motor) permanently, unless the period of disuse exceeds five days; but this may not be generally applicable. To switch on well before weighing-out and making-up solutions of samples, and then not switching off until evening, is a good stability safeguard for any all-mains instrument, and for most others.

To summarize:

(1) Adopt and diligently follow a daily routine of checking an accredited photometric standard by making *one* reading and plotting it on a control chart.

(2) Work out a weekly routine of inspection, cleaning and (if necessary) adjustment, to suit your own instrument(s) and laboratory conditions.

(3) Monthly, check for stray light with either a solution or a suitable glass.

(4) Register and where appropriate chart the results (slit-widths in particular) as a means of detecting drift and incipient trouble.

(5) At regular longer intervals of 3 to 6 months, depending on local conditions, have a ' proper ' top-overhaul by the Man from the Works.

Finally, ' Thou shalt refrain from such comments as " This instrument is no good," but instead shalt intelligently specify the nature of the problem, lest thou forfeit the co-operation of those that can assist thee ' (*Control*, 1962 Sept.).

CHAPTER 12

STRAY LIGHT

Company, villainous company, hath been the spoil of me
HENRY IV (I) iii 10

Stray light (or stray radiation) has been variously defined: pseudo-poetically as Spectroscopic Deviations from the Purest Ray Serene, or The Spectre at the Feast; near-scientifically as the presence in the light emerging from the exit slit of radiations other than those intended. The first better captures the spirit of the thing, though it doesn't bear close analysis. The second tells only part of the story.

Because a slit necessarily has a finite width (if it were ideally infinitessimally narrow it would show diffraction bands, or wouldn't let through any light at all) it is bound to allow a little of any continuous spectrum to emerge alongside the nominal wavelength. The only chance of getting a genuinely monochromatic beam (as implied by the reading on the wavelength dial) is to isolate one spectral line, and a singlet at that, from a line emission spectrum. So, in the most literal sense, a few AU of stray light must be accepted as inevitable at the best of times. And unless the slit is unusually wide in relation to the absorption band(s) being measured (see, for instance, Fig. 6.5 on the benzene spectrum) the effect is harmless. Stray light as generally understood—*instrumental* stray light, due to scattering and random reflection from various internal parts onto the inward-facing aspect of the exit slit—is however not to be confused with this relatively minor spectral impurity due to the finite band-pass of a wide exit slit, though the demarcation is blurred in many people's minds.

Manufacturers usually issue, or will supply on request, charts or tables for specific instruments relating the physical separation of the slit jaws in mm to the different wavelength ranges that the same width represents at various parts of the spectrum. Refractive index is different for each wavelength: hence the dispersion of the entering ray into a spectrum. In a prism instrument a physical slit-width of 1 mm can represent a spectral slit-width (or band-pass) of 1 mμ at 200 mμ (500oo cm^{-1}) and perhaps 50 or 60 mμ at 700 mμ (143oo cm^{-1}) (Fig. 3.1). This latter will provide all the '*finite slit* stray light' anyone could want, amounting in fact to gross misuse of a spectrophotometer. You encounter conditions like these if you misguidedly use a hydrogen lamp and a blue-sensitive phototube for work in the deep red region. In addition to the finite-slit-width effect, you get also true (instrumental) stray light from the strong UV emission of the H-lamp, which is many times more intense in the UV than in the red. And the greater sensitivity of the Sb-Cs phototube to UV than to red radiations, for which it was not designed, further aggravates the effect. A simple absorptiometer with a 650–750 mμ (154oo–133oo cm^{-1}) light filter would be much less costly and give better results without any misleading pretence at absoluteness or loss of reproducibility.

For analogous reasons, a tungsten-filament lamp is less useful in the near-UV than in the visible, not so much because its UV emission is barely high enough, more because its visible emission is relatively too high—so high that even the best matt-blackening and light baffles are unable to cope with the excess of visible light that floods in through the necessarily widened entrance slit. No matt black is perfectly non-reflecting, nor can all edges and surfaces of baffles be kept completely and permanently free from specks of dust—though one tries. And there is inevitably some random reflection from prism faces, and scattering from aging mirrors.

That explains why many instruments are fitted with a built-in slidable filter to cut out visible light and transmit only the near-UV for use when the filament lamp is probing just beyond the 'edge' of the visible into the near-UV region. The resulting absence of stray visible light amply makes up for any ill effects due to the extra slit-width needed (in completely cutting out the visible, the filter also inevitably attenuates the UV). And it also explains why the H-lamp does not need any such filter for UV work: its visible emission is already relatively weak enough for any stray visible light to be effectively intercepted by the baffles (etc.) and reduced to an acceptably low level in relation to its high UV emission, at least down to (say) 240 mμ (420oo cm^{-1}).

Even this high UV emission, however, does not entirely compensate for the falling-off in sensitivity of the normal photodetector as 200 mμ is approached. To correct this deficiency, the entrance slit must be opened still wider. That is why stray-light troubles are always worse in the further-UV. The assorted radiations falling on the entrance slit are qualitatively the same as before; but, because the slit is wider, more of them enter the spectrometer, including both wanted and unwanted radiations. And the unwanted ones, especially those of near-UV wavelengths contributing strongly to the total instrumental stray light, are the very ones to which the phototube is preferentially sensitive. Without decreasing the proportion of stray light, therefore, much the same improvement can be obtained in practice by increasing the further-UV sensitivity of the phototube by, for instance, replacing a glass envelope by good silica. User-replacement of a tired phototube often alleviates (at least temporarily) many of the symptoms of stray-light trouble. Though more lasting, and always worth while, a good internal clean-up is sometimes less rewarding.

Published work on stray light is voluminous. Half a dozen papers deserve special mention because of their clarity and easy availability: Holiday & Beaven (1950), Martin (1950), Perry (1950), Donaldson (1950), Slavin (1963), Hartree (1963). The first four are all in PSG Bulletin 3. Together with the two others, they give enough practical and theoretical information, and further references, to provide many happy days of literature browsing. I select here a few practical pointers, but I do seriously advise you to consult at least all six originals. By the way, in Dr Slavin's excellent paper, the most generally accessible of them all, the name Zscheile is misspelt; and in col 1, page 563, the reference to ‘ Figure 4 ’ should read ‘ Figure 1 ’. With these corrections, this paper should be permanently accessible to every spectrometrist.

DETECTION AND MEASUREMENT

In practice, any UV/visible spectrophotometer should not give significant stray-light trouble between about 230 and 750 mμ (43000–13000 cm^{-1}) and then only because too much is being asked of various components. Professionally quantitative direct measurements of stray light in the middle of the wavelength range are beyond normal users, but fortunately are rarely needed. Detection at any wavelength, on the other hand, is easy and should be a part of your routine checking; and direct semi-quantitative assessment at the extremes of the instrument's range, where stray light is most apt to be troublesome, is also fortunately easy. There is some consolation in the fact that the values obtained at the extremes are most unlikely to be exceeded elsewhere.

The direct approach is naturally the simplest. Unless you are interested in the spectrum of the stray light itself (for which you would use a set of appropriately selective filters or arrange for the emergent beam to enter another spectrometer—a tricky exercise in alignment) your test substance should be transparent over almost the entire spectrum, but opaque at the test wavelength. For quick checking of the further-UV a small disk of Corning's Vycor silica which cuts off at about 220 mμ (45000 cm^{-1}) is very convenient. Ideally, the recorded or plotted absorbance curve should soar skywards at lower wavelengths and not come down again; in real life, it probably will show a false maximum at somewhere around 200 mμ, and if the absorbance registered at this maximum is *not less* than 2·5 you haven't much to worry about. That figure represents 0·3% stray light at 200 mμ, which indicates the probability that over most of the spectrum it is very much lower still.

If a handy solid test-piece is not available, there are several solutions that can be used. Dr E. A. Johnson recommends, as a rough-and-ready test material, well suited to the less energetic user because weighing is not necessary, a saturated solution of lithium carbonate: shake up a pinch of lithium carbonate with distilled water in a test-tube, let it settle, and try a 1-cm cuvette-ful of the supernatant liquid. This should cut off all light below about 225 mμ. If the instrument is in good condition there should be no signs of light transmission at 210 mμ, and only minimal transmission (well under 0·3%) at 200 mμ. I can vouch for the efficacy of this test as a reliable ' stray-light watch-dog '.

A more stringent test is provided by a solution of potassium chloride, which gives a steeper cut-off (Slavin, *ibid*, quotes several other examples). In general, a steep cut-off is desirable because the most reliable estimates of stray light are made at a wavelength just beyond the cut-off edge, inside the region of complete opacity, and the meaning of ' just beyond ' becomes progressively more and more vague with less steep curves. Vycor, lithium carbonate and potassium chloride provide between them all the further-UV stray light information needed by any but the most sophisticated spectro-metrists, to whom this book is not addressed.

As an adequate first approximation a $\%T$ reading made at about 5 mμ inside the cut-off edge is equal to the percentage of stray light contaminating the emergent beam at that wavelength. Readings made further ' inboard ' away from the edge tend to underestimate the seriousness of the local situation, despite the fact that they already look, and in fact are, worse than readings nearer the edge. At 20 mμ ' inboard ' the underestimate of stray light may amount to 50%. For practical purposes dependable information is obtained from $\%T$ readings at:

225 mμ (44400 cm^{-1}) with saturated lithium carbonate, 1 cm cuvette.

205 mμ (48800 cm^{-1}) with Vycor.

190–195 mμ (52000 cm^{-1}) with 15% w/v KCl, 1 mm (in 1 cm thickness, distilled water itself absorbs appreciably at 180 mμ, 55600 cm^{-1}).

The spectrophotometer must, of course, be set for high absor-bances—the ' 0·1 ' range-setting, or its equivalent, or a still higher range if one is available. An expanded scale is always essential for readings below $1\%T$. And any confirmed reading here which isn't well below $1\%T$ calls for immediate remedial action.

The other end of the spectrum, upwards of 700 mμ, is unlikely to give trouble if a filament lamp is used in conjunction with a red-sensitive photo-detector. Most photomultipliers are, however, based on Sb-Cs, nominally blue-sensitive. Some Sb-Cs surfaces are nevertheless eminently satisfactory at quite high wavelengths well into the red: you have to take them as you find them. To check whether your photo-detector is, or is not, unduly afflicted by stray light when long wavelengths are being used, Corning 4–96 glass should be practically opaque from 650 mμ (15400 cm^{-1}) upwards. If it is not, consult the manufacturer.

If, despite good performance at both ends of the spectral range of your instrument, you are still dubious about the mid-range regions, try the indirect approach (see below), based on deviations from photometric rectilinearity, which is one of the major ill-effects of stray light. The other, which follows from it, is the appearance of spurious maxima due to the severe falling-off of all absorbance readings beyond a certain point on the wavelength scale (Fig. 12.1).

EFFECTS OF STRAY LIGHT

The presence of 1% stray light prevents any readings from being made at over 2·0 absorbance ($=1\%\,T$); in fact, a true 2·0 will read about 1·7, or 15% too low (page 160). This emphasizes the importance of minimizing stray light in analytical procedures. The effect is less severe at lower readings, but still undesirable.

The percentage error in measurements at maxima is never less than the percentage of stray light, and is usually several times greater. Even the 0·3% mentioned earlier as ' not much to worry about ' in normal work if it is found only at around 200 mμ, is serious if far-UV readings above 1·0 absorbance are contemplated:

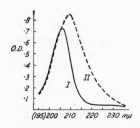

FIG. 12.1. Two spectra of 1-cholesterol-2-acetic acid (pure) in cyclohexane, as normally measured. Both have their true maxima below 200 mμ. (By courtesy of Dr F. D. Collins, 1951.)

at 1·0 absorbance, the error (underestimate) is 1·3%; at 2·0, about 6%.

The quantitative side is complicated by the fact that published formulae for the calculation of the effect of stray light usually assume, for simplicity, that the sample itself is fully transparent at all wavelengths except the one being used. This, of course, is seldom true. Most samples absorb enough of other parts of the spectrum besides the region being tested to filter out an appreciable, sometimes useful, proportion of stray light. In the chromate and dichromate spectra (Chapters 15, 16), for instance, tests at the 229–235 mμ (43700–42500 cm^{-1}) minimum turn out far better than they ' should ', partly because the readings are fairly low and partly because so much of the rest of the spectrum has been largely absorbed by the solution. For this reason, indirect estimates of instrumental stray light based on apparent deviations from Beer's law are literally no more than estimates, and often only very rough estimates at that. In practice, more than this is not required, however. Stray light has such a catastrophic effect on results that it matters little whether the amount be 1% or 5%; it must be eliminated or reduced as far as possible.

In general, stray light decreases the observed optical density. An obvious exception occurs when measurements are made at an absorption *minimum* in a curve that shows substantial absorption everywhere else—for instance, a typical highly selective light filter, which allows the passage of light within only a small range and cuts out all other wavelengths. Wood's glass is an example, transmitting fairly freely at 360 mμ (27800 cm^{-1}) plus a practically insignificant fraction in the far red. Readings at 360 mμ on the Wood's glass sample are enhanced by instrumental stray light because stray light (*a*) makes the blank setting artificially low, but (*b*) is absorbed almost completely when the sample is in the test beam.

The only part of the stray light that can then get through to the photo-surface is the small fraction around 360 mμ and the still smaller fraction in the far red. (Not that one expects stray light trouble at 360 mμ, unless one uses the unfiltered radiation from a tungsten filament; This is an extreme example, but it emphasizes the hazards of making generalizations about the effects of stray light. Study the spectrum well before applying corrections; they might operate the wrong way or be unnecessary.

In the direct test for stray light, an essential condition is sensibly complete transparency at one side of a sharp cut-off, complete opacity at the other. For the indirect test, based on deviations from strict proportionality, a single fairly narrow absorption band is required, with its absorption maximum in the test region and as much transparency each side as possible. Make a solution of a light-stable non-fluorescent material strong enough to give an absorbance reading of about 0·4 at 1 mm thickness, and repeat at 2, 3, 4, 5 (etc.) mm, as far as the nominal and expanded absorbance scales will take you. A pair of micrometer cuvettes will be found most convenient. They can be set with considerable accuracy if care be taken to avoid parallax errors. When a series is completed, interchange the cuvettes, solution and solvent, making sure that traces of solution are not left on the threaded portions to contaminate the fresh solvent. Calculations are based on the mean of each pair of readings.

Alternatively, if micrometer cuvettes are not available, equal accuracy can be attained—though less conveniently—with two rectangular cuvettes having a path-length ratio of 4 or 5 to 1; but first check the spacing of the end-plates with an engineer's internal-caliper micrometer. Again interchange to cancel-out minor errors. With a 1 cm and a 4 or 5 cm cuvette, choose a solution strength that will register in the 0·3–0·5 absorbance region with the smaller cuvette, so that the larger cuvette will read near the limit of the chart or scale. If there is a choice of several expanded scales, try to get ' one foot in each camp ' with adjacent appropriate ranges; this tests the potentiometers as well. Be wary lest this obscures the main issue of stray light. At least keep to one concentration, and so avoid the complications of ionic dissociation, etc. This, I believe, has in the past caused much false accusation of poor Beer and his law.

Under these constant ionic (etc.) conditions, deviations from strict proportionality are almost exclusively due to instrumental stray light; but not always. Fluorescence could be a contributory cause. To test this, try the sample in two positions in the cuvette compartment, (1) as near as possible to the photo-surface, and (2) as far as possible away from it. If fluorescence is interfering, it will cause higher $\%T$ (lower absorbance) readings in the ' near ' position. The obvious remedy is to use a non-fluorescent sample. But remember that not all fluorescence can be seen. Fluorescence in the UV is not uncommon, so a check like this is a wise precaution at all times when it can be applied. (See Chapter 17.)

Other possible causes of non-proportionality include defects in the darker potentiometric recesses of the instrument (check everything else first before calling-in the manufacturer), or to a light-leak from outside. This last, if it isn't due to carelessness, such as faulty replacement of the cuvette compartment lid or complete withdrawal of the filter slide, can arise from a crack in the casing or a faulty gasket somewhere. A quick test (Slavin, 1963) is that estimates of instrumental stray light *plus* light leaks show a marked decrease when the slit-width is increased (with, of course, appropriate adjustment of the sensitivity or gain control to maintain steady performance) because the leaks, remaining constant, become less important in relation to the increased incident energy, in which the proportion of instrumental stray light changes by only that small fraction ascribable to the ' finite slit ' effect. Having thus estab-

lished the probable presence of a light-leak, find where it is by
systematically scanning every part of the outside of the instrument
with a very bright light while the instrument is ' on ' and set for a
visible wavelength. The galvanometer needle or recorder pen will
jerk as the beam traverses the defect.

A stationary crack or gap in a defective gasket can be filled-in
with soft modelling wax, preferably black, and then covered over
with insulating tape secured with rubbery adhesive. If this cures
the fault, leave well alone until the next ' works service '.

ESTIMATION OF STRAY LIGHT
BY THE INDIRECT METHOD

A variety of formulae can be used for the estimation of stray light
from observed deviations from strict proportionality. One of the
simpler-looking is:

$$S=(10^{-D_o}-10^{-D_t})/(1-10^{-D_o})$$

where S is the fraction of stray light in the emergent ray (i.e. one-
hundredth of the percentage of stray light), and D_t the true and D_0
the observed absorbance (or extinction or optical density). Simple
though it looks, this isn't very usable as it stands, but it can be re-
written:

$$S=\left(\frac{1}{\text{antilog } D_0}-\frac{1}{\text{antilog } D_t}\right)\Big/\left(1-\frac{1}{\text{antilog } D_0}\right)$$

The equation can be further re-arranged to assess the effect of
reliably known stray light on any reading:

$$D_0=\log\frac{1+S}{(\text{antilog } D_t)^{-1}+S}$$

And you can estimate what any reading should have been from:

$$D_t=\log\frac{\text{antilog } D_0}{1+S(1-\text{antilog } D_0)}$$

This forms a salutary exercise for the Junior Staff. But be sure to
emphasize that any correction so derived applies only to the same
spectral region for which stray light has been estimated. Tests

with Vycor, KCl, Li_2CO_3, etc., are valid only for the far-UV, and will most probably considerably over-correct any readings made elsewhere. Trouble with instrumental stray light is rare above 230 mμ (43000 cm^{-1}) until the long-wave extreme is reached.

Example 1: Assuming 1% stray light, what is the true absorbance if the observed reading is 1·70?

$$D_t = \log \frac{\text{antilog } 1\cdot70}{1 + 0\cdot01(1 - \text{antilog } 1\cdot70)}$$

$$= \log \frac{50\cdot12}{1 + 0\cdot01(1 - 50\cdot12)}$$

$$= \log \frac{50\cdot12}{1 - 0\cdot4912}$$

$$= 1\cdot9934$$

Thus at an absorbance level of 2, the presence of 1% stray light lowers the true reading by about 15%. Anything over 0·2% stray light should be regarded as serious enough to warrant remedial action if quantitative work is required. This amount sets an upper limit of 2·7 to absorbance readings. A true absorbance of infinity (zero transmittance, complete local opacity) will read 2·7 and

> 2·7 itself becomes 2·4, 　i.e. 12% low
> 2·0 itself becomes 1·92, 　i.e. 4% low
> 1·0 itself becomes 0·992, 　i.e. 0·8% low
> 0·5 itself becomes 0·4976, i.e. 0·48% low
> 0·2 itself becomes 0·1995, i.e. 0·25% low (or thereabouts)

As zero absorbance is approached, the error approximates to the % stray light itself. In fact, at such low readings, another very small photometric error may conceivably creep in, operating in the opposite direction and slightly exaggerating the absorbance. This may well cancel or even over-correct the stray light error (page 212 Goldring, 1950).

Example 2: At the same wavelength and temperature, the same stable solution reads 0·375 absorbance at 1 cm thickness, and 1·470 at 4 cm. What is the effective percentage stray light at this wavelength?

If the lower reading is correct, the higher reading should be exactly 1·50. Certainly both can't be right, and the weight of evidence (including the comment above) points to the lower as inherently the more dependable. Accepting this as a reasonable assumption, $D_0 = 1·470$ and $D_t = 1·500$, so that:

$$\%S = 100 \left(\frac{1}{\text{antilog } 1·470} - \frac{1}{\text{antilog } 1·5} \right) \Big/ \left(1 - \frac{1}{\text{antilog } 1·470} \right)$$

$$= 100 \left(\frac{1}{29·51} - \frac{1}{31·62} \right) \Big/ \left(1 - \frac{1}{29·51} \right)$$

$$= 100 \times 0·0023$$

$$= 0·23 \% \text{ stray light}$$

This is on the borderline of acceptability. A repeat should therefore be done before any remedial action is taken; but if the result is confirmed, quantitative work at this wavelength should be limited to the lower part of the absorbance scale pending overhaul.

PRACTICAL REMEDIES

The aim should be to bring the % stray light down to 0·1% or less. In a double monochromator this should not be difficult. Two isolated monochromators, the only optical link between them being a ray of light from the exit slit of the first to the entrance slit of the second, should easily give better than 0·01% instrumental stray light. This is obtainable with a contribution of 1% from each, so there is, from the start, some excuse for minimizing the complex maintenance of double monochromators. Maybe that accounts for the poor performance of some of them in routine laboratories where time is at a premium. Time ' wasted ' on regular maintenance is time well spent.

If two optical systems of a double monochromator are not separately boxed-in but are lying side by side in a single large casing, maybe for the sake of neatness (sometimes non-technical stylists get the upper hand) much of the essential virtue of double monochromation is lost. The simplest remedy for the user is to fit his own light baffles between the sections, even to the extent of boxing-in the two systems completely except where light legitimately enters and leaves. Matt-blackened stiff card is suitable, but be careful to use good ' instrument black ' and not to overlook any metalware used in securing the baffles. Rubber-based adhesive is satisfactorily strong and does not damage the framework. Mix a little lamp-black with the adhesive, if it is colourless, to prevent random reflection.

In a normal single monochromator, inspect all edges and surfaces that are potential light-scatterers, and as a first stage remove any dust. A convenient tool for this is a small soft camel-hair brush with a thin polyethylene tube bound to it; the more dexterous may even be able to bind the brush hairs or a few really soft feathers (down) round the end of the tube (Fig. 6.17). Connect the other end of the tube to a gentle suction line (a domestic suction cleaner, for instance, or a battery of water pumps) and systematically brush away any dust. Being dry, it will go easily and quickly, and the soft ends of the hairs or softest parts of the down will not damage the average delicate optical surface. Fingerprints and suchlike call for more drastic measures, even a visit from the service engineer.

Often the various mirrors will be found to be either tarnished or patchy because the metal reflecting surface has peeled, corroded, or worn off its optically-worked support. Here, renewal is necessary, usually a manufacturer's job. Sometimes, for instance on the large mirror in the lamp house, heat + atmospheric corrosion takes its toll fairly quickly. If you have access to the ancillary equipment pertaining to an electron microscope, you can re-aluminize such mirrors almost as well as the manufacturer, and maybe make them last even longer by giving the aluminium a flash of silica. This will stand up to mild washing with dilute detergent on cotton wool, and is suited to mirrors in the main instrument as well as in the more rigorous conditions of the lamp house. Claiborne (1947) reports that rhodium is a good replacement for aluminium; its extreme toughness more than compensates for any minor losses of reflectivity.

USE OF LIGHT FILTERS

Having reduced the stray light to as low a level as you can by generally cleaning-up, some further improvement, if it is needed, can still be made in selected spectral regions by using appropriate light filters. This is not necessarily a confession of failure; it can also represent the intelligent use of an inexpensive short-cut to success, with the sole disadvantage that a wider slit-width will be needed when the filter is in use. After all, what is the first member of a double monochromator but a rather superior, adjustable, and very costly light filter? The second monochromator alone determines the resolving power and dispersion-mode of the complete instrument.

A filter can be located almost anywhere in the light-path so long as the reference and sample beams are equally affected. Just preceding the photo-surface, or just before or after either the entrance or exit slits, are convenient positions. The Hilger Spectrochem (for visible and near-UV) has a set of automatically selected filters covering various regions, and the promotion literature shows them in two different positions. The Beckman DU and Unicam SP. 500 and 600 are examples of instruments with a slide large enough to carry extra filters besides what is provided as standard equipment. The extremes of the spectral range of any light-source/photo-detector combination are the regions most susceptible to the ill-effects of stray light, so they are the obvious ones to need protection: the near-UV from all visible stray light, the far-red from visible stray light below 500–600 mμ (20000–17000 cm^{-1}) and from near-infra-red if the photo-surface is red-sensitive, and the far-UV from all radiations above about 230 mμ (43000 cm^{-1}).

A deep blue-purple filter in a slide is conventionally fitted for use with the tungsten filament to let the user probe the near-UV without interference from visible stray light. The slit-width has to be increased, but the increased dispersion of UV wavelengths partially compensates for the increase in spectral slit-width.

If absorbance readings are regularly needed near the extremes, it is probably worth while having filters specially made to fit the spare apertures of the slide, or even making a special slide with more apertures. Corning, Chance, Jena, all have ranges of potentially suitable permanent glasses that cut off the entire visible and UV spectrum for use around 700–800 mμ (14000–12000 cm^{-1}) and only a red-sensitive detector will respond appreciably to anything higher. Stray light from the infra-red can usually be ignored in the UV/visible instruments that concern us here. But try for yourself at different path-lengths to see whether a stray-light effect is in fact noticeable.

It is almost certain to be noticeable at the far-UV end of the spectrum. Dr Hartree (1963) says very truly: ' In practice, the lower limit on the wavelength scale is not the one engraved by the manufacturer but the point below which stray light errors rise above a tolerable level.' The wavelength calibrations themselves are, however, probably reliable enough, and it is a pity not to be able to use them at their face value. The least expensive answer is to filter out residual stray light. Filters that transmit from (say) 220 mμ down, but are opaque from there upwards, are difficult to come by. Solutions are available for below 250 mμ (Childs, 1961) but these would not be convenient in routine work. Nor would liquid sodium (Shaw and Foreman, 1959) which cuts out from 210 mμ upwards, but transmits well below this.

The ' armchair remedy ' seems to me to be an interference filter based on best UV-quality Spectrosil, with a fairly broad-band transmission centered around 210 mμ. Even though wavelength accuracy is not critical here, because there is no sharp line of demarcation where stray light begins to become obtrusive, I am told by a manufacturer of these things for wavelengths in the visible that fabrication for so far in the UV would not be easy.

In the present state of the art, an interference filter passing some 25 mμ at half-peak height would transmit only 7–15% of the incident light between 195 and 220 mμ (51000–45000 cm^{-1}). The range is admirable. Two such filters (the other giving an alternative band-pass of maybe 210–235 mμ) would cover our needs. But the extra $\sim$10$\times$ amplification required to move the pen or galvanometer pointer would probably add too much electronic noise to be practicable.

There is renewed hope in work now (1966) being done at Hull University under Professor J. Ring, of the Department of Applied Physics, on multi-layer filters potentially capable of transmitting some 60–80% at peak. The main difficulty lies in finding a non-hygroscopic substance for the spacer-films, with a high enough refractive index in the far-UV. Leakage of stray light through the inevitable side-bands is no problem: at worst, they never transmit much; and even an improbably high leakage of 4% of the original total would attenuate an unacceptable 0·5% stray light to an exceptionally good 0·02%. But when such filters do become available, don't let them beguile you into neglecting the usual routine of Preventive Maintenance (Chapter 11).

CHAPTER 13

DIFFERENTIAL AND ADDITIVE
ABSORPTION SPECTROMETRY

The little more, and how much it is
R. BROWNING *By the Fireside* xxxix

In conventional quantitative determinations of absorption spectra, two cuvettes are used. One, the 'sample' cuvette, contains a solution; the other, the 'blank' or 'reference' cuvette, contains the uncontaminated solvent. The blank compensates for any slight light absorption by the solvent, which has been made as transparent as possible, at least in the spectral region tested, and also for reflection losses at the interfaces where the light beam enters and leaves the cuvette. With a good solvent the reflection losses exceed the extinction. It is therefore realistic rather than lazy to use the same blank cuvette for more than one path-length of solution. But be very careful that the solvent is in fact transparent enough for this to be justified. Incidentally, an empty cuvette is apt to over-compensate because reflection losses are then higher.

In quantitative differential absorption spectrometry (usually called—more conveniently but, I think, rather loosely—differential absorptiometry) the blank itself is a solution of known and often considerable absorbance. Readings represent the difference between the two solutions. This technique has two major applications: (1) Improvements in precision (which are automatic) and improvements in accuracy (which depend entirely on the reliability of the nominal absorbance of the reference solution), subject always to stray-light effects (Chapter 12); and (2) Qualitative confirmation or denial of the presence of a component in a mixture, and sometimes an estimate of its concentration.

IMPROVEMENTS IN PRECISION AND ACCURACY

These are discussed more generally in Chapter 17, but differential absorption spectrometry is a subject on its own. The difference-

G

reading can be assessed with much the same degree of exactness as a similar normal reading. When the difference-reading is added to the accurately known absorbance of the reference solution, the result carries only the error of the difference-reading itself, a percent or two of quite a small amount, representing a proportionally even smaller percentage of the total, true absorbance. The probable error in an absorbance reading of 0.2 is about ± 0.003. If the reference solution has a nominal absorbance of 2.0, and the difference-reading is 0.20, the sample's absorbance is probably 2.20 ± 0.003, i.e. between 2.197 and 2.203; which is a good deal better than you could depend on by direct reading—perhaps, with luck, 2.19–2.21. (For every reader who considers this is pessimistic, there will be at least another who will accuse me of optimism.)

Papers by Bastian (1949 on), Cannon (1955), Gridgeman (1955), Hiskey *et al.* (1949 on), Kortum (1937), Lothian (1956), Neal (1956), Reilley *et al.* (1955 on), Ringbom *et al.* (1939, 1953), all give useful practical and theoretical details and (many of them) bibliographies. There is, for instance, much to be said for and against reading in $\% T$ instead of absorbance, calibrating the responses and reading-off from the calibration curves instead of directly reading absorbance-differences. As Lothian (*ibid.*) says in another connection: 'Stop talking, and go away and try it', taking as your guide the advice in the above papers.

Neal (*ibid*) gives an honest assessment of the expectable errors at various stages in preparation and measurement and attributes his strikingly better-than-average results (about 0.03% estimated over-all error, which is the same as the coefficient of variation he finds in practice) to such niceties as gravimetric instead of volumetric dilution—irksome, but well worth while. (See Chapter 17.)

Gridgeman (*ibid*) comments more on the theoretical and mathematical aspects, and gives a comprehensive bibliography.

APPLICATION TO MIXTURES

By the use of two cuvettes, one filled with the solution of a mixture and the other with a comparable solution of one or more of its components (in their correct ratio) a ' difference spectrum ' is obtained of the remaining, possibly unidentified, component(s).

Micrometer cuvettes are particularly useful here. Kendall and Huke (1963) give a good account of how they 'tuned out' the known component of binary mixtures by varying the path-length until the strongest of its bands were cancelled out. This, of course, presupposes that the spectrum of the unknown component is in fact identifiable with certainty: often it may not be; but at least the operation provides a spectrum for possible future reference. If a guess can be made at its probable identity, prepare a solution of a sample of the suspected material and subtract it optically, systematically tuning-out the main bands. The difference spectrum will now either support or refute your suspicions, especially if the remaining components are already known. If they are not, the progressive removal of obscuring spectra will make their own spectra more readily identifiable, or at least potentially so. And the process can be repeated *ad libitum*. Difference spectra are also discussed by Beaven and Johnson (1961).

The principle is the same in all these endeavours, namely the optical removal of a component rather than its physical isolation, which may not always be possible because of questions of stability, etc. But subtraction is not the only possibility. It is also feasible to *add* the spectra of components, to make an optical mixture without the components contaminating each other. Having perhaps taken great trouble to prepare pure specimens, one is naturally reluctant to do more than dissolve them in purified solvent and then recover them by gentle distillation.

For an optical mixture two or more cuvettes are aligned in tandem instead of side by side, the light beam passing through the lot in series. Not all cuvette compartments are capacious enough for this, but often manufacturers have suitable accessories for long-path cuvettes which can be used equally well for two or three shorter cuvettes. The product of concentration × path-length for each is varied by individually adjusting the appropriate micrometer cuvette(s). The substantial expense of several micrometer cuvettes could be money well spent, and is not a large proportion of the cost of the rest of the equipment.

Such 'additive spectrometry' can be used for establishing whether certain solutes interact when mixed, or remain in solution as separate entities. If the physical mixture gives the same spectra as the optical mixture there is a good case for assuming non-interaction. Kendall and Huke (1963) give a striking example of the success of the method as applied to an ionization problem concerning the anomalous spectral behaviour of sterically hindered phenols at different pH values. They found that simple phenols in very dilute alkali behave exactly like hindered phenols in strong alkali. Two 5 mm cuvettes in tandem were used. To maintain quantitative accuracy, extra compensation for increased reflection losses is needed. An additional small cuvette or two, filled with transparent solvent, in the reference beam will suffice. Always keep the number of reflecting interfaces equal in both beams.

'ARTIFICIAL HORIZON'

A pleasing novelty in the original Beckman DU was the use of a potentiometric range selector, whereby the readings on the transmittance scale were divided by ten at the touch of a switch. $0-100\% T$ became $0-10\% T$, and $1\cdot0$ was added to all absorbance readings, so that the useful ranges were $0-1\cdot0$ and $1\cdot0-2\cdot0$ (readings beyond the $1\cdot0$ calibration were too crowded to be conveniently usable). The general idea has been freely followed by other manufacturers, and several spectrophotometers now incorporate means for selecting at will anything up to half a dozen or more ranges by potentiometric networks that attenuate the signal to the required degree (Chapter 6). At least one, I hear, uses the alternative approach and attenuates optically. The effect is the same. The potentiometer is probably simpler from the manufacturer's point of view: you can do almost anything with a potentiometer. But I won't take sides. There are advantages both ways.

Customarily (there are exceptions), the range covered at each setting of the selector is $1\cdot0$ absorbance, and this can be arranged to come almost anywhere on the scale, subject to mechanical and optical limitations (stray light, etc.). Thus one well-known instrument gives a choice of $0-1$, $0\cdot5-1\cdot5$, $1-2$, $-0\cdot3-+0\cdot7$, this latter being specifically aimed at work with difference spectra. And (although this looks at first sight like a figment of a distorted imagination) $75-125\% T$, $90-110\% T$ and $95-105\% T$, also for difference work. Values exceeding $100\% T$, negative absorbance in a mathematical sense, mean that the sample absorbs less than the reference. (' Blank ' is hardly the appropriate word here.)

The effect of using one of these odd-looking but most useful ranges is to locate the zero absorbance (or $100\% T$) line deliberately higher up the chart, to provide an 'artificial horizon' in effect. With the same solution at the same path-length and concentration in each beam, a horizontal straight line should be recorded: differences between solutions will appear as deviations above or below the line, magnified according to the range selected. In establishing identity or non-identity this is very convenient. And tuning-out differences by adjustment of a micrometer cuvette is greatly simplified. Remember only the *differences* are recorded.

CHAPTER 14

ATOMIC ABSORPTION: A BRIEF NOTE

Paint shadows in imaginary lines
SAMUEL DANIEL *Sonnets to Delia* 46

The technique of quantitative atomic-absorption spectrometry has been described flippantly, but fairly correctly, as ' cashing-in on Fraunhofer '. Dr A. Walsh (1955) pioneered it in Australia.

The emission spectrum of the sun is crossed by a number of dark lines due to absorption of many wavelengths by vapour-state atoms in the relatively cooler outer parts of the sun's gaseous envelope (chromosphere), which resonate with corresponding radiations shining through from the much hotter photosphere beneath, and partially absorb them. A few of the dark lines are due to absorption by components of the Earth's upper atmosphere: the line at 7621 AU in the deep red, for instance, is due to atmospheric oxygen; but most of them originate in the chromosphere. Better-known examples are 5269 AU, iron; 5896 and 5890, sodium; 5875, helium; 6563, 4861, hydrogen (seen as intrusive but useful emission lines in the hydrogen lamp continuum); 4308, 3969, 3934, calcium; and many others. The effect is one of the minor, but usually avoidable, hazards of ordinary flame photometry, cooler parts of the flame absorbing some of the very radiation whose intensity you are trying to measure. In atomic absorption spectrometry advantage is taken of the easier and more precise control that you have over the behaviour of many atoms as absorbers than as emitters, by deliberately measuring the amount by which the intensity of a steady emission line is decreased by passage through a flame of lower temperature containing controlled amounts of the element being assessed.

The quantitative technique is still fairly new, although its qualitative basis dates back a century and a half to Fraunhofer (1787–1826). I will not mislead the reader by attempting to give practical hints on a subject unfamiliar to me. I include this note solely because in any book on absorption spectrometry some mention must be made of what promises to become a major interest in quantitative spectroanalysis by the World's most selective possible absorption of light. Meanwhile, most of the instrument manufacturers mentioned in these pages have suitable apparatus either available now or scheduled for introduction.

In a typical assembly, the sample solution is drawn steadily through an atomizer into a mixing chamber with air and acetylene, and the mist burned in a stainless-steel burner. The a.c. mains-modulated emission from a cold hollow cathode made of, or coated with, the element to be estimated passes through the length of the flame and into a simple monochromator with photomultipler and tuned amplifier. This responds only to signals at the modulated frequency of the source, and not at all to the steady emission from the flame, which acts as if it were a cuvette containing the sample in a transparent solvent. Out of the total radiation, only the lines emitted by the element are absorbed, and the spectrometer deals with only a selected one of these at a time. Usually one line is more suitable than others and is chosen for routine work. To suit the concentration of the solution, the path-length (compare cuvette) can be adjusted by rotating the burner.

Many variants are possible, and more and more papers are appearing in *Applied Spectroscopy*, *JOSA*, *Analyst*, *Analytical Chemistry*, etc. One of the Specialist Groups of The Society for Analytical Chemistry (The Atomic Spectroscopy Group) is wholly concerned with the subject. Elwell and Gidley (1960) have dealt with it in detail. Dr Walsh (1965) has himself brought the subject up to date in an interesting review.

CHAPTER 15

'LINKS WITH SANITY'

*... confirmation strong
As proofs of holy writ*
CORIOLANUS III iii 323

Even in the best-run laboratories there are times when one doubts the validity of a reading. Indulgent credibility reaches breaking point. In theory, of course, this should never happen. In practice it sometimes does, and all too often the doubt is well-founded.

Extinction readings go astray for the most trivial and foolish reasons, such as massive fingerprints on an optical surface; simultaneous use of cuvettes made of visually alike but optically dissimilar materials (for instance, silica ' compensated ' with glass); wrong combination of light source and photo-surface, needing excessive slit-widths or sensitivity (gain control); light-leakage past a badly replaced sample compartment lid; cuvette wrongly orientated so that the opaque side-faces are in the light beam (incredible, but it has happened); forgetting to remove a stray-light filter after you have finished with it; use of the wrong flask or pipette in dilutions (20 and 25 ml glassware are easily confused; decide which is the more useful in your work and *never* let the other one loose in the lab; if it might be needed, keep it under lock and key); incautious use of plastic ' squash ' bottles or rubber bungs, the plasticizer in which can be leached out by your carefully purified solvent (as Dr Roe will attest) and so contaminate your solutions; even weighings can go wrong if they are not independently checked—you should very rarely accept an unchecked weighing or dilution, especially your own, if only to set a good example.

Wavelength readings are usually more reliable. Short of severe mechanical wear or damage, or an unexpected change in temperature causing thermal distortion (a very real possibility, often ignored), there is little to go wrong suddenly, although Chapter 16 mentions some unexplained maladjustments that must have been most unexpected at the time.

One embarrassingly sudden traumatic incident in my old lab is worth recalling, even though it was rather in the nature of an unnatural hazard and most unlikely to recur. It arose from the over-conscientiousness of an ' occasional spectroscopist ' who had acquired the nominally praiseworthy habit of leaving things as he found them. He found the wavelength control at the lower end of the scale, so he returned it there, vigorously, with all the rotational inertia a solid-cast helical cam, which fly-wheeled itself well past the end of the groove guiding the cam-follower. The temporary couple of dozen mμ error was fortunately soon rectified by cautiously lifting the cam-follower back to its rightful part of the groove. Thereafter, all was well. But the mechanism could easily have been strained, to say nothing of diplomatic relations.

All such elementary defects obviously must be eliminated before you bother to check whether the instrument itself behaves properly when it is given a fair chance. Then you bring out your ' Link with Sanity '.

The essential feature of a link with sanity is immediate availability. No one is likely to use it, except *in extremis*, if more than a moment's preparation is necessary. That is why I prefer solids, or something built-in, though in a leisurely laboratory solutions can be useful, and are therefore included here. The idea is to test a known specimen and compare the actual result with the nominal, correct, result. If they agree, the spectrophotometer is behaving itself and the fault is elsewhere: look for the more obvious gaffes first, cuvettes, dilutions, etc. If they don't agree, or rather differ by more than some small acceptable ' fringe ' (Chapter 17), clear the decks for remedial action—if necessary by the Man from the Works, though most probably a minor replacement or adjustment will suffice.

WAVELENGTH STANDARDS

The quickest checks of wavelength are the three well-separated 6563, 4861 and 3799 AU hydrogen lines, built-in and ready for instant use wherever a hydrogen light source is fitted. The same is true of the rather brighter deuterium-filled lamp, with the reservation that the wavelengths are longer by about one part in 2000.

G*

Few routine instruments will reliably detect this difference. (The corresponding wavenumbers are 15230, 20580, and 26330 cm^{-1}.) In an instrument with a fixed prism (quartz spectrographs, for instance) any three correct wavelengths theoretically guarantee the accuracy of all the others; with a fixed grating, two suffice, because dispersion is rectilinear along the whole wavelength scale. Clearly, any fiduciary points must be spaced reasonably far apart to be of practical value. When they are all correct, the three wavelengths here quoted for immediate use cover a wide enough range to inspire confidence elsewhere. If any one of them is significantly ' out ', consult the maker's handbook or call for help. (See Chapter 12.)

If, as is usual in photoelectric instruments, the prism or grating (etc.) is rotated slightly to select the desired wavelength, much depends on the mechanical linkages involved. A single ' gentle ' cam, with one rigid lever carrying the cam-follower on one end and a mirror or dispersing medium on the other, is less liable to derangement than any more complex assembly. Reputable manufacturers can, however, be relied on to have computed the contour(s) of the cam(s) correctly, and all you have to do is to see that the cam face remains undamaged and the instrument temperature sensibly constant. Some instruments have an internal thermostat; others, a bi-metal strip to make minor corrections automatically. The correct functioning of this sort of refinement is worth checking from time to time. In two modern instruments (so I hear) the temperature inside the cuvette compartment rises during a recording to 35–38°C, which could vitiate absorbance readings on any sample with a normal rate of expansion. Sudden impact of a cam follower against a cam face can damage either or both beyond repair, though fortunately not beyond part-replacement, and must be deliberately avoided unless the design already automatically prevents it by restricting movement, or by the use of damping devices.

The ' instant wavelength check ' itself is simple. On a manual instrument, set the sensitivity control a little short of maximum gain so that a narrow slit can be used, and scan over a few mμ on either side of the nominal line position. Watch for a vigorous little ' kick ' of the galvanometer needle, and read the wavelength at the moment of maximum deflection. Over such a short wavelength range the slit should not need adjustment to keep the needle on the scale. We are not concerned here with exactly how far the needle is away from zero (or the balance point) when the kick occurs, so long as it stays on the scale and within the limits of free movement, which by the way are seldom symmetrical. By gently oscillating the wavelength control under these conditions some idea can also be obtained of the amount of backlash, if any, in the operating mechanism. The maximum deflection (to the left on the Beckman DU and Unicam SP.500, to the right on the Uvispek) should ideally occur at the same reading from whichever side it is approached; but, in general, settings are more closely reproducible when they are always made in a direction against the return spring of the cam-follower.

What if hydrogen lines are not available? Many visible-region instruments are equipped, adequately enough for their intended purpose, with only a tungsten lamp, emitting no lines. Here the most convenient answer is a ' glass ' containing a rare earth oxide or mixture of oxides, such as holmium and/or didymium oxides fused into silica (Vandenbelt, 1961). Holmium oxide shows several usable absorption bands, some almost like lines, covering 241–637 mμ (415oo–157oo cm^{-1}); didymium oxide extends this to 803 mμ (124oo cm^{-1}). (See adjoining table on Corning 3130 and Chance ON 12.) Use the very narrow bands as you would use emission lines. The only difference is that the kick of the galvanometer is in the opposite direction, and the maximum deflection of the needle is more easily held because the absorption peaks are naturally blunter than emission lines, so the changes in needle position with small changes in wavelength are correspondingly less sudden. For the same reason, it is advisable to take the mean of say three or four readings on sharp bands, where one reading might suffice with a strong emission line. On a recording instrument one slow run-through should be enough, with air as blank. (Try it at different speeds.) If the same chart can be used more than once despite a long interval of time, drift is easily detected. Alternatively, transparent charts can be superimposed. Either way, always date your charts.

Many recording instruments have available what is called an ' energy ' mode of operation, in which only the total energy of a single beam is recorded, not its intensity relative to a standard or blank. Here, as on a visual spectrometer or a spectrograph, a suitable line source (flame, spark, gas discharge lamp) can be mounted so that its light is directed by a tiltable mirror into the entrance slit. The source can be almost anything luminous, including the hydrogen lamp itself.

My favourite for a visual spectrometer is a neon ' pilot ' or indicator lamp, permanent and automatically switched on with the spectrometer light source. Neon gives a bright beacon at 5852 AU and weaker lines at 6402, 5400, 4800 AU. Sodium (5896 and 5890 AU—the famous doublet—and several fainter lines at, *inter*

DIDYMIUM (CHANCE ON 12) AND HOLMIUM (CORNING 3130) GLASSES
Characteristic Wavelengths and Tolerances

	$m\mu$	$\pm\ m\mu$	cm^{-1}	$\pm\ cm^{-1}$
Holmium	241·5	± 0·2	41,410	± 30
Holmium	279·4	± 0·3	35,790	± 40
Holmium	287·5	± 0·35	34,780	± 45
Holmium	333·7	± 0·55	29,970	± 55
Holmium	360·9	± 0·75	27,710	± 60
Holmium	418·4	± 1·1	23,900	± 70
Holmium	453·2	± 1·4	22,070	± 75
Holmium	536·2	± 2·3	18,650	± 85
Didymium	573	± 3	17,450	± 85
Didymium	586	± 3	17,060	± 85
Holmium	637·5	± 3·8	15,690	± 90
Didymium	685	± 4·5	14,600	± 90
Didymium	741	± 5·5	13,490	± 90
Didymium	803	± 6·3	12,450	± 95

(By courtesy of Unicam Instruments Ltd)

alia, 6161 and 6154 AU), or cadmium (6438, 5086, 4800, 4678 AU) discharge lamps, as used in polarimetry, are switched on only when needed, and give a brighter spectrum over a wider range at the cost of extra complication. A quartz mercury lamp, or one of the foregoing with a silica envelope or window, with or without added mercury, is useful for covering the whole UV and visible spectrum, but is naturally costly and must be shielded to prevent damage to the eyes. Good wavelengths to use are: sodium, 3302/3303; mercury, 5461, 3650, 3132 AU; cadmium, besides 6438 used so much in polarimetry, and 4800 which so dominates the spectrum that the light is blue instead of the red that most people expect, also has useful UV lines at 3611 and 2288 AU. For a quick check *in the absence of inflammable vapours*, I have on occasion used the flame from a match or taper dipped in table salt to get the major sodium lines. Held in a crucible tongs, a match burns for quite an amazingly long time.

The position of a line source is not critical so long as intensity requirements are satisfied. The position of the entrance slit relative to the rest of the instrument is however extremely critical. The ' line ' as seen, or photographed, or photoelectrically detected, is an image of the slit. In some instruments the slit has one jaw movable and one fixed (i.e. the slit opens unsymmetrically). When checking wavelengths, always use the same slit-width as you would in corresponding absorbance measurements to prevent the slight sideways movement of the ' centre of gravity ' of an unsymmetrical slit. The same applies when you record lines as landmarks on a chart. You use the ' energy ', single-beam, mode of working, and each line appears as a more or less sharp profile, sharper with a narrow slit. Often, slit-width is regulated automatically. A pair of unsymmetrical slits can be so arranged that the moving jaws compensate for each other. Find out by trial whether the slit(s) can be depended on to maintain a steady centre of gravity for the recorded profiles. Usually they can; but it is comforting to be sure (see Fig. 6.5).

A very quick test for wavelength scale correctness is to put one small drop of pure benzene in a dry 1-cm silica cuvette on one of the internal side-faces, blow gently across the top to mix but not blow out the vapour, cover the cuvette, and then check for the benzene vapour peaks at 2584, 2593, 2595 AU. Only an excellent modern instrument will discriminate as finely as this. If an older instrument gives a single ' kick ' at 259 mμ (38600 cm^{-1}) it is doing pretty well. Care is needed to avoid confusion with neighbouring bands. I am not keen on using vapour bands as wavelength standards—too fiddly, possibility of contamination, etc. But some people like them, and they are certainly useful if a Corning 3130 holmium glass is not available.

How necessary are wavelength checks? Very necessary, of course, if measurements of wavelengths are required, or if an extinction reading has to be made at some specified wavelength(s)—for instance, isosbestic point(s). Quite unnecessary, if an extinction reading is to be made *at* a maximum or minimum ' regardless ', because here the shape of the curve shows where the reading should be made, irrespective of a wavelength scale, in fact perhaps mildly contradicting it.

In this case, the correctness of the wavelength scale doesn't matter (though it should be put right as soon as possible); all that does matter for the moment is that the point(s) chosen shall be the highest or lowest on the curve, as proved by adjacent portions of it. Nevertheless, as a matter of principle, it is good to be able to depend on wavelength readings even if they are seldom needed as such, in case they are so needed in a hurry on some occasion. Besides the unnatural hazards mentioned at the beginning of this chapter, it is remarkable what aberrations can slowly develop without the user's being aware of them (see Chapter 16).

PHOTOMETRIC STANDARDS: (1) LIQUID

I am unenthusiastic about liquid standards, and I would use one only while a solid standard is temporarily unavailable. The three most widely tested are potassium nitrate, chromate, and dichromate (see next chapter), but there are others (cf. Taylor, 1942; von Halban *et al.*, 1936, 1941, 1944; Vandenbelt *et al.*, 1945) that may have more to recommend them when fully authenticated absorptivities are published. As a quick but frankly rough check, make up from a freshly opened bottle of AnalaR (or highest reagent grade of equivalent chemical purity with a full analysis on the label) KNO_3, 200 mg/20 ml, in distilled water, and measure the *OD* with interchanged cuvettes at 302 mμ and 262$\frac{1}{2}$ mμ (331oo and 381oo cm^{-1}). The absorptivities should be 0·70–0·71 and (about) 0·14$_8$ respectively. Make sure that the temperature is not abnormal. A small volume of liquid soon attains lab temperature, or the temperature of any other surroundings it may be in. There should not be any change in cuvette temperature during this brief test—but check it. I suspect that some of the observed discrepancies have been due to temperature differences in the cuvette compartments. The temperature gradient of KNO_3 may be lurking somewhere in the literature; I have never seen it; but this is only a rough check, and about 20–21°C will be in accord with most conditions.

For a more certain check, try potassium chromate, 35 mg in a litre of water containing 2 g of KOH. At 373 mμ (268oo cm^{-1}) you should get an absorptivity of 248·5 ± 1,* even with an old solution if the solution has been well looked after (Chapter 16). For some reason, the other chromate band seems a little temperamental; but

---

* E.g. Vandenbelt and Spurlock (1955).

E_1^1 373 mμ is beyond reasonable dispute, and we even know its temperature gradient, which is 0·001 absorbance per °C.

More searching still, covering most of the UV with E_1^1 values that can (I believe) be trusted, is potassium dichromate 60 mg/litre in faintly acid solution, which I dislike least of the currently available liquid links with sanity: four useful landmarks, 235, 257, 313, 350 mμ (42500, 38900, 31900, 28600 cm^{-1}) alternately min-max, cover a useful range of absorptivities, 125, 145, 49, 107 $\pm$ 1. Fuller details are given on page 189. So far, dichromate has not to my knowledge had the benefit of an NPL or NBS official blessing, nor do I know its temperature gradient except that it is low enough not to be troublesome. Aim as usual at 20–21°C for your tests, and beware of high-temperature sample compartments because of solvent expansion.

For a quick check of the rectilinearity of the photometric scale in the absence of more convenient solid standards, use any handy stable solution in a couple of thicknesses, say 1 cm and 4 or 5 cm, interchanging cuvettes. A pair of micrometer cuvettes is still better and allows a wider, and lengthier, test over anything up to a 10 or 20:1 range. The nominal range is much greater than this, but the probable *percentage* error in micrometer scale readings below a few tenths of a millimetre raises doubts. Don't introduce any questionable extra complications such as dilution. One variable at a time is a good rule in anything except the higher flights of statistical analysis; in this case be very careful to vary only the path-length. One solution of potassium dichromate in one cuvette covers an extinction range of about 3:1 between its maxima and minima; so by using a pair of checked 4:1 cuvettes you can cover an actual 12:1 range, without prejudice to the 'absolute' correctness of the recommended standard values, although I believe them to be correct $\pm$ 1 as shown. This range is more than adequate to reveal non-linearity.

PHOTOMETRIC STANDARDS: (2) SOLID

Solid standards are manifestly much more convenient and inherently more stable than liquid standards. There is a distinction between those that can be calibrated accurately and absolutely by independent means, and those that must be calibrated by direct photometry. The old sector photometer, for instance, was

' absolute ' in that the ratio between the area of the aperture and the light-impervious metal disk was measurable by mechanical means—micrometer, protractor, engraved scale on the periphery, etc. A rotating sector has obvious disadvantages in a photoelectric instrument, quite apart from the need to cope with the flicker effect. We may pass it by.

The stationary aperture, however, has possibilities. Among variants, two are worth comment: (1) the Winther gauze, blackened to discourage minor complications due to reflection, is 'absolutely' calibratable by lantern-projection onto an accurately ruled screen; or by examination under a low-power microscope with a built-in scale; or more simply by calculation of the ratio between the average size of the holes in the mesh relative to the area blanked-off by the wire, whose mean diameter can be non-destructively measured by micrometer at several ends and whose number per unit can be counted.

In a conventionally woven gauze, wires must be spaced no closer than their diameter to avoid unduly sharp local bending. This limits the available OD to a maximum of about 0.6 ($=25\% T$). Cleaning, and especially freeing from dust and fluff, is a major problem, not fully solved by sealing between silica plates because reflection losses must then be quantitatively compensated. A system of roughly parallel, $\frac{1}{2}$-mm thick, corrosion-proof wires, horizontal if the slit is vertical, is better. The aperture across which they are mounted must be appreciably larger than the cross-section of the light beam. This assembly is easier to blow clean, and need not be enclosed.

(2) Perforated screens, made by electro-etching small conical holes in metal sheet, have been tested by Vandenbelt (1962) and also Slavin (1962). Distribution and size can be controlled fairly accurately, and the final product checked by direct micrometer measurement to arrive at an absolute ratio between aperture area and total area. The cones are orientated with the narrow end towards the incident light. This minimizes light scattering. As only the narrow end is optically operative, area calculations are based on this end alone. The screens are easily cleaned with acetone. The average light beam is small in cross-section, so the exact location of a screen is no easy choice and should be left to the expert: risks of inhomogeneity are considerable with a small number of holes in the beam. However, if at some stage in the

optical system the reference and sample beams pass through, and are partially masked by, two exactly equal apertures as part of the design, even a single smaller aperture of known relative area (easily measurable) can be arranged to act as either a standard or, in the reference beam, as an optical attenuator for high-absorbance measurements. Built-in by the manufacturer for quick change-over—three positions: sample beam for an instant OD standard, reference beam for attenuation, neither beam for normal use—this would be most convenient. But that is a matter for the manufacturer, not the average user. Amateur use of perforated screens as photometric standards could give misleading results. Don't attempt to make up a high OD standard by superposing sets of screens, wires or gauzes.

A glass or silica photometric standard is the sturdiest and most usefully practical for the average spectrometrist. When I had my first Link with Sanity made from Wood's glass, I had little choice. Within its limitations it served me well for nearly 25 years, during which it led a treble life, first as a standard ($1 \cdot 18$ OD) for spectrograms, then as two separate standards ($0 \cdot 459$ and $0 \cdot 668$ OD) for photoelectric spectrometry. An absorption minimum at 360 mμ (2790o cm^{-1}) with everything else completely blacked out is not ideal, and it presents problems of detection of possible internal imperfections (bubbles, striae, etc.) which only sophisticated optical equipment can solve. I couldn't, so Hilger's rescued me (Chapter 16 gives more details). The Hilger–Watts amalgamation hadn't then occurred. There are now two (there may be more) glass or silica materials for use as standards commercially available: (1) Chance-Pilkinton's ON10, which covers the whole visible region and so is equally suitable for all instruments operating within the 200–800 mμ (5000o–12500 cm^{-1}) range; and (2) Hilger's rhodium-coated silica, which is about equally tough and covers also the entire UV range. Such standards *can* be superposed quantitatively if they are separated slightly.

ON10 has been available for several decades. I used it as a visual standard (or rather sub-standard, as it didn't have any certificate) in the early nineteen-forties, at a 3-mm thickness which I took as having an OD of just under $2 \cdot 0$ at 640 mμ. I see that Slavin (1962) gets this value for $3 \cdot 06$ mm; Chance's have maintained remarkable consistency! Being translucent, its bubbles, striae, etc., if any, can easily be seen without optical aid. Usually there aren't any. Slavin points out that by using three thicknesses separately, 1, 2, and 3 mm (or thereabouts), you can cover a useful photometric range from about 0·4 to near 2·0 by shifting around from one maximum or minimum to another. Test points used by Slavin were 402 mμ (min), 445 (max), 535 (max), 560 (min), 595 (max), 640 (max), 740 (min). The 740 mμ values were too low to be of anything but academic interest. And there is a flattish region around 500 mμ (200oo cm^{-1}) which looks promising but may possibly be unsuitable in some undisclosed way. There doesn't seem much object in testing at so many wavelengths *routinely*—as distinct from in the research Slavin was doing, or in manufacturers' special tests. One 3-mm and one 1-mm Chance ON10, optically polished and certified at 402, 445, 640 mμ (249oo, 225oo, 156oo cm^{-1}) cover the OD scale adequately, and include readings that involve both blue- and red-sensitive photosurfaces. The two glasses in tandem will be strictly additive; take care to keep them as nearly parallel as you can, e.g. by mounting them with an old spacer-ring between them, not in contact. Reflection losses (about 0·043 per surface) are already allowed for in the certified OD, which is preferably uncomplicated by compensation. Specify that the certified test shall be against air, and ask for the OD at one wavelength to be tested also at 5°C above and below the normal temperature of your laboratory so that you can get an idea of the temperature gradient. The preferred light direction should be indicated by an arrow on the edge or mount, or a mark near the edge on one of the optical faces, and the certified OD also engraved thereon. Any slight oxidation film that develops on the glass, and does not readily wipe off with lens tissue, can be removed with acetone. Over-vigorous dry wiping for many years can appreciably wear the glass; gentle wiping first with acetone and/or alcohol followed by tissue is harmless.

The Hilger rhodiumized silica photometric standard gives an almost horizontal spectrum. This carries the ideal of wavelength independence to pleasant extremes. You can give the NPL or NBS a free hand in choosing a wavelength, or several. Again I think it wise to have a couple of standards of different ODs, one about 0·4–0·5, the other 0·8–0·9; and to arrange for a means of mounting in tandem when necessary. Rhodiumized silica is probably tougher even than ON10. Wear is not a problem; chipping is, and it can be minimized by mounting the standard in a cuvette-sized metal or tough plastic block, protected yet accessible for wiping. The ' orientation arrow ' and also the official reading should be deeply engraved on the block—arrow on top, reading on one or both sides.

That NPL/NBS-certified reading, by the way, is a challenge to you. See whether, if necessary with the aid of the service engineer, your mean of 10 readings (Chapter 18) comes close to the official figure.

CHAPTER 16

COLLABORATIVE TESTS

Quot homines, tot sententiae
TERENCE *Phormio* II iv 14

Collaborative tests are more usual in the measurement of biological response—bioassay of drugs, vitamins, plant stimulants, insecticides, cosmetics, flavours, preferences and other imponderables generally—than in the physical sciences, which are optimistically credited with being somehow above such things. This feeling of the infallibility of instrumentation is the laboratory equivalent of another social stratum's blind belief in the newspaper: ' If it's in print it must be right.' It is only when people begin to disagree over results that a call is made for a test on a wider scale than is possible in one laboratory, involving several different instruments in different laboratories, all testing the same material or method. Understandably, such inter-laboratory tests almost always show substantially greater divergences than intra-laboratory tests (made on different instruments within one laboratory). A psycho-ergonomic study of this difference in behaviour might be rewarding.

The nature of the test can vary considerably. Sometimes the objective is to establish which of various available physico-chemical methods is to be recommended for preparing the final test sample. This is not so much a test of instrument performance as a way of testing whether the instructions are fool-proof enough to be followed exactly by conscientious operators doing their best.* The more experienced an operator, the more individual quirks are liable to be introduced, often unconsciously. Some of them may be improvements, and it can take a long time to find this reason for discrepancies. No set of instructions is able to cover *everything*. The problem is to know where to stop, at what stage detailed instructions become mere verbosity.

---

* cf. *Collaborative Tests* (1965).

Sometimes, and more generally useful to the spectrometrist, the objective is to compare readings on the same stable sample; for, unless agreement is obtained here, the preliminary preparative processes are wasted. The sample is distributed either as a solution in contamination-free containers (e.g. sealed ampoules); or as a solid to be weighed and made up in solution; or circulated as a single solid specimen to be tested directly as received. This last is the most convincing test of photometry as such, but quite the lengthiest and most frustrating to accomplish, even if, by cunning organization, messenger-delivery can be arranged within groups of neighbouring laboratories. A large batch of specimens cut from a supposedly uniform sheet of solid material always raises doubts as to uniformity (unless the test is for wavelength only). Ampoules of one solution solve the problem of uniformity but introduce questions of stability. A time limit must be set, and the contents of ampoules should never be used more than once because of possible contamination and evaporation. Decomposition during sealing-off must also be avoided.

Three readily obtainable substances have been used more than others in collaborative tests of spectrophotometers: potassium nitrate, potassium chromate and potassium dichromate. Each has its adherents and has been widely misused. None should ever be used for the purpose of *correcting* readings in the way that I routinely and successfully, whether legitimately or not, used the first ' link with sanity ' on my absorption spectrograms (1948; also Chapter 4). That was (and presumably still is, if anyone nowadays has the misfortune to have to strive after quantitative results with absorption spectrograms) useful enough in its limited local context. But it would be rash indeed to apply it in this way indiscriminately.

In a characteristically thoughtful paper, Glenn (1965) outlines the many pitfalls of collaborative tests, constructively criticizes previous attempts, and castigates the misuse of the results thereof. As Dr Glenn points out, the ' cosy situation ' within a laboratory— where a sample of a preparation (not necessarily pure, but at least standard) is always available for the establishment of ' local absorptivity '—is regrettably beyond the reach of the public analyst, for instance, who is ' bound to employ published figures and so run the gauntlet of instrumental differences.' Distribution of reference compounds (see, *inter alia, Pharm. J.*, 1963) ' seems to be the analyst's best hope of compensating for the relatively large instrumental differences that collaborative tests have revealed.' As a practical alternative to the desirable reduction of instrumental differences, such use of reference compounds is earthily realistic, akin to constructing calibration curves. Glenn further asks where, however carefully you maintain and check your own instrument, ' is the guarantee that any given published absorptivity was obtained under similar excellent conditions?' Sound enough. But the argument could go too far: a general improvement in inter-laboratory instrumental agreement would, I contend, be preferable to any number of reference compounds, which I regard as valuable but essentially temporary crutches for use only until the instrumental gap has healed. And that, I believe, is the ideal to aim at, even though it may take a long time. Intelligently used, any two engineers' micrometers agree pretty well. Why shouldn't spectrometers? The fact that they manifestly don't, must be faced; but it shouldn't prevent our trying. And the only way to find out how much disagreement to expect—useful information to have in case of arguments (Chapter 18)—is by collaborative tests.

POTASSIUM NITRATE

At a concentration of 1% w/v in distilled water, neutral potassium nitrate shows a broad absorption band at 302 mμ (331oo cm^{-1}) with an absorptivity or E(1%, 1 cm) value of—what? Opinions differ: seriously quoted figures range from 0·68 to 0·72, not counting rogue results which run up to 0·78. This is one of the unsolved mysteries, a *Mary Celeste** of spectrometry. I expect there will be a fair amount of embarrassment here and there, if or when it *is* solved.

The present position (1966) is that absorptivity of KNO_3 seems to be 0·70–0·71, give or take 0·005, and that if your instrument reads within this range it is in fit condition for most work on routine absorption spectra. If it doesn't, it isn't.

The evidence for this uncertainty is interesting. In 1948, soon after the Photoelectric Spectrometry Group was formed, I distributed samples of KNO_3 solution, 1% and 0·7% approx, ampouled by my friend Dr J. I. M. Jones of Crookes Laboratories, to the users of twenty-eight Model DU Beckmans. Another friend (and

---

* Not *Marie Celeste* (Furneaux, 1964).

at that time, Port Sunlight colleague) Norman Gridgeman did a statistical analysis of the results of this collaborative test, published in the first PSG Bulletin (1949). The grand mean absorptivity was 0·713, about 1% higher than anything I had seen in the literature. This could not be related to any known cause. The presence of a few percent of nitrates of lower molecular weight, etc., was excluded by the analysis printed on the BDH AnalaR label, which showed spectroscopically harmless impurities collectively amounting to well under 1%. This was confirmed later, and found to include not more than a few ppm of sodium nitrate. Sodium nitrate is particularly undesirable as a major contaminant. It is slowly and insidiously hygroscopic to the point of deliquescence, which lowers extinction readings, while its lower molecular weight raises them; the net effect either way is decreased by this opposition, but remains unpredictable. Fortunately, sodium nitrate is easily eliminated, or rather reduced to a level where only the faintest yellow tinge is imparted to the flame, by repeated recrystallizations from distilled water.

A larger test involving ninety-four assorted recording spectrophotometers was organized by a PSG Sub-Committee (see Bulletin 16, 1965). One of the solutions distributed was potassium nitrate (1·170%). This time, the grand mean absorptivity was 0·705. This is significantly different from ' my ' value, but Heaven alone knows what it signifies; especially as an impressive group of DB, DK1, and DK2 Beckmans, twenty-four of them altogether, averaged 0·716. It is interesting, though confusing, to note that an NPL estimate on this same solution was 0·697, the same as the mean returned by fourteen Cary instruments, and that Vandenbelt (1945) reported 0·699 for a DU Beckman. The standard deviation was twice as high in this ' recorder ' test as in the earlier manual one. It is worth noting that the Works Entries as a group did conspicuously better than the Private Entries, better even than in the manual tests. This suggests to me that the routine visit of the Man Who Knows could well be made more frequently and would be good value for the expense account.

There still seems room for yet another collaborative test on KNO_3, this time with more attention paid to temperature and to the cuvettes, particularly the interchange of sample and blank. Although over a large number of instruments cuvette errors cancel out in the final result, they do exaggerate the standard deviation

(Chapter 18). And preferably one of the two materials that now follow should be included immediately before or after the run on KNO_3. See also Vandenbelt (1954), Hogness and Zscheile (1947).

POTASSIUM CHROMATE

I confess to a mild prejudice against K_2CrO_4, probably because of disappointments with it in the early nineteen-thirties. It seems nevertheless to have been quite a favourite for many years with the National Bureau of Standards, Washington, D.C., whence absorbance data in considerable detail (temperature effects, etc.) can be obtained. It is usual to prepare a 0·0025% solution in distilled water containing 2 g/litre of potassium hydroxide (uncritical), about 0·05-N KOH. The purpose is to ensure that it really is chromate and not dichromate in solution, and to suppress ionization by introducing a vast excess of K· ions, so that the observed light absorption can be limited to undissociated K_2CrO_4. Such control is not possible with 1% KNO_3, which is probably pretty completely dissociated, and may be partially hydrated as well—but by natural causes not under human control and probably highly sensitive to temperature changes. The advantage of being able to weigh out man-sized amounts of neutral potassium nitrate, less liable to sampling errors (Chapter 17), is more than counter-balanced by the stability of the chromate solution. Kept in the dark in glass containers (NOT in plastic) no change in absorbance above 260 mμ (3850o cm^{-1}) was observed in eight years; Haupt (1952) claims that it is ' safe for five years '—always assuming no evaporation, no contamination, etc. Nitrate at 1% is said to grow bacterial whiskers after a while. The addition of an effective bactericide would not be good for the spectrum.

As a subject for yet another collaborative test, potassium chromate would be admirable if only in an attempt to clear up another minor mystery—why everyone agrees about one of the absorption bands, but not the other. The spectrum shows two maxima (373, 273 mμ; 2680o, 3660o cm^{-1}) and two minima (312, 229 mμ; 320oo, 437oo cm^{-1}, or thereabouts). Several collaborative tests have been done in U.S.A. with satisfactory agreement between themselves and isolated spectrometrists elsewhere, within a mμ or two and a percent or two—except at 273 mμ. In all the published results I have seen, the absorptivity at 373 mμ lies between 247 and 249, mean 248$\frac{1}{2}$, which can, I think, be taken as being as nearly definitive a value as any in spectrometry. But the reported absorptivity at 273 mμ wavers hazily over the range 189–199, and I, for one, would be interested to know why. Maybe further tests including KNO_3 and $K_2Cr_2O_7$ in the same session might provide a clue.

If ever you do organize a test with chromate, be fair to the participants by weighing (or telling them to weigh) a known amount that does not need diluting, into a *checked* one litre (or at least 500 ml) flask. Rather than risk the real or potential errors of dilution, I would prefer to weigh as many separate amounts of 20, 40, 60 (etc.) mg as may be necessary to look for deviations from rectilinearity. I wouldn't trust the results otherwise, unless dilution were gravimetric.

POTASSIUM DICHROMATE

Potassium dichromate (or bichromate), $K_2Cr_2O_7$, in very dilute acid solution, has a happier collaborative test history, perhaps because it is shorter. Even if ampoules are not distributed, instructions are still simple: Dissolve 25–30 mg of accurately weighed dry analytical grade dichromate in a couple of hundred ml of distilled water in a checked 500 ml flask; add 0·15–0·2 ml of concentrated clear sulphuric acid; adjust to the calibration temperature; make up to the mark at the calibration temperature. Remember the acid is essential, just as the KOH was previously. This amount of acid gives about 0·01-N H_2SO_4, which is enough to ensure the absence of any contaminating chromate ions in the dichromate solution. The ensuing ionic goulash is enough to daunt any but the staunchest theoretical physical chemist, but the reported results are gratifyingly concordant in practice, despite differences in techniques. I hold that to be a strong point; when the same result keeps on turning up under a variety of test conditions my confidence in it increases. Absorptivity of dichromate remains unchanged over at least the concentration range 0·005–0·010%, probably further. This is worth investigating over a wider range, together with concurrent tests for stray light; cf. Slavin (1963) and Chapter 12.

In two collaborative tests involving seventy-five and seventy-nine manual instruments, one test conducted in England (Hartree;

Gridgeman; Lothian; Morton; 1951). In the Netherlands (Ketelaar, Fahrenfort, Haas and Brinkman, 1955) agreement was good, with the same coefficient of variation (1·6) for both. This was despite the fact that in our test two solutions of different concentrations were distributed in ampoules, whereas in the other the participants made up their own two solutions from crystals distributed by Professor Ketelaar. Except for one recorder, all 150-odd instruments in these tests were manual, and included eighty-seven DU Beckmans, fifty SP.500 Unicams and fifteen Uvispeks. Results were:

Mean wavelength	235 min	257 max	313 min	350 max	mμ
Mean wavenumber	42500	38900	31900	26800	cm^{-1}
Mean absorptivity 1951	125·2	145·6	48·9	107·0	
Mean absorptivity 1955	124·6	144·8	48·8	107·3	
Acceptable for use as Standard	125	145	49	107 ± 1	

Remembering that these values are all based on manual spectrophotometers, a collaborative test on (preferably) transparent charts of 0·0035% K_2CrO_4 (alkaline) and 0·006% $K_2Cr_2O_7$ (acid), made almost concurrently on recording spectrophotometers, with cuvettes interchanged as I have suggested and with strict temperature control, should be particularly instructive. (*Pace* Alan Glenn!)

SOLID PHOTOMETRIC STANDARDS

My first ' link with sanity ' (Chapter 15) was a piece of Wood's glass of good optical quality, free from internal bubbles, which Hilger's worked up for me to mount in a Spekker photometer for use with E.498 and E.528 medium quartz spectrographs. The relevant NPL certificate gave the optical density at 360 mμ, the wavelength of greatest transparency, as 1·18, which was what I had asked for as being best suited for my spectrographic measurements assessed with the unaided eye. With the photoelectric ' invasion ', and having in mind the fact that the new instruments were (fundamentally) of the ' transmittance read-out ' type best suited to the 20–60% T range, I got Hilger's to split the glass into two

COLLABORATIVE TEST ON TWO WOOD'S GLASS PHOTOMETRIC
OD STANDARDS AT 360 $m\mu$

Instrument	Standard A			Standard B		
	H-lamp	Tungsten lamp		H-lamp	Tungsten lamp	
		No filter	filter		No filter	filter
Beckman	·664	·663	·661	·460	·460	·458
	·664	·664	·664	·461	·461	·462
	·667	·667	·659	·463	·462	·456
				·459	·459	·456
	0·6650	0·6647	0·6613	·461	·460	·454
				·460	·458	·456
				·464	·464	·459
				·461	·460	·458
				·460	·459	·459
				—	·458	—
				·470	·464	·462
				0·4619	0·4605	0·4572
Unicam SP. 500	·670	·670	·667	·463	·461	·459
	·664	·663	·661	·463	·460	·458
	·670	·670	·670	·460	·463	·462
	·669	·668	·662	·465	·462	·459
	·670	·662	·668	·463	·457	·460
	·669	·669	·670	·468	·460	·460
	·668	·670	·667	·464	·463	·461
	·672	·673	·669	·467	·466	·460
	·664	·664	·665	·461	·463	·461
				·469	·461	·459
	0·6684	0·6677	0·6665	·467	·460	·460
				·460	·461	·460
				0·4642	0·4615	0·4599
Uvispek	No Tests			·459	·463	
				·455	·458	
				·461	·463	
				·459	·464	
				·456	—	
				·461	·462	
				·461	·462	
				·458	·467	
				0·4588	0·4627	

Over-all *CV* for one reading   0·44
Over-all *CV* for one instrument 0·33
NPL Double Monochromator mean *OD* value   0·4581 (*CV* 0·15)
OD Value used for Control Chart (chapter 18)   0·459

unequal parts, and polish the ends plane and parallel. These were then mounted in solid brass blocks of the same over-all size as the standard 1 cm cuvettes, again making sure that the faces were truly normal to the light beam. They were automatically maintained that way by the little bowed springs in the cuvette carrier, which pressed the brass blocks against the machined face of the carrier. I filed a little arrow on the top of each block to indicate a standard direction of light—possibly unnecessary, but a reasonable precaution. Also, the brass was machined away where appropriate, to allow the glass to stand *locally* proud of the metal by maybe $\frac{1}{2}$ mm; this made it much easier to wipe clean. Other parts of the brass, standing *generally* proud, protected the glass from contact with the carrier or springs.

After fairly prolonged preliminary organizational correspondence with quite a lot of friends in several laboratories, I circulated the two standards among them for testing on Beckmans, Unicams, and Uvispeks, and the NPL kindly also tested the smaller of the two on a double monochromator. Results are given in the adjoining table.

Excluding the NPL result (which, incidentally, was 0·001 lower than the mean result in Chapter 18 and can be regarded as pleasantly confirmatory) the over-all coefficient of variation for one reading was 0·44%, about a quarter of the value ' expected ' in collaborative tests of manual instruments, and supporting the roughly predicted optimum uncertainty of $\pm\frac{1}{2}\%$ for readings uncomplicated by cuvettes (Chapter 17).

The slight but significant difference in the Filter and No Filter columns relating to the smaller standard (B) can be plausibly attributed to the effect of stray light (something of the order of 0·1% average here) which would not be intercepted quite so strongly by the less opaque material; Chapter 12 explains why in this case stray light will tend to raise rather than, as is more usual, to lower an extinction reading.

COLLABORATIVE WAVELENGTH TESTS

In the course of the foregoing tests, wavelength maxima were also reported. This was not taken seriously enough by most of the participants, or so it seems. However, for what they are worth, the following results emerge:

The 302 mμ maximum of KNO_3 was variously estimated as lying between the limits 300–302·5 mμ, and the associated 262 mμ minimum, 259–263 mμ, in the 1949 PSG test of manual instruments; and 298–312 mμ in a recent test on recording instruments with comparable *OD* uncertainties (Tarrant, 1965).

In the first $K_2Cr_2O_7$ test we had:

> 235 min, range 232–237 mμ
> 257 max, range 256–260 mμ
> 313 min, range 311–315 mμ
> 350 max, range 345–352 mμ

With fairly broad ' peaks and troughs ' estimation of the precise wavelengths of the highest and lowest extinctions is a matter of practice, and even skilled operators can honestly differ. But I would have thought that differences of much more than 1 mμ were instrumental rather than due to human misjudgement. Which means simply that many instruments were in a poor state of wavelength adjustment and hadn't been checked (Chapter 11) for a long time. (Or as the Hopi Indians are said to say: ' Since very very when '.)

These findings are roughly confirmed in another recent paper by Auerbach, Bauer and Nachod (1964). They distributed holmium oxide ' glass ' filters among eighteen laboratories in thirteen countries, involving twenty-seven spectrophotometers, manual and recording. The test was well organized, but apparently the instructions were (as usual) not always understood, or at least not carried out. Most results clustered expectably round a mean value, indicating *some* consistency, at least, but there were rather a lot of stragglers: the band about 361 mμ (27700 cm^{-1}) was quoted as from $359\frac{1}{2}$–367 mμ; the band at 460 mμ (21700 cm^{-1}) as $457\frac{1}{2}$–464 mμ. There is a bit of mystery about this latter—readings by two operators on one instrument were 460 and 464! No amount of regular testing will cure this. Possibly not even psychiatry.

CHAPTER 17

THE QUEST FOR ACCURACY
AND PRECISION

Believe those who seek the Truth; distrust those who claim to have found it ANDRÉ GIDE

In order to evoke the right atmosphere I want to quote two sobering texts from U.S.A.: (1) ' The public would be astounded if the truth about laboratory errors were known ' (Professor K. F. Meyer); (2) ' One should be slow to attribute significance to discrepancies of 5% or less in the *E*-values reported by different laboratories ' (Professor W. O. Caster). Although dating back to the early fifties, these remarks are still largely true. And to them I would add a couple of axioms: (*a*) No measurement is dead accurate except by accident; and (*b*) There is no way to tell when it does happen to be dead accurate. Does this shock you? I hope so. Raised eyebrows stimulate thought.

Despite popular usage, *accuracy* and *precision* are not the same. Accuracy is closeness to the truth, nearness to reality, almost a philosophical abstraction. Precision is a measure of repeatability irrespective of correctness, and is mathematically calculable.

A measurement can be exactly replicable and yet not be accurate. By repeatedly bringing a control up against a wrongly set stop, for instance, a ' perfect ' series of readings will be obtained, all of them wrong. If ever you get more than three consecutive results agreeing perfectly, look for what is making some part of the mechanism hang fire at some fixed point. In spectrometry, as elsewhere, results can literally be too good to be true. Although consistency is an obvious primary aim, remember that results are at least as likely to be consistently wrong as consistently right. But don't let your armour of healthy scepticism become so inflexible that you can't recognize and admire real precision when you see it: to suspect is not necessarily to reject.

Precision is amenable to strict mathematical treatment on which

194

an intelligent guess at the truth can be based. Many readers shy away from trying this: but the elementary treatment I advise later gives a lot of useful information and needs very little mathematical prowess. If it needed more, I would long ago have given it a miss.

Whether we like it or not, we have to face the fact of experimental error. For our own satisfaction we should know (at least roughly) how much error to expect under different experimental conditions, and how by changing the conditions we may to some extent be able to control the degree of uncertainty. *All* measurements are subject to error. Measurement is, of course, to be distinguished from counting. There should be no error at all in a statement like ' there are five cows in that field ' even if the number has been derived by the time-honoured, but probably apochryphal, method of counting the legs and dividing by four. But in the statement ' there are two cows per seven acres ' a measurement (of area) has been introduced, and with it an uncertainty of perhaps 0·001 cow—more or less, according to the skill and sobriety of the surveyor and the dependability of his instruments.*

Sir Charles Darwin, when he was Director of the NPL, Teddington, was of necessity acutely aware of the limitations of even the finest measurements; and when he remarked that every measured result has a 'fringe' he also pointed out the corollary that unless the probable size of the fringe is known the result itself doesn't mean much. The size of the numerical fringe in manual absorption spectrometry seems to average about $\pm 1\% - \pm 2\%$, with occasional ragged edges extending untidily—but with strict statistical sanction—to $\pm 10\%$ or more in collaborative tests (Chapter 16). Recording instruments roughly double the ' basic fringe ', leaving the ragged edges about the same as they were. Is none of this reducible? What are its causes? What can be done about it?

An equally important question that can receive only brief mention in a small book is whether a precise result means anything when you've got it: unless it does, precision is pointless. Some colour reactions, for instance, are difficult to replicate quantitatively. If the range of variation here, at the preparative stage, is

---

* *Added in proof.* Gridgeman's (1966) plea, ' Stand still while I count you,' seems apposite. At the first Ecumenical Council (Nicaea, A.D. 324), he says, 318 Bishops are reputed to have taken their places on their thrones. When they arose, they seemed to number 317 and could not agree on a definitive figure. There may be a moral in this: perhaps if they had sat down again . . .

±5% it is a waste of both effort and instrument to strive after ±1% photometry. You must maintain a sense of proportion. Much the same applies to the study of wide trends, such as the effect of different kinds of pasture or fertilizer on milk output or on the concentration of carotenoids in butter. In the earlier stages of such a study, differences of less than 10%–20% are usually not worth considering. In the later stages, when it comes to choosing between a final pair or so of pastures, it becomes economically worth while to split hairs—or grass blades. But before that, speed is more important than precision. A large number of samples, *collected in duplicate* as well as roughly tested in duplicate, preferably not side by side, will give a more dependable picture of the over-all situation than a few painstakingly precise assays which might not be representative. Much good nutritional work has been done with wide analytical tolerances, ±10% and more. But as a matter of general principle, and especially in the spectrometric assay of buying-and-selling samples which have already been tested elsewhere, the closer the tolerances one can work to the better.

Incidentally, if ever you work out a useful but frankly rough ' sorting ' test and are rash enough to publish it, be sure to specify its probable limits of error and rather labour the point in your paper. It might even be as well to exaggerate the limitations slightly. In 1940, I devised a quick visual spectrometric sorting-test for vitamin A in margarine* (which was dropped only recently from Martindale's B.P. Extra) based on the range through which the transient $SbCl_3$ reaction colour faded from its initial peak value. This was to allow for the presence of a dye (no longer used) which also reacted with $SbCl_3$, but did not fade. I did mention casually, in passing, that the result would probably lie within ±15% of the truth, i.e. ±a couple of International Units in those days, which was near enough for the purpose; but it wasn't long before people were phoning me to say ' So-and-so gets 15·2 units. I can find only 15·1. What went wrong?' For two people doing this rough test in different labs to agree within 2 units was a minor miracle; to argue over 0·1 unit shows that I had failed to get my point over. To

---

* Correctly pronounced by most of the 3×10^8 English-speaking people, though rarely in the U.K., vItamin (long i, because accessory food factors are vital but not ' vittles ') and marGarine (hard g as in Margaret, which derives from the same Greek root). This respects both etymology and the wishes of the late Sir Gowland Hopkins and Mège Mouriés, who coined the names and have a right to the last say in their pronunciation.

tell the truth, this test was neither more precise nor more accurate than Andersen and Nightingale's (1929) dilution test was in expert hands; but mine had the advantage of not needing an expert. The dilution test depended on assessing how much dilution was needed before the blue colour could only just be detected; I have often wondered whether a dose of quinine (which is said to increase the sensitivity of the human eye to blue) would give higher values, or santonin (to yellow) would lower them. But I could never get any expert volunteers.

Morton and Stubbs (1946) devised a simple UV test for estimating the vitamin A in cod liver oil by making three readings at selected wavelengths from which the irrelevant absorption (light loss due to substances other than vitamin A) could be assessed and deducted from the gross observed absorption, without purification or separation of the vitamin. This simplifies procedure and decreases the precision of the estimation, but greatly enhances its accuracy, which is what counts therapeutically. The method has however been much misused by application to contexts for which it was not intended, and unjustly maligned as a consequence. One widespread trouble is that commercial contracts are more concerned with precision than with accuracy: at all costs, even at the cost of truth, agreement between Seller's and Buyer's testing-laboratories is the aim, even if the results don't mean anything. Although on a low aesthetic plane, this is understandable as an easy and usually harmless way out of a practical difficulty. Another is that sometimes the absorptivity of a substance in its pure crystalline state is still often not known accurately (maybe for reasons of instability when it is pure and stripped of natural inhibitors and stabilizers). Examples are α- and β-carotenes. They can be separated out of (say) red palm oil unsaponifiable (alumina followed by active magnesia) and then tested for absorptivity at appropriate maxima with some exactness. From this information it would be possible by simple proportion to calculate the amounts of both carotenes in the sample—if only we knew the true absorptivity of the two pure carotenes. But the literature quotes a variety of figures, not more than one of which can be right, and possibly none. The range is not large; in academic work one just chooses the most likely figure and works to that, with the reservation that the assay can later be revised in the light of further experience. And a lot of useful work has been done by taking, provisionally and

H

without prejudice, the richest concentrate so far prepared as the reference substance, as if it were pure. As long as the characteristics of the reference substance are exactly specified, the system works well. But always specify the characteristics for the sake of future readers.

ERRORS AT VARIOUS STAGES

Let us look at what is involved in making a spectrophotometric measurement. Customarily, a solution is first prepared. It is amazing what delusions of accuracy persist over this deceptively simple process. If you don't already know all about it, study a book on sampling for quantitative analysis. There is much more in it than meets the eye. To be brief, a small sample taken at random is rarely representative of the main bulk. The sample you weigh *must* be small, or the necessary amount of progressive dilution becomes unwieldy and itself introduces errors. A fair solid sample is obtained by the contamination-free breaking of a large bulk into fairly small pieces, mixing these thoroughly by ' quartering ' on a clean surface, rejecting one pair of opposite quarters each time, and repeating the mixing and quartering until a sample weighing maybe 200–300 g is left. This is then ground to small grains, spread on clean paper, and repetitively quartered again down to 20–30 g, ground finely with a clean pestle and mortar, and bottled appropriately. At all stages, it may be necessary to avoid oxidation, etc. Quite a performance, but essential if a ' fair ' solid sample is to be obtained from a large bulk.

Cattle feeding-stuffs are usually well enough mixed for almost any sack to represent a consignment fairly. Here 100 g from each of two or three sacks, mixed and quartered as above, will suffice. Biological products generally are minced, or chopped if the scale is large, well stirred, and then, before anything has time to settle out, a 100 g sample comminuted in a *clean* high-speed blendor. Contamination is all too easy. Sometimes it is wise to run a small sample through the apparently clean blendor before the main sample, as a final precaution. Except with a sample consisting of a single chemically pure compound, fine division is essential. To be fairly representative, any mixture must contain several hundred particles per weighed-out portion, aggregating maybe a total of 20–200 mg. That is why solutions (oils, for instance) are so much easier to sample fairly than solids. Only very thorough stirring is necessary.

Assume you have a fair sample. There is a small but finite error even in weighing. In refined work, correct temperature limits must be respected, and at the very least you should allow the sample and whatever you weigh it in (small flask, weighing bottle, watch-glass) to attain thermal equilibrium with the balance. Read a book on analytical procedure.

You must never heat a calibrated flask. Some samples do not dissolve readily without heat, so choose your solvent with care. As an example, carotenoids are normally freely soluble in light petroleum (often confusingly miscalled ' petrol ether ', which should anyway be ' petrol aether ', meaning ' very volatile petrol '). If the carotenoid is already in solution (e.g. red palm oil) it dissolves easily in any petrol. If it is in the pure crystalline form (e.g. synthetic β-carotene) it will begin to oxidize superficially long before it shows any signs of dissolving. The answer is to run an ml of pure benzene onto the weighed crystals, which are thereby wetted instantly; then proceed with diluting. Dilution in this case is so considerable (absorptivity=about $2\frac{1}{2} \times 10^3$) that the trace of benzene in the final solution is insufficient in practice to affect the wavelength or heights of the carotene bands significantly; in fact it would be difficult to detect even the presence of benzene itself at 250–260 mμ, which is the only potential trouble spot, except with a Holiday Cam (etc.)—Chapter 4. This is one of the few exceptions to the rule that mixed solvents are inadvisable (Chapter 10).

HOW IMPORTANT IS TEMPERATURE CONTROL?

In everyday work, the test-temperature is the laboratory temperature, which is best brought up to, or in kindlier climes, down to 20–21°C. The temperature of the optical system is sometimes thermostatted to a higher temperature, and the photo-surface to a much lower temperature to reduce ' noise ', but an effort should be made to maintain the cuvette temperature at a steady 20–21° unless there is some special reason. Most published absorption spectra were obtained at about this temperature; or at least the operators thought so—some sample compartments are known to rise to 35–40° with little provocation. If nothing else, this thermally expands the sample and makes nonsense of the calibration of pipettes and flasks. A permanently fitted thermometer, with precautions to ensure light-tightness, is well worth while. A ventilated sample compartment also helps. *Latitude of a degree or two either way is seldom important even in quantitative work*, but ± 10° could be unpleasant.

Deliberate low-temperature work is another matter, rather beyond our present elementary practical scope. To show the trend of the temperature effect, however, a brief note on ' how the other half lives ' is instructive.

A substantial lowering of the temperature, by 100° or more, causes profound changes in the character of absorption spectra. The principal effects to be expected are a sharpening and intensifying of the bands, with possible further resolution into sub-maxima. When comparing spectra, especially if any attempt is made to standardize band-shapes (Chapter 19), a mild degree of simultaneous temperature standardization is therefore also desirable as a precaution. For deliberate low-temperature work, −50° and below, a cryostat holds the specimen, whether it is a solid, or a non-freezing solution in a cuvette, or a frozen ' glass ' of glycerol and water in a cuvette. Few such set-ups are suitable for use in commercial spectrometers without the sort of structural alterations that only the manufacturer can do properly. Some manufacturers supply them.

Hartree (1951) makes interesting practical remarks on visual work. Lipsett (1961, 1965) describes a liquid helium cryostat, which goes as low (−269°C) as most people would want. Beale (1951) gives a theoretical background plus several practical details.

HAZARDS OF DILUTION (ETC.)

Dilution is not foolproof. The average small pipette has a probable delivery-uncertainty of about 0·004 ml. This, from the start, makes the use of normal (bulb-type) 1-ml pipettes unacceptable unless ± 0·4% error can be tolerated in the first dilution. Graduated 1-ml pipettes do better than this *if* you calibrate them and draw out the delivery tip to a finer point; but they are not easy to handle with this precision unless you blow a small bulb near the other end, and use a rubber or plastic bulb to control filling and delivery. Practice is needed. I won't stress the point, but dilution of 100× is less liable to error as one 0·5 ml delivery from a good graduated pipette into a 50 ml flask than as two 10× dilutions with most normal 10:1 flask:pipette combinations, and the inevitable, though small, errors of both members of the pairs.

For the record, I found that 2 ml pipettes had the same probable absolute delivery-uncertainty as 1 ml and 5 ml, so that the percentage uncertainty with these was about 0·2% and rather less than 0·1% respectively. This was with cyclohexane. Always check (by weighing) that both the flasks and pipettes you use really are as calibrated, and check them with the solvent you are using: ' run-out ' times vary not only with temperature but also with solvent. Isopropanol drains much more slowly than water, and is not suitable for use in small pipettes without re-calibration and more-than-usual temperature control; hexane drains much faster than water. The standard calibration on pipettes is for water only at a specified temperature. It is not meant to apply to other solvents, and it does apply only when the viscosity (etc.) behaviour simulates that of water. And even an NPL-calibration for water is likely to be wrong if the pipette has been recently heated. All this, of course, is true for any analytical work, not only absorption spectrometry.

It is both instructive and chastening for several members of the staff, senior and junior, to weigh ten successive deliveries from one pipette (cf. Chapter 18). Besides its salutary ego-deflationary value, this incidentally calibrates the pipette + operator complex. And if the deliveries are made into a weighed standard flask of ten times the pipette's nominal volume, a fresh calibration mark on the flask (don't be in too much of a hurry to do this without cross-checking) provides a useful pair for obtaining reliable 10:1 dilutions within known fiduciary limits, independent of the absolute accuracy of either pipette or flask. Mark the attested pair, indelibly but distortionlessly, for future easy identification. It is rare outside differential spectrometry (Chapter 13) that the final photometry has effectively closer fiduciary limits than you can achieve this way. When it has, gravimetric dilution becomes necessary. This is less irksome than it seems, apart from the extra time involved. As results are ultimately expressed in volumetric terms—percent is always w/v in calculating absorptivity—you must know, accurately, the specific gravity, which can be looked-up in tables for pure solvents or determined in the laboratory. More than usual care is needed with very volatile solvents. Use glass stoppers.

There is no doubt that volumetric dilution is quicker and more convenient than gravimetric dilution. I am not in favour, however, of sequential volumetric dilution beyond twice. Even though errors *might* cancel out, they are as likely to multiply. For enormous dilutions there is much to be said for the intelligent use of a micro-syringe, delivering in mm^3 rather than cm^3; μl instead of ml. That gives you a $10^3\times$ dilution advantage for a start. In the ' Agla ' syringe (Burroughs Wellcome & Co.) a stainless steel plunger is used and one turn of the micrometer head delivers 0·01 ml, accurately. Each of the 50 divisions on the circumference therefore corresponds to 0·0002 ml. Subdivision of this into three or four is easy if parallax is avoided. It is simple to dismantle for cleaning. Use a little of the last solvent, and use it immediately. Practice is of course needed to achieve quantitative results. Consult your local GLC expert. Micro-syringes (the name derives from the integral micrometer) are capable *in expert hands* of delivering $\pm 0·00005$ ml. Try for yourself. Practice by weighing ten deliveries of 50 μl into a flask on a semi-micro balance (you won't have the patience to fill the flask). Find how much the aggregate differs from whatever it should weigh, and also how the individual deliveries vary among themselves. (See *Standard deviation*, etc., Chapter 18.) Really pure solvents being so hard to come by, small calibrated flasks are a great asset. With skill you can get a $10^3\times$ dilution in one stage to within $\pm 0·1\%$ by diluting 20 μl in 20 ml. Choose a flask with a nice narrow neck. Don't spoil things by not using NPL- or personally-calibrated flasks.

Avoid openly stocking both 20- and 25-ml flasks and pipettes. They are too much alike, and therefore too easily confused, to be safely let loose in the same laboratory. If you *must* use both, keep one or the other under lock and key; or, somehow, colour them distinctively and indelibly; or blow a small bulb near the suction end of one size of pipette and choose different basic shapes for the flasks, round for one, conical for the other. This is not fussiness; it is just a precaution to prevent inevitable errors from being made worse by avoidable mistakes.

I said a page or two back that ' for our own satisfaction we should know (at least roughly) how much error to expect under different experimental conditions '. Quite the simplest way is to do an elementary statistical analysis by estimating the standard deviation (' *SD* ') of a set of ten results (Chapter 18). If you want to extend this test of consistency, don't do a run of twenty, but two runs of ten, and compare them. They should agree fairly well. If they don't, brush up your manipulative technique. I seriously advise applying this ' ten-repeats ' idea to every stage of your spectrometry, including weighing, which is usually taken for granted as above suspicion. Here, the *SD* should be negligible, but probably isn't. Try it, with a small flask lifted off the balance between weighings. Details are given later of all the statistical treatment that I think is essential in practical absorption spectrometry, a basic minimum without which you are ' flying blind '. Many people are, and don't know it. To have a good idea of the approximate *SD* of every type of routine measurement you do, and of every routine method of analysis that concerns you, can be very useful in arguments and will very often prevent them. Statistics can be even more blinding than science. The tactless use of statistical analysis in argument is also one of the quickest ways to lose friends without influencing people.

CUVETTES

Having thus made sure of your solution, how well matched are the cuvettes? Manufacturers are understandably getting cautious in their claims, and may even decline to supply guaranteed matched pairs. In normal use cuvettes that are ' matched ' today probably won't be tomorrow, or even later today at *every* wavelength. There are several possible reasons for this, including minor optical imperfections leading to variable location of the light spot on the photo-surface—which is seldom perfectly uniform in response from point to point, though some Sb-Cs surfaces are commendable—and visually imperceptible ' UV dirt ' on the outside of a cuvette face. The simplest remedy is to interchange sample and blank and their respective cuvettes, without altering their orientation (i.e. keep them facing the same way, and if they are cylindrical don't rotate them) and without touching the end faces. The simple arithmetic mean of the two observed extinction readings is then usually satisfactory, though the differences between the readings themselves can be disquieting (see next paragraph). If cuvettes are not already marked, inscribe an indelible arrow on a non-optical face so that they can always be used the same way round in the light beam. And make sure that the springs in the carrier press the cuvettes firmly against it and hold them normal to the light beam. A degree or two aslant makes very little difference to the length of the light-path, but it can displace the beam to a different part of a non-uniformly responsive photo-surface. The red-sensitive surface is worse than the UV-sensitive surface in this respect.

A record kept of the same two 1 cm cuvettes over a period of about a month showed an average *OD* difference of 0·0175; in one case, 16% of the reading. The range of differences was from +0·066 to −0·014, with no difference at all in only 5 out of 56 readings. The probable mean error of omitting the interchange (we called it ' reversed cells ') was about $2\frac{1}{2}$% of the observed readings on the average, at a level of about 0·4 extinction, that is ±0·01 absolute. Not terribly bad, for routine work, but not very good either. Omission of interchange when the ' 16% ' episode occurred would have meant an error of anything up to 8% low or high; in the event, the mean agreed to within $\frac{1}{2}$% of the mean on another pair of cuvettes, which were tried ' just in case '. What happened to make the ' regular ' pair misbehave? They behaved exemplarily next time, so I can only assume that UV dirt was the culprit and that it was routinely cleaned off before an inquest could be held. Put it down to human fallibility.

Single-cuvette working—the use of one cuvette successively for compensator and solution by measuring the *OD* of both the blank and the sample separately against air, and then subtracting—is inconvenient and demands a truly stable light source over long periods while the cuvette is emptied, drained, and refilled without the optical faces being touched. But, if the cuvette is replaced the same way round every time, this method does avoid the problem of a mobile light beam. It is especially useful in assays where the ' blank ' is blank only in name and shows substantial absorption of light (e.g. total tocopherol+dipyridyl; Edisbury, Gillow and Taylor, 1954) so that more conventional working involves large slit-widths. Make very certain that the amplifier is stable, however, and that the blank is reproducible. This latter condition also applies to recording instruments.

ERRORS IN SETTINGS

In making a manual reading of *OD* or %*T* there are basically three knob-settings: First you balance the dark current—that trickle of electrons which erupts from the photo-surface even when the shutter is closed—hoping it will remain constant for the next minute or two. Then you directly adjust the effective light intensity via the slit-width, and hence, indirectly, the amplified phototube or photomultiplier output stimulated by ' 100% ' illumination through the solvent alone. Finally you balance potentiometrically, and thereby compare with the effect of ' 100% ' illumination the diminished output arising from the attenuated illumination that now emerges from the solution. (What you have really done is to compare the ratio between two lengths of potentiometer wire, and then translate the answer, through electrical, into optical terms.) As a refinement, you should now also check whether the incident light and the dark current have, in fact, remained constant during the operation, as you have assumed. Incidentally, this tests photo-surface fatigue as well, but usually there just isn't time after every reading. The process takes for granted rectilinearity of photo-surface response; Sb-Cs UV-sensitive surfaces are more reliable in these respects than red-sensitive caesium oxide.

In a null-point instrument, linearity of amplification does not have to be assumed, nor linearity of galvanometer response, since the galvanometer needle is returned to the same arbitrary setting every time. This is conveniently mid-scale; but if the galvanometer sensitivity is appreciably better elsewhere, there is sometimes an advantage in using an easily identified graduation somewhere away from the official position, at least until the next overhaul. We do however have to assume rectilinearity of the potentiometer + photo-surface complex; and we trust our ability to detect very small movements of the galvanometer needle after they have occurred—not while they are occurring, which is much easier.

In each of the basic knob-settings there is an expectable small error. What is the absolute minimum aggregate? In practice, the routine minimum seems to be about 0·5%. The NPL seem able to bring theirs down routinely to a fraction of this; whether they do it by sheer instrumental excellence or by averaging a large number of results, all checked against some arcane standard, I don't know (see table on Wood's glass, Chapter 16). Keeping to real life, 0·5% seems a good enough goal to aim at for routine work, even for commercial contracts; but *between laboratories* $\pm 1\frac{1}{2}\%$ seems as good as can at present be expected, and rather more if recording spectrophotometers are involved. In differential spectrometry

(Chapter 13), Neal (1956) claims and justifies $\pm 0.03\%$—but this is in one laboratory, and the precision is not of direct extinction-reading but of an analytical result deduced from a calibration curve expressly designed to expand a small part of the scale, whereby it cunningly, yet quite honestly, evades the issue of more precise readings. It just does not need them. We do.

The steadiness of the hydrogen- or deuterium-lamp, stabilized, is variously assessed at $\pm 0.01-\pm 0.2\%$, which introduces a corresponding uncertainty into the results. The absorbance (extinction, OD) potentiometer consists of a coiled coil of some 10^3 small turns curled round in a circle against which electrical contact is made. Settings are therefore 'quantized' in steps of about $0.1\% T$ from 0 to 100%, in the sense that the contact slides from one turn to the next, bridging the gaps as it travels. There can never be anything but a whole number of turns involved—no fractions. Roughly, $0-100\% T$ (from infinity down to zero extinction) is therefore representable by the first 1000 integers, or maybe a couple of hundred more. This introduces a small irreducible uncertainty into the readings from the start. Each reading will inevitably register either a little too high or a little too low unless the true value luckily happens to coincide with one of the turns. The possible error from this cause alone is equivalent to half the distance between turns, $0.05\% T$. As the true value will not fall exactly mid-way any more often than it comes accidentally on a turn, the uncertainty will in practice average-out to something lower than 0.05, say $0.03\% T$ to the nearest figure. As an *absolute* quantity, and in the absence of parallax, electronic quirks, etc., this remains constant—or rather remains between zero and 0.05—from one end of the scale to the other. As a *proportion* of a reading, it varies continuously, reaching a minimum percentage of about three times the absolute error at the $37\% T$ or 0.43 extinction setting (Twyman and Lothian, 1933). This percentage uncertainty changes but little over the range $20-60\% T$ $(0.7-0.2$ extinction) rising sharply at low values of $\% T$. Only ten or a dozen turns cover from $0-1\% T$ and also carry the extinction calibrations from 2.0 to infinity. As an extreme example, at $0.2\% T$ the uncertainty is half the reading: the next turn ' up ' is 0.3, the next one ' down ' is 0.1; or in terms of extinction, 2.7, 2.5 and 3.0 respectively. This is one good reason for 'expanded scales', the '0.1' selector setting, for instance. Above $80\% T$ the percentage uncertainty again rises, but less rapidly. (The question of a ' best ' reading is raised again on page 212).

Over the normally used extinction range of a manual spectrophotometer, therefore, the fundamental uncertainty of the potentiometer itself can be taken as at best a little over 0·1% of the reading. Now if this were readily detectable by the galvanometer, the needle would jerk intolerably as the potentiometer jumped from turn to turn and would make readings difficult to register. Fortunately for users, galvanometer response normally comes just short of this: on the Uvispek, the individual potentiometer turns are discernible as little flicks, too small to affect readings or irritate the operator; on the Beckman DU and Unicam SP.500 the gain control (' sensitivity ') has to be turned hard right, for high amplification, before a slight tremor sets in. This makes me think that the dark current and slit-width settings, which also work with exemplary smoothness, must also be subject to a broadly similar galvanometer ' reluctance ', giving in the aggregate an instrumental uncertainty of the order of $\frac{1}{2}$%. There is not much likelihood of this being appreciably reduced without some basic change in the design of commercial spectrometers.

In support of this broad generalization we have quite a lot of evidence. Hogness, Zscheile and Sidwell (1937) came to a similar conclusion on their own early but refined instrument. Caster (1951) deduced much the same from statistical reasoning applied to the Beckman DU. And the following table, based on six series of ten consecutive readings at a level of 0·7 absorbance, made on a single sample which was not moved during the test, further amplifies the theme and also shows how repeatability is affected by the setting of the sensitivity control on the SP.500:

| | Position of sensitivity control (Number of turns from left) | | | | | |
	0*	1	2	3	4	7†
SD of single reading	0·047	0·0111	0·0039	0·0028	0·0022	0·0014
CV of single reading	±6·7%	±1·6%	±0·56%	±0·40%	±0·31%	±0·20%

* Hard left, narrow slit, high gain
† Wide slit, low gain

This means that at each setting the readings would be likely once in every three times to fall outside the ± ranges indicated, the C of V (*CV*) being the standard deviation expressed as a percentage.

Each reading was preceded by resetting the dark current and slit controls as if a complete curve were being plotted; but the figures are uncomplicated by the foibles of cuvettes or the vagaries of making-up solutions. The over-all uncertainty revealed therefore represents what would probably happen if a solid standard were being tested. At the customary mid-range sensitivity setting—a fair compromise between responsiveness, slit-width and precision, recommended by the manufacturer for normal use—the *SD* for a single reading amounts here to $\frac{1}{2}$% as predicted. See also p. 191.

This would satisfy most people, even accountants. A vast amount of useful research information can in fact be derived from *OD* readings with 10 or 20 times this range, and if a ± 1% range could be really depended on, even commercial contracts would rarely call for arbitration. But there is an uncomfortably wide gap between this and what we encounter in real life. Collaborative tests show that an over-all spread of ± 10% is not unheard of, and once in three times any two randomly chosen manual instruments in different laboratories can be *expected* to disagree by more than $1\frac{1}{2}$%; recording instruments, by 2 or 3%. There is more than a hint in all this that improper use of cuvettes, ignorance of their increasing optical imperfections as we descend the wavelength scale and of the means of minimizing the effects thereof, and unsuspected interference by stray light, are major contributary causes of discrepancy. But there remains a large inter-instrumental disagreement largely unexplained.

The paper by Caster (1951), already mentioned, goes a long way towards clearing the air, including discrediting the all-too-common use of numbers with four or five digits in reporting results. On the mainly mathematical side, Gridgeman (1952) summarizes and clarifies much that has already been published and adds some valuable observations of his own. And a truly monumental paper by Goldring, Hawes, Hare, Beckman and Stickney (1953), goes into so much candid detail concerning practical reasons for ' Absorption Anomalies ' that I used it, liberally and gratefully, in a couple of post-graduate lectures a year or two later, and would do so again if the occasion arose, for much of it goes beyond my own experience. No one, fortunately, is at all likely to encounter more than a fraction of the possible snags in spectrophotometry in one lifetime, or could survive them without psychological trauma; but it is well to be ready for them.

WAVELENGTH COMPLICATIONS

Errors in wavelength calibration can cause mystifying irregularities in extinction readings made at a specified wavelength away from an absorption maximum or minimum, where the spectrum is momentarily ' horizontal '. Obviously enough, the steeper the slope, the greater the probable error. The useful isosbestic point, where individually variable curves intersect under all conditions (Chapter 2), loses most of its value if it can't be reproduced exactly in different laboratories. One mμ either way shifts the measurement onto a slope and up to a higher extinction. The effect of an over-wide slit is however less noticeable at the isosbestic point that at a point on a steep slope, where the more effective lower-extinction side of the slit aperture dominates the reading (because more energy gets through). Figure 17.1 makes this clear, even though it does exaggerate the situation.

A new instrument takes some time to settle down and the original works adjustment is apt to drift quite considerably. This is a good reason for having a control chart of standard wavelengths as well as of extinctions (Chapter 18). Drifts are conspicuous on a chart, not in a table. One cause of changes in wavelength adjustment is variation in temperature. The effect of a change of 10°C on the far-UV adjustment is hardly noticeable (often of the order of 0·03 mμ) but increases to upwards of 1 mμ in the visible region. Some instruments are thermostatted; some have a simple bimetal strip to trim the position of the dispersing medium continually. Make sure that these corrective precautions are in working order. Methods of adjustment are given in the manufacturer's instructions (see also Chapters 11 and 15) but two points are worth special reiteration: One is that a habit should be made of always setting the control from the same direction, against the spring loading, which usually means from longer to shorter wavelengths. Find out which; neglect of this can lead to errors of from ½ mμ to 2 or 3 mμ or more according to region. The other is that the hydrogen or deuterium emission spectrum has too many faint lines in the visible region for the useful 486 and 656 mμ lines to be picked out with certainty unless the adjustment is already fairly good. Judging by collaborative tests, a wavelength spread of 4 or 5 mμ or more is not unusual, so precautionary checks are well worth while. As a minimum requirement, don't be satisfied with anything worse than $\pm\frac{1}{2}$ mμ in the far UV, and about $\pm 1\frac{1}{2}$ mμ at

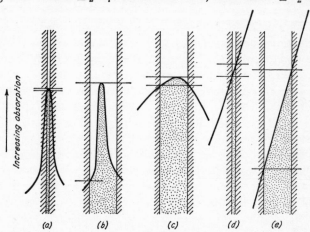

Increasing absorption

(a)   (b)   (c)   (d)   (e)

FIG. 17.1. Effect of excessive slit-width (see also Fig. 6.5). Unshaded areas represent light that has not been absorbed by the sample. The roughly triangular unshaded parts between the horizontal lines behave in the manner of stray light (q.v.) and lower the observed *OD* readings.

(a) and (b) A narrow absorption maximum, first with an appropriate slit, then ' swallowed ' by an over-wide slit. An *OD* reading obtained with (b) will be nearer the lower horizontal line than to the correct top one. Conversely, of course, with a narrow minimum.

(c) The effect is smaller, but still appreciable, with a broad band. Even the comfortably wide 302 mμ (33100 cm^{-1}) band of potassium nitrate can be ' moved up and down ' 2% by varying the slit between 0·05 and 0·65 mm.

(d) and (e) The effect on a steeply sloping curve. The white triangle, small in (d) and large in (e), will lower the *OD* reading and also bias the wavelength reading towards whatever wavelength corresponds with, in this instance, the left jaw of the slit.

486 mμ. You might be able to do better, with luck. And the work will benefit correspondingly.

It is rare in a modern instrument for the slit-width to have much effect on apparent wavelength, at least over the range of widths normally used (but see Fig. 6.5). Slits nowadays either open symmetrically, so that the ' centre of gravity ' does not change;

or two slits in series (entrance and exit, for instance) with one fixed jaw in each are so arranged that the movable jaw of one compensates for the other. Find what system is used on your spectrometer, and test whether one or two known wavelengths apparently vary in position when you vary the slit-width. Except at extreme widths, there will probably not be any significant difference. In general, down to the point where diffraction occurs, the narrower the better. Unless there is a considerable instrumental light leak (page 158) a wider slit will always lower the apparent extinction of a band—maybe not much, but usually perceptibly (Fig. 17.1).

This is fairly obvious with very narrow bands. Take an extreme case, a band only 1 mμ wide. If the spectral band-width of a slit, or spectral slit-width, at the wavelength concerned exceeds 1 mμ, the band will be ' lost in the slit ' and passed over unnoticed. In practice, even a narrow band is usually substantially wider than the spectral slit-width, and its presence will be duly registered; but the principle is the same, and a lower extinction will be registered at a maximum in the absorption spectrum (or a higher value at a sharp minimum) than the true value. This effect will be repeatable as long as the width remains unaltered; accuracy is impaired, precision remains as it was. Just how much error this involves in real life depends on the relative widths of slit and band. But the effect is noticeable even with fairly broad bands, such as the wide and harmless-looking potassium nitrate band at 302 mμ (33100 cm^{-1}). An admittedly generous variation in physical slit-width from 0·05 to 0·65 mm separation of the slit jaws here caused a difference of 2% in observed *OD*, 0·014 on a reading of 0·7. This was a genuine difference, statistically significant, based on the arithmetic means of 10 readings at several widths. With narrower bands the difference would be greater. Try it, without touching the wavelength control between readings. Or try different rates of recording.

Both Cannon (1955) and Lothian (1956) sound notes of caution concerning differential spectrometry with excessively high ' blanks ' requiring wide slits. At high extinction levels, the difference between blank and sample can seemingly vary with slit-width, particularly at lower wavelengths, and this variation is anomalous—an increase in width can increase the difference, instead of decreasing it. The effect is sometimes so large that it ' warrants a careful check at two or more slit-widths when making differential measurements at high optical densities.' The convenient ' 0·1 ' selector position allows the use of radiation intensities at one-tenth the normal level; but don't push your luck too far.

At the opposite end of the scale, 80–100% T, under 0·1 OD, both accuracy and precision suffer, mainly because of difficulties in compensating for reflection losses, which are comparable with the light absorption, and partly because response is less definite. Maybe the ' difference ' scales (such as 95–105 % T, or 80–102% T) electronically expanding a small range over most of a chart ordinate, would help the photometry; but even that would not eliminate the reflection difficulty.

Nor would the possible complication raised by Goldring (1950): ' At any absorption band there is a so-called anomaly in the refractive index. This is in the proper direction to cause an increased reflectance loss at the absorption peak. Confirmation or discard of this idea awaits further experimental work '. This would only operate at low readings, and would raise their apparent value. I don't know the answer. Just distrust low readings.

I do know, however, that the chief obstacle to replacing the intensely subjective Lovibond Tintometer by a simple spectrometer for such tests as the red component of the yellow colour of whale oil or groundnut protein is the low level of the readings. I have tested the red Lovibond glasses used, and found them to be in a remarkably consistent logarithmic series when allowance is made for reflection, so well graded in optical densities that anyone who doesn't get exactly double the reading at double the solution thickness is not as good at Lovibondery as he/she thinks. For the record, an empirical relationship for yellowish samples that would be hard to refute except by a collaborative test on a huge scale is

Lovibond Red (2-in. cell)=$10 \times E$(4 cm) $_{525\ m\mu}$

WHAT IS THE 'BEST' LEVEL OF READING?

As I see it, there is no single ' best ' level of reading. As design improves, the range widens. For absorption spectrograms, the combined responses of photographic emulsion and human eye demand an extinction of about 1·2 for even moderate accuracy and precision. Visual spectrometry seems to call for something not much under 2·0 for what seems to be purely physiological reasons which would be interesting to investigate. Photoelectric devices cover a wide range of designs, and each must be taken as you find it. The old Twyman-Lothian (1933) figure of 37%T or 0·43 OD still holds good for all 'transmittance read-out' instruments in which (nominally) no error is involved in setting 0 and 100%T. Depending on the design of the instrument, 'absorbance read-out' instruments increase in precision with increasing readings, coefficient of variation decreasing rapidly between 0 and 1 extinction, and levelling-off thereafter, while standard deviation increases slowly and apparently rectilinearly all the way. Slavin (1965) gives a good account based on his own and also on Gridgeman's (1952), Cahn's (1955), and Crawford's (1959) findings. As usual, try for yourself, remembering the acute mechanical and stray-light complications of high readings: getting a $>10^2$:1 attenuation accurately and/or precisely is no mean manufacturing achievement.

EXTRAPOLATION AND INTERPOLATION

To arrive at the true height of a really narrow absorption maximum it may be impossible to do more than take a series of several readings (not necessarily 10, but as many as you have time for, and the same number of each) at a series of slit-widths—accompanied by appropriate adjustments to the gain control—and then to extrapolate the results graphically to zero slit-width. Extrapolation is rarely a practice to be recommended. It is always mathematically risky; but sometimes it can't be avoided. In this case the approach to the truth is asymptotic and correspondingly safer.

A couple of examples will illustrate the need for caution in the absence of asymptotic guidance:

(1) Mark Twain had a keen eye for the more bizarre *extrapolatio ad absurdum*. At any bend in a river, centrifugal scouring undercuts the outer bank. When two such bends come back-to-back, as happens so often along the Mississippi, it is only a matter of time before the river takes a short cut across the isthmus, leaving a horseshoe-shaped lake alongside. In the previous century, the Mississippi had thus shortened itself by 130 miles. *At this rate*, Mark Twain remarked (correctly; for a century was not an adequate sample), a million years ago next November it was 1 300 000 miles long, and stuck out over the Gulf of Mexico like a fishing rod . . .

(2) I remember reading a few years ago in an excellent textbook (I wish I could think of the name; can someone tell me, please?) about an Awful Example of the dangers of extrapolation without adequate knowledge of the full circumstances. What, for instance, are the next four terms in the series 2 4 6 8 . . . .? Obviously, you say (with memories of very early schooldays), 10 12 14 16. You have reasonably, but prematurely, assumed that the series is based on $x=2n$. And so it might well be. Or again it might not. The next four terms could be . . . . 34 132 374 856, based on the equation $x=2n+(n-1)(n-2)(n-3)(n-4)$, which also is not unreasonable, though one wouldn't be expected to think of it. Many series of observations start like this with a simple rectilinear relationship and then curve off for no apparent reason—unless you know the basic equation or have seen the behaviour before. Familiarity breeds expertise.

Interpolation is not nearly as risky as extrapolation, but even this has its hazards. For the sake of neatness, I suppose, or because it 'looks right', most people like to smooth-off curves drawn through the fixed points on a graph. But again, know your subject first. Some curves are known to be smooth. Some are thought (wishful thinking?) to be smooth until someone finds that a small inflexion keeps on appearing in the same place time after time, so often that it is unlikely to be due to either error or coincidence. A case in point is the little, almost insignificant, shoulder on the short-wave slope of the vitamin-A band. For years this was deliberately smoothed out from hand-plotted curves, until recording charts showed it as well, and kept on showing it, in exactly the same place. ' The multiplication of seeming coincidences ', said Professor Baly in one of his 1924 lectures, ' must sooner or later engender a belief in their physical reality.' Slow recording is less likely to miss such features as faint inflexions that regularly elude hand-drawing of curves because a chart record comprises an almost infinite number of balance-points instead of one every 5 or 10 $m\mu$. The moral is obvious: Get to know your curve by slow recording or finely-spaced plotting before you try to take short cuts.

MANUAL USE OF '0·1' NETWORK WITH 100% T

Slit-width requirements are conflicting. Too narrow a slit, and the sensitivity (gain) control has to be wound round till the galvanometer hardly responds and precision is lost: too wide, and precision is regained, but accuracy is lost. A compromise is, however, possible if the operator is prepared to exert a little more effort than usual. Undoubtedly more *mental* effort is needed, because for a short time your reflexes, nicely conditioned to work the instrument in normal routine fashion, have to omit one step in the operational sequence and insert another which in ordinary working you never think of because it is done for you.

Turn the selector switch to the ' 0·1 ' position and leave it there. With shutter closed, balance the dark current as usual. Set the transmittance to exactly 100% (this makes you appreciate the convenience of the ' check ' position!) Open the shutter, and with the solvent cuvette in the light beam zero the galvanometer by means of the slit control. Now slide the sample cuvette into the light beam and make a normal reading—all the time leaving the switch at ' 0·1 ', but taking the readings at their nominal face value. Don't, as is conventional when using ' 0·1 ', add 1·0 to the OD readings or divide the nominal transmittance by 10, because you haven't used the ' check ' network of resistors at all, and your comparisons have all been made along the same 0–100% T stretch of potentiometer wire. For the same reason, your sensitivity is less affected under these conditions and you avoid that embarrassing loss of galvanometer responsiveness which accompanies the conventional and much more convenient use of ' check ' and ' 0·1 '. The conventional usage is of course expressly designed for readings much higher than 1·0 absorbance (under 10% T); we are concerned here with readings under 1·0, whether they be absolute or relative (i.e. differences between sample and blank, see Chapter 13), and our aim is to reduce the slit-width needed for coping with perhaps an untractably semi-opaque solvent. The only difference between this and differential spectrometry is that here the same semi-opaque *solvent* is present in both beams. The effect on the spectrometer is the same: a vast reduction in incident light. This is one good way to handle it without appreciably altering either the sensitivity setting or the slit-width. An incidental benefit (this depends on the instrument; not all are alike) is a probable suppression of a considerable proportion of any stray light, with consequent improvement in rectilinearity of performance.

Rectilinearity is very desirable indeed, but often elusive. The whole point of using a logarithmic function like absorbance, log I_0/I, is lost unless the readings are truly proportional to cuvette path-length and solution concentration. Deviations from rectilinearity should NEVER be blamed on the late-lamented Beer. Apparent violations often do occur, and much information can be derived from the manner of their occurrence (Lothian, 1963). Possible causes of trouble include association of solute molecules, dissociation, ionization, interaction with the solvent, charge- or energy-transfer, modification of electron atmosphere by changes in temperature, emission of fluorescence under excitation, light-scattering, photo-lability during exposure, birefringence, interference between wave-fronts when very thin films are used (for instance, if a micrometer cuvette is closed down to the point where interference fringes are seen; at this level, the scale on the micrometer will read less than one division and the error of reading it will necessarily be excessive). Without invoking metaphysics, it is clear enough that all these things involve qualitative changes in the absorbing molecules and/or in their environment. Beer's law explicitly insists that the 'absorbing entities' shall remain the same in quality, whereupon the extinction of light attributable to them will be proportional to their multitude in the beam, that is, proportional to concentration × path-length. It is therefore of primary importance to specify and maintain the exact conditions of test. In practice, one can usually choose conditions of pH, solvent, temperature, permissible concentration-range within which significant variations do not occur. If this is done, reasonable agreement should be attained even between different laboratories.

An interesting horror story has been thought-up by Tarrant (1965), based on possible wear of potentiometer slide wires. The possibility is mercifully improbable, but worth keeping a wary eye on. A transmittance wire will tend to continue to produce consistent results if it is evenly worn, while an absorbance wire will produce low results with an error proportional to the absorbance. Heavy wear is necessary before much effect would be noticed.

LIGHT SCATTERING

Some of the foregoing items have already been considered. Others are worth further mention. Light scattering, for instance, can be troublesome in unexpected ways. In quantitative work, a solution should as a minimum requirement be visually bright and clear. The faintest suspicion of dullness can conceal a sort of ' UV-cloudiness ' which you obviously can't see. The Tyndall effect, in which a transverse light beam reveals the presence of micro-cloudiness, is a borderline case. It is even possible for this effect to be ' seen ' only by a UV detector, so its visual absence is no guarantee that a solution is truly ' UV-clear ' of turbidity. Especially insidious is the case where the solute is sparingly soluble and the solution, although initially clear, begins to crystallize—because, perhaps, of a fall of a degree or two in temperature, or unsuspected seeding by a speck of atmospheric dust. At the onset, cloudiness will not be visible, but could well affect a far UV extinc-tion reading, raising it appreciably; later, visible crystals may deposit here and there, some obscuring the light beam and raising the reading, while the solution itself becomes weaker and so lowers the reading. The whole effect is unpredictable quantitatively. Always use solutions well below saturation point, *if you can*. Optically clear polyphenolic quebracho extract, for instance, actually precipitates on dilution (Knowles, 1952). There are exceptions to almost everything.

Quantitative turbidimetry is an art in itself, and rather beyond the scope of this book. It must however be mentioned in passing. As a rule, precise temperature control is important in turbidimetry because of its effect, slow or immediate, on particle size, which governs the wavelength and amount of absorption by the cloudy solution. If the sample is far enough away from the detector, measurements can be made on a spectrophotometer, but a simpler filter instrument is usually equally useful and precise. Goulden (1961, 2) gives details of the evaluation of globule diameter (fat emulsions, etc.) and particle size from a limited number of readings. His curves show clearly why a correction for turbidity cannot be applied *reliably* by taking a reading at a long wavelength and deducting this value from a reading lower down the wavelength scale. Sometimes this works well; more often it doesn't. Better not to risk it. In general spectrometry, turbidity has more nuisance value than use. If you suspect UV-turbidity and can't see a Tyndall effect, remember that its magnitude will depend on the geometry of the optical system, detector size, distance between sample and detector, etc. If you can vary the distance, which is possible only with a capacious sample compartment, there should be no difference in readings obtained in extreme positions. Be sure that the blank and sample are similarly positioned in their respective beams, and that the rays all pass properly through the middle of the cuvettes without touching the sides, even when the cuvettes are away from their normal stations.

Attempts to read paper chromatograms directly on a spectrophotometer are beset with similar problems of background opacity. But the technique described by Kendall and Lloyd (1956) is worth noting. Qualitative results are good. Quantitative results are complicated by the variability of the blank paper as a translucent medium. Moistening with *pure* glycerol+water sometimes helps. In practice, it is generally better to use UV scanning to locate otherwise invisible spots and then to elute them for ' proper ' tests in solution.

IRRELEVANT ABSORPTION

The simpler a measurement is, the less likely it is to go wrong. In the absence of interfering sources of error, of which irrelevant absorption is probably the most common, a single extinction reading (*a* in Fig. 17.2) at the peak of an absorption band, where wavelength effects are minimal, provides a valid datum for quantitative assay. If, however, there is interference of any kind (fluorescence, inhibition, irrelevant absorption, etc.) *a* as observed is not a valid measure of concentration. At best, it is then no more than a rough estimate, setting an upper limit if interference is solely in the form of irrelevant absorption, or a lower limit if fluorescence or inhibition preponderate. Physico-chemical removal of the interfering component(s) is the obvious remedy if it can be applied without damage to the component being assayed. But this is not always practicable or expedient. Sometimes a correction for irrelevant absorption can be applied with excellent results (e.g. Morton and Stubbs, 1946). Although unintelligent use has brought this idea into undeserved disrepute it is worth trying if there are many similar samples. Sometimes the contribution of irrelevant absorption can be calculated from the spectral curve of a known component; for instance, in a mixture of carotene and vitamin A, proportional allowance can be made for the unwanted contribution of the carotene to the UV absorption of the vitamin on the basis of a single measurement in the visible, where vitamin A is transparent and carotene absorbs strongly.

Alternatively, the persistence (Figs. 2.1 and 19.7) of the relevant band occasionally provides a more reliable measure of concentration than does the 'gross' absorption; but this is true only when either irrelevant absorption is absent or it runs nearly parallel to the baseline, as it does in most cloudy solutions (which should if possible be avoided as a matter of principle).

A convenient and almost self-compensating evasion is possible when the relevant band is flanked by two minima, as in Fig. 17.2. On the recorded chart or hand-drawn graph, draw a tangent to the two related minima. Then *b*, the tip-to-tangent distance or

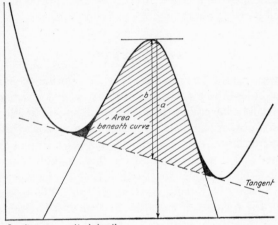

Fig. 17.2. Assessment of concentration from a single optical-density reading at an absorption maximum is valid only under strictly defined conditions. Alternatives are shown here and discussed in the text.

average persistence, comes nearer the truth than any other single reading, in that it remains more closely proportional to concentration × path-length under varying conditions. The magnitude of *b* must, of course, be established for whatever reference preparation is used, whether pure substance or standard mixture, in the final proportionality calculation. Because *b* is necessarily smaller than *a*, precision will be a little lower; but accuracy will be substantially improved.

There are theoretical advantages in taking the area beneath the curve as a measure of concentration. This area can be assessed by planimeter or some other integrator, or by counting squares, or even by carefully cutting out the shape and weighing it in comparison with a known area of the same paper. Crude though this procedure seems, it can be remarkably precise. Take into account only the shaded area above the tangent; ignore the little triangle at each side. Attempts to include all or parts of the area below the tangent are rarely successful: the whole affair becomes bottom-heavy and accuracy generally deteriorates.

In case of doubt, try the variants for yourself. I prefer the simple non-destructive *b* unless a demonstrably irrelevant-absorption-free sample can be easily obtained. See also Chapter 13 and Vandenbelt and Henrich (1953) on ' Spectral anomalies produced by the overlapping of absorption bands '.

FLUORESCENCE

Cloudiness, latent or obvious, always spuriously raises OD readings, unless the blank happens to be even cloudier, when the readings will be lowered, or a balance unobtainable at all. Fluorescence, on the other hand, always lowers apparent absorbance, raises apparent transmittance. The effect is not often serious, but must be watched for. Test the sample (or rather a sample of the sample, in case it is photo-labile) in strong UV light—mercury lamp or H-lamp. Use a high concentration for this. Fluorescence then occurs in the menisci, if anywhere, and in the first mm or so of solution, and is most easily seen there if it is visible at all. What happens during a measurement of absorbance is that, unlike the radiation you are interested in, any fluorescence that has been excited usually passes on substantially unattenuated by the solution, and affects the photo-surface. Even if you don't see any, there may still be some UV fluorescence. Check as for invisible turbidity, by testing your working solution at the two extremes of the compartment. Fluorescent emission is radiated randomly, unlike the genuine ray which is directed along a well-defined path, and so lower OD readings are obtained when the sample is nearer to the detector if fluorescence is interfering. The effect is decreased by dilution, the solution behaving as if stray light were present (as, in a sense, it is). Readings in the higher part of the extinction scale will be much lower than they should be; lower readings are less affected.

An estimate of true, fluorescence-free, extinction can therefore be obtained by using progressively more dilute solutions in longer cuvettes, and risking extrapolation to infinite dilution. Fortunately the approach is again asymptotic, and ionization complexities are infrequent. *Inter alia*, see a couple of revealing papers by Braude and Timmons (1953) and Ovenston (1953), with evidence to support both sides according to conditions, by Vandenbelt and Henrich (1954).

The potential seriousness of fluorescence in quantitative spectrometry is obvious, but there is no need to panic over it. Check the magnitude of the effect as above. If you can't effectively eliminate it by interposing a suitable interference filter between cuvette and photo-surface, you can at least minimize it by working with dilute solutions located as far from the detector as possible. If, as often happens, the fluorescence is due to a minor contaminant try to remove it from the sample. Usually fluorescence is also a symptom of high reactivity with adsorbents, and removal by chromatography is feasible.

Fluorescence by the material of a cuvette (older cuvettes, made of natural crystalline quartz before the advent of the much superior Spectrosil, for instance) is fortunately rare. If you find it, there seems nothing you can do except to break the offender and throw it away. It is far too ' dangerous ' to leave lying about.

LABILE SUBSTANCES

Not every sample is stable. Photochemical decomposition due to action of daylight on either the sample or its solution is an effect to be looked for in any material, particularly biological. The effect is often enhanced by the solvent. Light also often augments the oxidizing action of the atmosphere. In general, it is wise to prepare solutions in a subdued light unless they are known to be stable. *Any material that absorbs light is potentially vulnerable to it*, the effect being greatest at those wavelengths which are selectively absorbed. Many years ago Dr T. Moore of Cambridge found that vitamin A is inactivated by UV radiation; this led Professor (then Dr) R. A. Morton of Liverpool to examine the UV spectrum of vitamin A for a suitable absorption band whereby it could be assayed spectrometrically without lengthy biological tests or the use of equivocal and messy colour reactions. In alcohol solution, the 325 mμ band of vitamin A is remarkably stable, even under strong UV light and bubbled oxygen; in chloroform, it disappears quite rapidly. You have to know your test substance.

There is little risk of photo-decomposition of any but the most photo-labile substances while they are in the cuvette compartment. In the older instruments, where the sample received the full glare of the light source, the risk was considerable. I remember a colleague's spectrogram (taken with the under-water spark light source, q.v., on an old Hilger E.3) of the carotenoid violaxanthin, in which a fresh solution had to be used for each exposure—two or three refills for each of the longer exposures which lasted up to 5 minutes. The stuff visibly changed colour while it was being tested. The resulting curved absorption band-shadows across the unattended spectrogram were more artistic than useful. In the modern instrument, radiation falls on the sample only after it has been through the monochromator and lost most of its optical sting. (You couldn't record those curved bands.) Nevertheless, I have encountered one or two samples that are stable enough in the laboratory, with artificial lighting and sunshine filtered through glass windows, that showed deterioration during test at around 250 mμ (40000 cm^{-1}). Even exposure in a silica cuvette to outdoor sunlight would not necessarily reveal this particular instability: an exceptionally clear atmosphere is needed before much radiation below 300 mμ gets through; but for most UV-lability checking, outdoor exposure to sunlight (even Port Sunlight) suffices. Be careful to avoid evaporation, which could mask spectral loss by increasing the concentration. As a precaution, you should repeat-test any ' unknown ' sample, preferably more than once on the same cuvette-full, over the peak wavelength range. If a change can't then be detected, forget the possibility in normal work. Not many substances give any trouble of this sort. If they did, spectrometry would soon become unpopular.

The possibility of chemical interaction in the cuvette must not be overlooked. A little knowledge of elementary chemistry will prevent the cuvette from being accidentally used as a reaction vessel. Remember the latent hazards of simple atmospheric oxidation.

POLARIZATION AND OPTICAL INTERFERENCE

In many monochromators, multiple reflections cause appreciable polarization of the light beam. Sometimes the quartz itself is optically active, which is one property synthetic silica does not show. If the sample itself is birefringent, a slightly undulating absorption spectrum will be produced. Usually, the effect is small, but the true curve can be appreciably distorted by its superposition. A quick check of the sample with a sensitive polarimeter is worth while if you have doubts.

A micrometer cuvette, adjusted to an absurdly short path-length, can act as an interference filter—not an efficient one, but sufficiently effective to superpose its own transmittance spectrum on the true absorption spectrum. The remedy here is obvious, and the likelihood of such a foolish mistake remote. Vigilance is a good habit. Here it will conserve the integrity of both the spectrum and the end-plates, which are all too easily damaged by mutual contact, especially if a particle of hard grit is trapped between them.

PHANTOM BANDS

Errors can be erratic or systematic. Erratic errors, due to evaporation of solvent, development of cloudiness (dust, micro-organisms, coagulation, partial crystallization, dirty cuvettes, etc.) have either been dealt with or are too obvious to stress further. A curious phenomenon noted by Beckman is worth comment (see also Chapter 6). Everyone has seen the galvanometer needle shake, or even seen a slight temporary shift in zero setting, when the amplifier box is tapped or the cuvette compartment lid is replaced with an unseemly clatter. This is attributed to mechanical meta-stability of the input valve filament or first grid, which, under a minor shock, can ' toggle ' over between two possible positions, both semi-stable. These positions are reproducible and so can escape detection despite a change in zero—which could have been due to drift—between opening and closing the shutter (etc.). This is tantamount to temporarily re-setting the controls, only it isn't you, but the electronic components, that have done the re-setting; and *their* re-settings, though limited in variety, are unpredictable. This can play some un-amusing tricks with an absorption curve, or readings generally. Always be gentle in operating controls.

If errors are systematic and follow some sort of trend or pattern, extrapolation to an extreme may be possible, though not necessarily desirable (page 213); or conditions of test need to be more rigidly specified; or a calibration curve can be drawn for use with one specified instrument (it is rare for calibration curves to work satisfactorily with more than one instrument, and rarer still between laboratories). Major causes of systematic and misleadingly reproducible non-linearity are stray light (Chapter 12), fluorescence, polarization if the sample is optically active (dealt with earlier in this chapter), and idiosyncrasies of the amplifier.

One of the hazards of stray light is the manifestation of Phantom Bands in the far UV (Figs. 7.1 and 12.1). Because the purest ray serene is accompanied by bright gate-crashers of different wavelength, and the photo-detector isn't very good at distinguishing between them, a majestically uprising curve droops suddenly away from its proper direction, passing through a maximum before descending. That maximum is a figment of the photo-detector's imagination. How do you tell a genuine band from a phantom? Halve the concentration, which is usually not enough to affect ionization, or—better, because ionization doesn't then enter into the matter at all—halve the cuvette path-length. If your suspected band and all its associated *OD* readings are also halved within experimental error (that is why a knowledge of what is and is not significant is so important) the band is no phantom, but genuine. If, on the other hand, readings are appreciably more than half, do a stray-light test at the appropriate wavelength inside the danger zone, and calculate how much correction to (approximately) apply. But use corrections only when you have to, as a last resort. Eliminate the need for them whenever you can. (cf. Johnson, 1962).

In certain circumstances, recording spectrometers sometimes trace quite convincing phantom bands, as reproducibly as if they really meant it, for a reason entirely unconnected with stray light— rather the reverse, in fact: namely, not enough energy to move the pen. Suppose a rising curve is being traced from the longer wavelengths downwards (usually you have no choice of direction, and the manufacturer's choice is the opposite; but no matter, the argument is unaffected). The solvent cuts off at (say) 230 mμ (43400 cm^{-1}) or maybe the instrument is off-colour owing to some maladjustment or other, so that response below 230 mμ has fallen off. At 230 mμ the pen will rise to some point short of its limit and stay where it is, drawing a horizontal line, because the energy in either beam is insufficient to activate the servo-motor and move the pen. Now suppose that, instead of recording from high to lower wavelengths, we are able to change into reverse and record from (say) 200 mμ upwards. From 200 to 220-odd mμ, the pen doesn't leave the baseline—not enough energy. Above this, a little unbalanced energy seeps through and the pen creeps up, until at 230 mμ it ' meets itself on the way down ' as it were, and thereafter traces the true curve to whatever higher wavelength may correspond with the beginning of another band, which it will probably trace with exemplary accuracy. The phantom band in this case gives itself away by its peculiar shape, which has an unusually unnatural-looking asymmetry with possibly a sharp kink where it rejoins the proper curve. For emergency use, all recording instruments should, I think, have provision for reversal of direction of scan, even if it has to have manual help to prevent the pen from digging into the chart.

Sometimes all that is needed is adjustment of the gain control. If the pen is *gently* moved a cm or two along the ordinate it should return to its original position without over- or under-shooting. If it over-shoots, the gain is too high; if it under-shoots, and moves sluggishly, too low. Compromise is essential. In general, adjustment should aim at just enough, but not more than enough, gain for no ' dead spot ' to be apparent. Too high a gain causes instability of the amplifier (page 207).

I imagine that it is an analogous effect which causes the ' tail-off ' below 230 mμ on many spectrograms: the absorption curve rises for a while, then suddenly turns away from the main exposures, giving an apparent lengthy match point along one of them, or between two of them, over a distance of perhaps 10 mμ down to where the spectrum finally peters out in the far-UV. If the emulsion were photo-sensitive at lower wavelengths, no doubt the curve would curl down again instead of ' tailing-off ' towards the edge of the plate. But I never saw any such evidence of stray light on the old E.3 or E.528 spectrographs.

MISCELLANEOUS COMMENTS

A few items in what follows have already been referred to earlier in this book. Repetition of the truth is sometimes mildly irritating, but gives less trouble than turning to previous pages. One item that has not been mentioned is that if the H-lamp power-pack of one of the older manual instruments is not quite able to cope with unusually wild mains fluctuations, fit a 1:1 constant-voltage transformer between it and the mains. This gives the stabilizing circuit a lot less work to do and really does discourage drift between readings.

Caesium oxide photo-surfaces are not concerned with measurements below about 600 mμ (1670o cm^{-1}) but it is worth mentioning that they occasionally suffer from a curious form of non-linear response due to photo-emission from the inner surface of the glass envelope. At low levels of illumination (high absorbance) this can, so it is said, even reverse the polarity of the signals. It could also conceivably happen to an aging Cs-Sb tube before it finally succumbs. Photo-surfaces themselves sometimes get tired. This can show up as drift during over-long illumination, though this is rare nowadays; or as a form of acute hysteresis, for which Beckman admits ' the only remedy, other than waiting for complete recovery after change of radiation intensity (at the risk of increased drift errors) is to replace the offending tube '. I am thankful never to have encountered this ailment. You are never likely to.

' An instrument is no better than its cuvettes ', said Mr W. H. Storey of Unicam on an epic occasion. I have already mentioned the risks of taking them for granted (page 204) and suggested a simple method avoiding errors of non-matching: interchange without rotating or external cleaning. The mean of the two results is as close, I think, as one can get to the truth in routine work. Interchange is however practicable only with one pair of cuvettes: any greater number becomes unwieldy. A method on which opinions differ to the point of friendly acrimony is described by Scott Archer (1954). It goes against many of the accepted canons of spectrology (for instance, by using empty as well as full cuvettes) but it does work well and is certainly more convenient than attempted interchange of more than two full cuvettes. Non-reproducibility of cleaning, Archer claims, has much less than the expected effect on results. Unprejudiced users should at least give it a trial: you match clean empty cuvettes against each other at several appropriate wavelengths and record the corrections needed. Then run in the solvent and solution(s) without removing the cuvettes from their holder or indeed touching them. Archer produces an impressive set of statistical evidence to support the claimed precision of the method.

The importance in either Archer's method, or in the simple

interchange method, of not touching the end-faces of the cuvettes is obvious. In a lighter moment, I tried just what the effect of an unremoved fingerprint would be. I made easily visible thumb prints on an empty cuvette (rather dusty on the inside so that it showed readings high enough to assess with reasonable certainty) and also on the optical faces of our ' link with sanity ' Wood's glass standard (Chapter 15). Four sets of five readings were made at 240 mμ (41700 cm^{-1}) on the cuvette, and at 360 mμ (27800 cm^{-1}) on the standard before and after soiling, and after dry-wiping with lens tissue. The effect was (not unexpectedly) a dozen times as pronounced at the lower wavelength, but was completely removed by simple wiping:

Extinction Readings (*means of* 5)

	Initial	Soiled	Wiped	Difference	
360 mμ	0·462	0·468	0·462	0·006	
		0·465	0·462	0·003	
		0·470	0·461	0·011	0·006
		0·466	0·462	0·004	
240 mμ	0·282	0·353	0·283	0·070	
		0·361	0·282	0·079	
		0·348	0·283	0·065	0·072
		0·357	0·283	0·074	

This test was simplified considerably by the use of a dry 'sample '. A thumbprint on an end-face of a cuvette containing a solution is not so easy to remove without spillage of some of the contents. It is better then to empty, wash clean, and start afresh.

The fact that a human (some would unkindly prefix ' sub- ') operator is involved in all tests introduces some of the less predictable qualities of a bio-assay. Even with the deliberate avoidance of parallax, skilled operators rarely agree exactly over their readings of the same untouched setting of a dial. Eleven pairs of operators, entering singly by one door, writing down their readings, and leaving by the other door without any chance of communication until several minutes later, showed the following pair-differences: 0·012 0·005 0·005 0·003 0·002 0·005 0·005 0·003 0·003 0·008 0·006. These do not at first sight look serious; but they actually amount to about 1% of a normal reading, although neither instrument nor test material was changed, only the operator. This takes us perilously near the realms of psychiatry, and prudence calls a halt.

Or at least for a diversion. Having, by attention to details, ' tuned ' an instrument to give a good performance, how does one tell when to order a periodic overhaul and when to leave well alone? Much depends on the work of the laboratory, but time should always be found for Preventive Maintenance (Dale, 1957; Spruit and Keuker, 1965; Chapter 11, *q.v.*); daily on a manual instrument, weekly on a recording instrument. The manual results are plotted on a control chart (see Fig. 18.1). Recorder charts are preferably transparent or at least translucent, *dated*, and filed for sequential comparison on the viewing stand (Fig. 4.4) by superposition against the light. This reveals even minor differences, and especially drifts. Apparently, some charts are sensitive to variations in atmospheric humidity, so that they change slightly in size. Be careful of this, because if one point marked on the edge has to be aligned against a mark on the chart holder on the instrument, any changes in chart dimensions will upset the official calibration of ordinate and/or abscissa. It is a wise precaution to mark at least one other point on both ordinate and abscissa remote from the maker's mark on the holder (frame, bed, or drum), and to check that all marks coincide every time you fit a chart. On a strip chart, wavelength ' landmarks ' are automatically made along the moving edge (abscissa) but the precaution of marking the extremes of the ordinate on the framework is still worth while. Permitted limits of air moisture are comfortably about 20–80% relative humidity. A hair hygrometer in the laboratory is sufficiently precise for this; but in everything else try to emulate the ideal of Ettore Bugatti: ' The best is only just good enough '.

CHAPTER 18

THE CONTROL CHART AS A PROPHYLACTIC IN ABSORPTION SPECTROMETRY, OR A CHILD'S GUIDE TO STATISTICAL ANALYSIS

In research, the statistician should be called in at the design stage, not as a rescue worker

DR E. C. WOOD (S.A.C., U.K.)

In intellectually humbler but financially more rewarding walks of life a control chart not only reveals (for instance) when a package is underweight—or, more rarely, and far more panic-provoking, overweight—but also warns when there is a *likelihood* of ' things going off the rails ' either side. A glance at the present chart (Fig. 18.1) shows the appropriateness of the metaphor. The livelier disputes in spectrophotometry usually centre around extinction (absorbance, or optical density) measurements, so that the usefulness of any early warning system designed to forestall derailments of readings needs no stressing. It is less easy to make out a case for a similar daily wavelength control chart; but a weekly plot at two or three well-spaced wavelengths or frequencies would disclose any incipient major drift before it went beyond a $m\mu$ or so, or the equivalent wavenumber. The extinction control chart given here illustrates the principles involved, whatever datum is chosen for plotting:

(1) Select a suitable solid extinction standard (or wavelength standard) capable of permanent calibration if possible by the NPL, Teddington, or NBS, Washington, D.C.

(2) Take ten consecutive readings, re-setting all controls *except* sensitivity (gain) between readings.

(3) Calculate the standard deviation (*SD*) of a single reading (see below).

(4) On a long sheet of graph paper (probably several joined together) with dates marked along the bottom edge, draw five horizontal straight lines, the middle one to represent the average

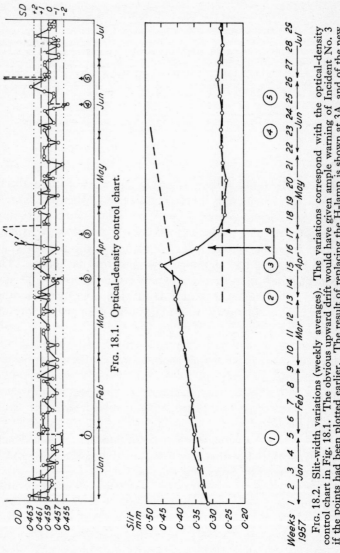

Fig. 18.1. Optical-density control chart.

Fig. 18.2. Slit-width variations (weekly averages). The variations correspond with the optical-density control chart in Fig. 18.1. The obvious upward drift would have given ample warning of Incident No. 3 if the points had been plotted earlier. The result of replacing the H-lamp is shown at 3A, and of the new mirror at 3B. The other four incidents would not be expected to affect slit-widths.

extinction derived from (2) above, and the others at distances from it of one and two *SD* above and below the fiduciary line. These are the 'rails' or confidence limits of the control chart.

(5) Every day, take a *single* extinction reading on the permanent standard and plot it on the control chart. Weekly, plot on a separate chart the slit-width required to give a balance under 'normal' conditions, i.e. with the usual sensitivity setting.

In order to confound the sceptics, I entrusted the construction of my first control chart to The Youngest Staff Member, unfortunately without enjoining her to plot the slit-width but merely to make a note of it daily. This was my mistake. After the third 'incident' (below) I told her to plot (once a week only) the average of the four or five relevant slit readings—four, when she spent one day a week elsewhere on 'further education', five normally.

All the above of course refers to a manual instrument. On a recording instrument a weekly chart would suffice, (or rather two charts, one for extinction, one for wavelength). The results would be read off the instrument charts and then plotted on a control chart as usual. To arrive at the initial 'chart *SD*' would consume a fair area of charts; but this would in my opinion be well worth while. Recording spectrometers are good value for money, but they are certainly not cheap, and to have all this usable extra information about them strikes me as money well spent.

USING THE CHART

If a reading falls inside the inner limits (± 1 *SD*), as it should do twice in three times, take no action, *unless* the reading stays on one side of the centre line for three successive days: this could indicate instrumental drift, which a repeat reading will at once confirm or refute. Otherwise, NO repeats; the whole thing is based on the assumption of single readings.

Once in twenty-two times, if your original estimate of *SD* still holds good, i.e. if the reading still belongs to the same statistical family, a single reading should fall outside the outer fiducial limits (± 2 *SD*). When it does, repeat it at once. This time it should be well within again, and the incident can be forgotten. Forgotten mentally that is; the routine reading must be plotted as usual, uncorrected, and a note of the repeat can be made on the chart. If the point is still outside, further investigation and/or adjustment is needed. Ideally, the points on the chart should scatter symmetrically (Gaussian distribution) above and below the central line, most often on or near it. A few consecutive readings falling near, but all to one side of, the central line require an improbable equal-but-opposite sequence to balance them. This is not impossible; but the chances are that a semi-permanent imbalance or skewness has developed. The most likely explanation is some instrumental misbehaviour (ranging from finger-marks on the standard to a drift away from rectilinearity of the amplifier or photo-surface) which was not operative when the position of the fiduciary central line was established. I was lucky, in that the Goddess of Chance granted me a set of reliable observations in the first place, and homogeneity of performance thereafter for a year or so before I went on to other things.

The control chart shown in Fig. 18.1 covers the first six and a half months of use. The vertical scale is necessarily exaggerated to show any variations at all. On the same scale as here, the zero or base-line would be some 2 feet (say 60 cm) beyond the bottom. (On the original, it would have been some 10^2 metres below ground.) Out of the 120 test-points shown, eighty-three lie within $\pm 1\ SD$ (eighty-two expected from purely random errors and a good initial estimate of mean extinction and SD) and six lie outside $\pm 2\ SD$ ($5\frac{1}{2}$ calculated). The estimated SD (0·0016) is interesting in that it implies a ' probable error ', to use an outmoded but convenient term, of 0·001, which is about the practical limit of reading the scale.

The circled numbers along the bottom of the chart represent ' incidents '. The first, second, and fourth arose from a barely perceptible slipping of the scale on its spindle, rectified in a few seconds without dismantling, and permanently fixed next time the lid was off. Neglected, they would have led in a week or two to a sizable systematic error with, insidiously, no effect on short-term reproducibility. The fifth was traced in a few minutes to a minor mishap to the sensitivity potentiometer connector-spring, fortunately accessible. All were detected and cured before they had time to develop beyond an error of 0·002 on the reading (about $\frac{1}{2}\%$ in routine analysis, on the average), which is less than the typical difference between pairs of cuvettes. Outfits costing ten times as much have differed by ten times more (Brode, 1953, *et al.*).

The third incident should never have happened and must be regarded as another Awful Example. It was associated with a failing (and aged) hydrogen lamp and a badly corroded lamp-mirror, both of which demanded the use of progressively wider slit-widths than usual. Together, somehow, they upset the photometry quite unexpectedly in the sixteenth week. Perhaps—who knows?—the increasing slit plus mirror-defects suddenly diverted an errant ray, hesitating on the brink, into the entrance slit at a slant and so raised the level of stray light, which had hitherto remained low and constant. An inquest is profitless, the moral obvious: Plot your slit-widths, averaged from your routine extinction tests. Slit-widths had been dutifully noted throughout, but they languished neglected and unplotted beneath a mass of more immediately interesting data. Dale's (1957) weekly routine—see Chapter 11—which hadn't then been published, would doubtless have revealed some falling-off during the previous month, maybe even earlier with the added visual aid of plotted slit-widths. The slightly smoothed plot of a weekly average of daily slit-widths would I think be preferable to a daily plot. Any drift is then less likely to be obscured by minor irrelevancies associated with erratic sensitivity setting, the control knob of which is not always graduated. Wise after the event, I exhumed the daily slit data and averaged them by the week. Figure 18.2 shows the result, which speaks for itself.

THE BASIC CALCULATIONS

Sir Herbert Dingle modestly claimed he would rather be master of a little mathematics than the slave of much. If without presumption I may string along with Dingle, a little statistical analysis provides considerable mastery, whereas a lot can become a fearful burden unless the user has a nice sense of proportion. All the statistical mathematics you need *for present purposes* can be summarized quite briefly:

Variance $(V) = (\Sigma x^2 - n\bar{x}^2)/(n-1)$, where Σx^2 is the sum of the squares of the observations and $\bar{x}$ is their arithmetic mean. The -1 is Bessel's correction for use when n is small. Independent variance of an extinction reading,

$$V_E = V_{\text{cuvettes}} + V_{\text{control settings}} + V_{\text{phototube}} + V_{\text{dial reading}}$$

each expressed as a small fictitious extinction. Of these the first is usually by far the largest, and the last should be—but sometimes isn't—negligible. Over-all variance of a spectro-assay similarly $=V_\text{preparative procedure}+V_\text{E}$.

Standard deviation (SD or s.d.)$=\sqrt{V}$. This is the SD of a *single* observation in a series. Extinction (optical density, absorbance) readings made on one instrument in normal good condition can be assumed to belong to one big series or statistical ' population '. SD is an absolute quantity, not a fraction of anything.

Standard error (SE)$=SD/\sqrt{n}$, i.e. the SD of the *mean* rather than of a single observation. Four times as many tests halves the error.

Coefficient of variation (CV, C of V, or c.v.)$=SD$ expressed as a percentage of the mean.

So much for definitions. Now for a couple of examples.

(1) As it stands, the variance formula gives no trouble if a mechanical or electronic calculator is available to discourage premature rounding-off of 6- or 7-digit numbers that differ only in their last couple of digits. Working by longhand, this is a severe temptation, but it *must* be resisted. Here is a way to avoid it. Spectrometric readings, being ' quantized ' in the sense that they can't be quoted honestly to more than three digits, are well suited to a simplified version that anyone can apply even without an abacus. Consider the ten consecutive readings on which the control chart in Fig. 18.1 was based. Multiply each by 1000 and substitute for x in the formula the *difference* from any convenient whole number ('false mean ') near the mean, say 459 (i.e. 0.459×1000):

$1000 \times$ reading	x	x^2
458	-1	1
460	$+1$	1
458	-1	1
459	0	0
457	-2	4
459	0	0
459	0	0
463	$+4$	16
459	0	0
460	$+1$	1

Sum: $+2$ $24=\Sigma x^2$

Here the readings × 1000 are given in the order in which they were made.

$$n=10; \quad \bar{x}=2/10=0.2;$$

hence the mean reading

$$=0.459+0.2/1000=0.4592$$
$$\bar{x}^2=(0.2)^2=0.04, \text{ so } 10\bar{x}^2=0.4$$
$$\text{Hence } V=(24-0.4)/(10-1)=2.62$$
$$\text{and } SD=\sqrt{2.62}=1.62$$

On the real scale, this represents 1/1000th of 1·62, or 0·00162, which honesty compels me to round off to 0·0016, as in Fig. 18.1.

(2) As an alternative, which incidentally shows the remarkable consistency of the instrument's performance, the whole 120 points on this chart can be analysed almost as simply as the above original 10, because the readings are limited to a similar small range of numbers. Multiply each difference from 459 (x, that is) by the frequency with which it occurs (N) to get the Nx column:

1000 × reading	x	N	Nx	Nx^2
463	+4	5	+20	80
462	+3	4	+12	36
461	+2	8	+16	32
460	+1	32	+32	32
*459	0	33	0	0
458	−1	18	−18	18
457	−2	14	−28	56
456	−3	5	−15	45
455	−4	1	−4	16
Sum:		120	+17	315 = Σx^2

* The mode or most frequent observation (but only by a short head). It also happens to be the median (p. 236).

Here $n=120$; $\bar{x}=17/120=0.142$; therefore you add 0·000142 to the false mean to obtain the *grand mean*=0·459142.

$$\bar{x}^2=0.02; \quad 120\bar{x}^2=2.4 \text{ (negligible)}.$$

$V=(315-2.4)/(120-1)=2.63$, which is not significantly different from the previous 2·62, and again corresponds with $SD=0.0016$ on the scale.

This sort of thing inspires confidence in the idea of basing a lengthy series of tests on the findings of as few as 10 results. Tyche does not always grant such homogeneity, but you can generally depend on her.

USEFUL APPROXIMATIONS

Most laboratories have in their archives long lists of results in duplicate. Dig out a few. Find out whether they are proper duplicates, done on separate days, on separate samples, by separate people, as Dr E. C. Wood so rightly recommends whenever this is possible. (They probably won't agree quite so well, but they carry far more statistical weight.) In any case, work out either the average difference (if the results are all at about the same level) or the average percentage difference (if they are not) between pairs. Then the *SD* (or, if on a percentage basis, the *CV*) of the assays concerned is very nearly 8/9ths—actually $\frac{1}{2}\sqrt{\pi}$ or 0·886— of the average pair-difference.

For a short run of observations, the range or spread gives a good rough idea of variability. With 8–10 observations or results, *SD*=about one-third of the range; for four, $\frac{1}{2}$ range. Beware here of freak readings, which are more likely to occur as the number of observations increases. All values based on only a few observations are at best no more than estimates of the truth, and are most dependable when the mean and median are sensibly equal. (The *median* is the middle reading, or the average of the middle pair of readings, in a series arranged in order of magnitude. The *mode* is the most popular value).

The *SD* is only a fraction of the result itself. An error in the estimate of it is therefore less important to the main findings roughly in that ratio. And it is usually close enough to base arguments on. Take the series near the end of Chapter 17, on different people reading the same dial-setting. The true *SD*, calculated the long way round, is 0·0026. The range of the 11 results, 0·012–0·002, is 0·010. Just under one-third of this is 0·003. Which is near enough to suggest that 0·012 is probably not such a rogue result as it looks. In practice it does not often matter whether the *SD* of a result such as 10·8 is 0·1, 0·2, or 0·3; that's hair-splitting; but it *is* important to know whether it is 0·2, or 2·0, or 0·02.

One in 3 observations differs from the mean by more than 1 *SD*.
One in 22 observations differs from the mean by more than 2 *SD*.
One in 370 observations differs from the mean by more than 3 *SD*.

(Theoretically, 31·73%, 4·57%, and 0·27% respectively.)

A *significant difference* is conventionally not less than $2\sqrt{(V_1 + V_2)}$, where V_1 and V_2 are the variances of two results in question. This represents a *confidence level* of just over 95% certainty (' $p = 0.95$ ') that the difference is genuine—which is also sometimes expressed as $p = 0.05$, meaning a probability of 20:1 that the results are really not the same.

A difference of more than $3\sqrt{(V_1 + V_2)}$ is virtual certainty: on paper, 99·73% probable. The values of V are of course derived from the already-known *SD* or *CV* characteristic of the method $[V = (SD)^2]$, and duly weighted according to the number of observations on which they are based. When the results are means, divide each V by its corresponding n. ($\sqrt{n}$ applies only to *SD* or *CV*.) Always make sure of such matters before you argue about discrepant data obtained elsewhere.

That summarizes all that I think you *need* to know to keep track of your own results and for intelligent argument about discrepancies; but there is a lot more for those who want to delve further. Whole series of popular articles (like Youden's, for instance, if you care to browse back through *Industr. Engng. Chem.* for several years) are to be found in non-statistical journals, and most of them are understandable by ordinary mortals. Look out for writings by (among others, to whom I apologize) Bliss, Daniel, Davies (O.L.), Fisher, Gridgeman, Hance, Kendall (M.G.), Snedecor, Yule. They usually contain an item or two that can be applied outside its original context. A notably useful section of a report which Technical Services, Dept. of Commerce, Washington 25, D.C., thought worth while to issue separately is *Statistical Shortcuts* by E. A. Waldfogel. The evergreen *Facts from Figures* by M. J. Moroney (Pelican Paperback A 236, available in U.S.A. from Baltimore 11, Md) is worth its price if only for the essay on the finer points of Crown & Anchor. Maybe all the misprints will be eliminated someday. But fortunately they don't affect the findings or the general usefulness of the book. This is a merciful characteristic of statistical analysis: perhaps because statistics is concerned with errors and not mistakes . . .

Note added in proof, December, 1965: A later and simpler book that admirably supplements Moroney's *Facts*, but which I regrettably and unaccountably did not encounter until these present *Hints* were in galley proof, is *Use and Abuse of Statistics* by Professor W. J. Reichmann (1961), now available as Pelican A707. Very stimulating and provocative—particularly on the sort of commercial manipulation of graphs I mention in Chapter 19.

PRESENTATION OF RESULTS

You __must__ draw the line somewhere
POPULAR SAYING

As long ago as 1949, Dr W. R. Brode of NBS, Washington, D.C., published a 10-page summary of the chaotic position both the nomenclature and graphical presentation of absorption spectra had got themselves into. It is worth studying. If Chapter 3 confused you, Brode's paper will show you that really I have over-simplified the situation. Personal preferences and prejudices are inevitable. When a meaning is clear from either the context or by overt definition I don't think they matter much to anyone except the writer. But sometimes I wish that a sense of euphony were more widespread, and that brutal logic did not lead to such words as *transmittivity*. On the other hand, I suppose we should be thankful that *opacitance* and *opacitivity* never caught on; nor *absorptance* (symbol α; meaning $1-T$) which would have been doubly confusing. As a personal reaction, Canutishly against the tide, I dislike absorbance and prefer extinction or OD. But that's a minority view. And I'd certainly discourage both *extinctance* and *extinctivity*.

This chapter deals briefly and generally with the presentation of absorption spectra on graphs and charts. After a certain amount of early vacillation, convention seems to have settled for absorptivity or transmittance as the ordinate (vertical), and wavelength or some function of frequency as the abscissa (horizontal). Almost always, wavelengths are now plotted or charted with the lowest value to the left, and (correspondingly and logically) the highest wavenumbers also to the left. Agreement has not been reached on various other features. Each mode of presentation has its adherents, but dogma is out of place. Merits vary according to circumstances.

There are three popular variants on the abscissa: evenly spaced wavelengths; evenly spaced frequencies; and a compromise based on the natural dispersion of the prism ('quartz dispersion'). Each has its practical advantages, including varying ease of manufacture (a diffraction grating automatically gives even spacing of wavelengths, for instance).

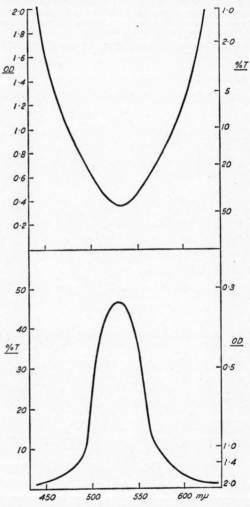

Fig. 19.1. Two portrayals of the absorption spectrum of the same green light filter. Above, linear OD; below, linear $\%T$. Note how the character of the curve changes, not only by inversion, but also by the ordinate compression at low values of linear $\%T$.

Use of a cam mechanism to select a wavelength makes it entirely a matter of manufacturer's choice which mode of presentation is employed. There is essentially no difference in complication once the cam profile has been worked out. There are substantial differences in the results. Evenly spaced wavelengths exaggerate the spread of UV absorption bands, and overcrowd bands in the visible. This is a practical disadvantage, but not noticeable unless your work covers a sizeable fraction of the spectral range at one time. From a theoretical point of view (comparison of energy levels and suchlike) even spacing of frequency has so many advantages that only the fact that you do lose some of the delightful, but misleading, UV-spaciousness of combined visible + UV ' wavelength ' instruments makes me wonder why *de facto* even spacing of frequency is not universal. I say *de facto* because on some instruments (Ultrascan, for instance) wavelengths and relevant rulings are evenly spaced on a frequency scale although they are labelled $m\mu$.

To me, this makes the best of both worlds. Or nearly the best: I would also print an evenly spaced wavenumber scale along the top, with corresponding wavelengths along the bottom and wavelength rulings between. I'm always grateful for help in converting cm^{-1} to $m\mu$. If you're young enough, try to get used to thinking in cm^{-1} or μ^{-1}. But there's still a lot of wavelengths in the literature, and likely to be for a long time, so the ability to convert quickly from cm^{-1} to $m\mu$ in your head will be useful all your life—like being genuinely bi-lingual. For the sake of your readers, many of whom will not be spectrometrically bi-lingual, it is a kindness to include both wavelengths and wavenumbers on your published graphs, always.

Some transmittance-minded manufacturers record extinction (' density ', OD, absorbance) upside down, with the higher E-values towards the bottom along with the lower $\% T$ values. So long as the printing is clear, the necessary mental inversion is easy enough, and is made easier still if the charts are transparent and can be physically inverted and read by looking through from the other side.

LOGARITHMIC OR PANORAMIC?

The figures are largely self-explanatory, except perhaps for Fig. 19.6. This compares two ways to draw the same lengthy curve: one by

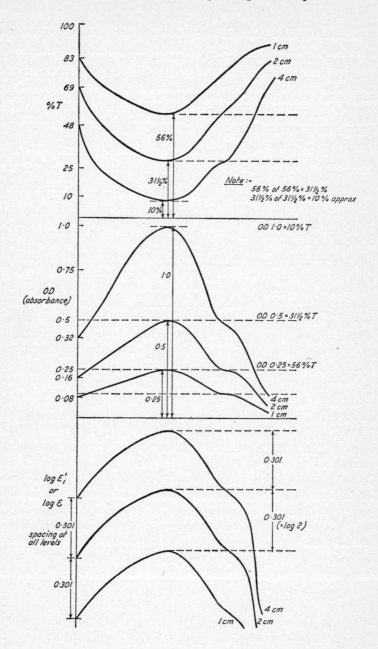

using the logarithm of absorptivity as ordinate; the other by plotting the whole curve directly against absorptivity itself, (*a*) as a single long curve of which the lower part is practically meaningless as it stands, and also (*b*) as progressively expanded sections where the trace comes too near the base-line for the bands to show up properly. The log-plot is ' all of a piece ' and rather under-plays— but consistently under-plays—the persistence (max—min) of the bands. The other approach gives a sort of perspective effect, small bands looming up successively into fuller and perhaps exaggerated view as you travel into the various sections. This is much the same as walking slowly past a sequence of several charts arranged in order of concentration × path-length. I call it *panoramic presentation*. I used it a lot at one time because some people were better able to grasp the meaning that way; and also, because I couldn't get logarithmic graph paper, it saved me the trouble of looking up a fearful number of logs, or using a slide-rule as a ruler on blank paper. But, if you can educate your audience up to it, I think that the log-plot is the all-round best. I hear that an accessory for at least one instrument is available which directly records log-extinction as the ordinate (I don't know the details of how this formidable problem was solved, but the Gilford patent mentioned in Chapter 8 provides a clue as to one possible approach). Until direct log-recording is common, hand-plotting from charts or tabulated results is all that can be done.

However they are obtained, log-plots are compact and so are easy to file, and they have a built-in bonus-advantage which is not sufficiently emphasized: the shape of the curve is independent of concentration and path-length so long as the ' absorbing entities ' remain qualitatively unchanged. As a consequence of the

FIG. 19.2. These nine curves all represent the same fictitious absorption spectrum plotted at different levels (1, 2, and 4 cm path-lengths) and against different ordinates. The inflection on the right side of the curve designedly has half the E-value of the maximum and therefore comes opposite the maximum shown by the next lower cuvette (half path-length) in all three sets. The shapes of the curves alter markedly with path-length, except in the lower set, where the ordinate is $\log E_1^1$ or $\log \epsilon$. Here, the shape remains unchanged at all levels and the curve merely moves bodily up and down by an amount equal to the logarithm of the path-length ratio. If the abscissa is on a rectilinear frequency basis (cm^{-1}, for instance), the curves can also be shifted bodily sideways and compared directly by superposition on a viewing stand (Fig. 4.4).

log-plot, the position of the curve shifts bodily up or down the ordinate by one unit per decade, 0·3 unit for every $2\times$ change in path-length (or concentration, Beer-complications permitting), so long as the logarithmic scale remains unaltered. The practical usefulness of this is obvious. Direct comparisons by simple super-position become possible without re-drawing (which has to be done *very* carefully indeed, to exactly the same scale) so long as the

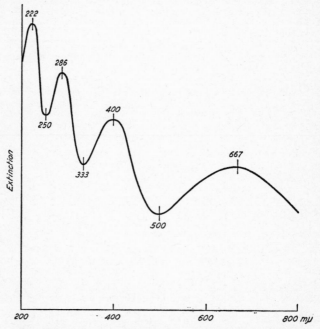

FIG. 19.3. A regular pattern is not obvious here, but these four maxima and their related minima are equally spaced on a frequency scale and are then all similar in shape. See Fig. 19.4.

abscissa remains the same. Just move your charts, or standard-abscissae graphs, up or down until they coincide—or don't. And with standardized even-spaced cm^{-1} abscissae you can similarly move them sideways (Figs. 19.2 and 19.4).

BAND-SHAPES

Proof of identity by comparison of absorption spectra *without other supporting evidence* is not often possible. Complete coincidence of two simple curves may in fact be just that: no more than coincidence. All diazo-compounds, for instance, look much alike in their UV spectra, because the powerful diazo-chromophore dominates the spectrum. Coincidence of complex spectra comprising several bands becomes more likely to mean genuine identity in what one could call galloping proportion to the number of coinciding bands, etc., particularly if they form a

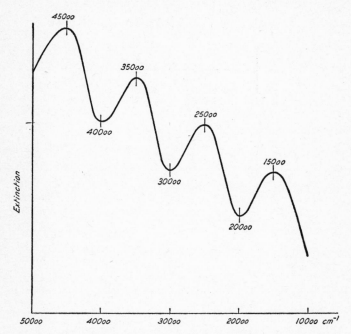

FIG. 19.4. This is the curve in Fig. 19.3 redrawn on a linear frequency scale, with ordinates unchanged. The regular 10000 cm⁻¹ spacing of the bands is now obvious.

pattern. There is usually also some other property which can be brought in—melting point, boiling point, chemical behaviour—to settle the argument. Establishment of non-identity requires the existence of only one discrepant feature; but be wary that the discrepancy is really fundamental to the absorbing material(s), and not merely due to an unsuspected impurity or some adventitious solvent effect acting on one of the specimens under comparison (pH, etc.).

You can ' prove ' almost anything with a graph. The shape of a curve depends on the ratio between the units used in the abscissa and ordinate. In Company Reports to Shareholders you will sometimes notice a tendency to show rising profits on a graph effectively

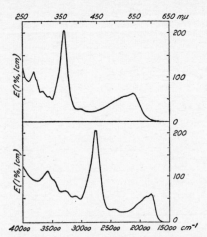

FIG. 19.5. Spectrum of vitamin B_{12} in water; the difference between wavelength and wavenumber presentation. (By courtesy of Drs G. H. Beaven and E. A. Johnson, 1956.)

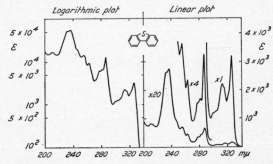

FIG. 19.6. Spectrum of dibenzthiophene in light petroleum. *Left*, logarithmic plot. *Right*, ' panoramic ' plot. The ordinate for both curves is log OD. (By courtesy of Drs G. H. Beaven and E. A. Johnson, 1956.)

without a base-line. If the percentage rise is meagre, even 1% looks impressive when it fills the expanded selected portion of ordinate. Declining profits, on the other hand, are shown with a proper base-line far below, so a loss of 10% takes up only one-tenth of the ordinate, and looks even less if the graduations below 90% are omitted and the y-axis is broken off short, low down, to make it superficially simulate last year's 1% graph.

Potentiometrically 'expanded' scales do much the same in spectrometry, but (so far) honestly. The expanded scale is used to achieve greater response from the galvanometer, or for better precision, or to emphasize a small spectral feature which might be important in itself but has been swamped by other larger features. A case in point is shown in Fig. 19.7.

In the spectrum of holmium oxide 'glass' (Corning 3130) there is a tiny band near 485 mµ (20600 cm^{-1}) with a small depression in the middle of the peak, only a few times the thickness of the pen trace. The left-hand transmittance spectrum shown here was

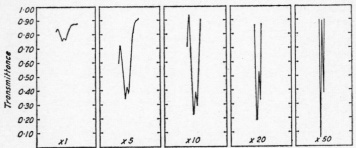

FIG. 19.7. The small doublet at 485 mµ in the spectrum of a thin sample of holmium-oxide glass. It is shown without expansion and with consecutive expansions of ×5, ×10, ×20, and ×50. (By courtesy of Perkin-Elmer Inc.)

recorded 'untreated' on a Perkin-Elmer 350, and the others were expanded 5×, 10×, 20×, 50×, respectively. All establish the reality of the resolved peak, with quantitative confirmation of persistence (max–min) and the positions of the component bands with some precision. The last two spectra (20×, 50×)* are effectively without base-line and must be regarded as qualitative so far as absolute intensities are concerned; but if the persistences of the last three are visually read-off and converted to *OD* (see table in Chapter 3) their ratios are, as they should be, 1:2:5, within experimental error (0·65−0·41=0·24; 0·75−0·26=0·49; and 1·22−0·046=1·17)—despite everything, including the vastly exaggerated band profiles. This, I reckon, is photometrically good going.

---

* Some prefer ' ×20, ×50'. It depends on whether you say 'by 20, by 50' or '20 times, 50 times'.

CHOICE OF SCALE

Of the various shapes or profiles shown by the different modes of presentation and at different concentrations, etc., which is correct? The choice is arbitrary, since any shape can be produced at will by merely changing the relative scales of ordinate and abscissa. Even the logarithmic presentation that I advocate is not immune from scale-tampering; but at least within an organization it should be possible to reach agreement about the size of graphs and/or charts for filing, and so arrive at more or less standard band-shapes. Without such standardization, routine superposition is impracticable. To re-draw as carefully as would be necessary all the curves you *might* want to superpose is too time-consuming a luxury for any normal laboratory. Re-drawing can't be hurried. If the recording is not already logarithmic—very few of them are—the only way to avoid a pile-up of charts is to re-draw each one that you *know* will be needed for later comparison, as soon as possible after it is recorded. One or two re-drawings at a sitting is quite enough hard work for most people.

What scale should you choose? A recent co-operative venture on a minor international level has already done this for us. Two scientific committees, drawn from the Photoelectric Spectrometry Group (U.K.) and the Institut für Spektrochemie und angewandte Spektroskopie (W. Germany), have together compiled a massive UV Atlas of Organic Compounds, which is now being published in five volumes by Butterworth's. Some 10^3 spectra are all presented on the same scale on standard-sized charts designed for superposition of up to five at a time for easy comparison. All are printed on standard DIN A4 sheets, 210×297 mm (i.e. $1 \times \sqrt{2}$). Normally, each chart covers an ordinate range in log ϵ from $\epsilon = 10$ to $\epsilon = 2 \times 10^5$ at 40 mm per decade. Depending on spectrometric context, there is a choice between 182–500 mμ (550oo–200oo cm^{-1}) and 222 to 1000 mμ (450oo–100oo cm^{-1})—that is, all charts cover a 35000 cm^{-1} range at the same regular scale of 10000 cm^{-1} per 4 cm of abscissa. (This, by the way, vividly highlights the contrast between the mμ and cm^{-1} modes of presentation! An extension of the 'long wave' chart 4 cm to the right would, rather overcrowdedly, encompass the whole of the 'eastern' half of Plate 1, radio and all.) For the kindly guidance of those of us who are still apt to get lost among the cm^{-1}s, the corresponding wavelengths in mμ are printed at intervals. Except for the wavelengths, the alternative charts are superposable in both directions, and can be displaced up, down, or sideways without mathematical offence. If you plot log E(1%, 1 cm) instead of log ϵ, the only effect is to shift the curve bodily downwards, without distortion, through a scale-distance of {log(molecular weight)—1} ordinate units.

Manual plotting on, or reading from, a cm^{-1} or permicron (Chapter 3) scale can be simplified by using a metric ruler to measure the distance of features from one edge of the chart. Find out how many mm there are per 1000 cm^{-1} (etc.), and use a table of reciprocals to calculate equivalent cm^{-1} if the printed data happen to be expressed in wavelengths on an actual cm^{-1} chart (as on the Ultrascan). If the wavelength rulings are not in exactly integral mm intervals, it is worth while indelibly marking-off cm^{-1} or μ^{-1} or dkB (etc.) against several existing graduations on the ruler; alternatively, make a transparent scale on the underside of a strip of plastic (to avoid parallax), or even on tracing paper. Band-spacings can then be traced and/or measured directly.

Incidentally, charts form one of the few subjects on which you can safely allow the stylists to let themselves go with impunity— and probably very good results. Superposed on the vertical wavenumber rulings, for instance, a dozen or so faint wavelength rulings in a contrasting colour both look pleasing and make the chart easier to read. Too many charts are uninspired and drab-looking. Some charts are already functional, clear, uncluttered, and also aesthetically pleasing. Why not all?

*   *   *   *   *

The next stage, as I see it, is 'Digital Read-out', with which several manufacturers are now toying. Existing recording instruments seem to be readily adaptable to this system of printing results as numbers instead of curves. More in keeping with the 'quote' at the head of this chapter, however, is the (I think) probable next stage after this again: cathode-ray-tube presentation, with a long-persistence screen. Permanent records can be made by laying photo-sensitive paper on the surface of the tube, so that an elementary dark-room might come back into spectrometry; or, more probably, one of the newer (e.g. xerographic) processes will be used. But although experimental assemblies show great promise, commercial reality still seems a long way off. When it does come, spectra will once again have to be properly *looked at* and adjusted before their pictures are taken. We shall return to being more nearly literally spectro*scopists*.

*   *   *   *   *

I end this book as I began it, with a disclaimer and a quotation. No textbook in the world is complete, not even those nice big books three times the size of this one. My aim has been to supplement and perhaps sometimes clarify these more comprehensive works, not—quite impossibly—to supplant them. The inevitable gaps in my narrative can be filled-in where necessary from the Big Books themselves, and from the periodic literature including manufacturers' catalogues, instruction manuals, house journals, all of which contain a wealth of generally useful information, even though it is understandably slanted towards each manufacturer's own products. This book will, I hope, help you to find your way intelligently through the maze. But, in the words of Liu Shih-An,

> My mind is filled to overflowing
> With the things I did not say.

REFERENCES

(The numbers in square brackets refer to pages in this book)

Andersen, A., and Nightingale, E., 1929, *J. Soc. chem. Ind. Lond.*, 139 T. [19, 197]

Archer, M. Scott, 1954, *PSG Bull.*,* No. 7, 1960. [226]

Auerbach, M. E., Bauer, E. L., and Nachod, F. C., 1964, *Industr. Qual. Contr.*, **20**, 45. [193]

Baly, E. C. C., 1924 and 1927, *Spectroscopy*, 2nd ed. (Longmans, Green & Co. Ltd., London). [26]

— and Tryhorn, F. G., 1916, *Phil. Mag.* (series VI), **31**, 417. [140]

Bastian, R., 1951, *Analyt. Chem.*, **23**, 580 (and other papers). [166]

Bauman, R. P., 1962, *Absorption Spectroscopy* (John Wiley & Sons Inc., New York and London). [21 f., 52, 73]

Beale, R. N., 1951, *PSG Bull.*, No. 4, 89. [200]

Beaven, G. H., 1950, *PSG Bull.*, No. 2, 30. [58]

—, 1954, *PSG Bull.*, No. 7, 171. [94]

— and Johnson, E. A., 1956, *PSG Bull.*, No. 9, 211. [246]

— — —, 1961, (with Willis and Miller) in *Molecular Spectroscopy: Methods and Applications in Chemistry* (Heywood, London). [167]

Beer, A., 1852, *Ann. Phys., Lpz.* **86**, 78. [11]

Braude, E. A., and Timmons, C. J., 1953, *PSG Bull.*, No. 6, 139. [221]

British Standards Institution, Part 1, 1954, B.S. 1991, *Symbols* (etc.). [20]

— — —, 1965, B.S. 3875, *Specification for Optical Spectrophotometric Cells.* [119]

Brode, W. R., 1943, *Chemical Spectroscopy* (John Wiley & Sons Inc., New York; Chapman & Hall Ltd., London). [100]

—, 1949, *J. opt. Soc. Amer.*, **39**, 1022. [14, 239]

—, 1955, ' Color and chemical constitution ', *Amer. Scient.*, **43**, 259. [Plate 1]

—, Gould, J. H., Witner, J. E., and Wyman, G. M., 1953, *J. opt. Soc. Amer.*, **43**, 862. [232, 239]

Cahn, L., 1955, *J. opt. Soc. Amer.*, **45**, 953. [213]

Cannon, C. G., 1955, *PSG Bull.*, No. 8, 201. [166, 211]

—, 1960 (ed.), *Electronics for Spectroscopists* (Hilger & Watts Ltd., London). [55, 64]

— and Butterworth, I.S.C., 1953, *Analyt. Chem.*, **25**, 168. [106]

Cary, H. H. and Beckman, A. O., 1941, *J. opt. Soc. Amer.*, **31**, 682. [58]

Caster, W. O., 1951, *Analyt. Chem.*, **23**, 1229. [194, 207, 208]

---

* PSG = Photoelectric Spectrometry Group, c/o Unicam Instruments Ltd, Cambridge, England. *Bulletin*, 15s., $2.00 post free.

Chapman, D., 1965, *The Structure of Lipids* (Methuen & Co. Ltd, London). [3]

Childs, C. B., 1961, *J. opt. Soc. Amer.*, **51**, 895. [164]

Claiborne, E. B., 1947, *Rev. sci. Instrum.*, **18**, 378. [162]

Collaborative Tests, 1965, *The Pharmaceutical Press*, London. [184]

Collins, F. D., 1951, *PSG Bull.*, No. 4, 96. [89, 156]

Crawford, C. M., 1959, *Analyt. Chem.*, **31**, 313. [213]

Dale, A., 1957, *Unicam Spectrovision*, No. 3, 3. [143, 228, 233]

Davey, S. C. B., 1963, *Hilger J.*, **8**, 30. [116]

Donaldson, R., 1950, *PSG Bull.*, No. 3, 45. [153]

Edisbury, J. R., 1940, *Analyst*, **65**, 484. [196]

— , 1948, *Spectrochim. Acta*, **3**, 420. [19, 185]

— , 1949, *PSG Bull.*, No. 1, 10. [187]

— and Sanders, E. T., 1954, *PSG Bull.*, No. 7, 174. [96–9]

— , Gillow, J., and Taylor, R. J., 1954, *Analyst*, **79**, 617. [204]

Elwell, W. T., and Gidley, J. A. F., 1961, *Atomic-Absorption Spectrophotometry* (Pergamon Press Ltd, London). [171]

Fischer, H., and Steiner, P., 1922, *C.R. Acad. Sci.*, *Paris*, **175**, 882. [140]

Food Standards (Margarine), 1954, S.R. & O., No. 614. (Taylor, 1955, below, is relevant.)

Fripp, D. W., and Powell, B. D., 1960, *Lab. Practice*, **9**, 319. [132]

Furneaux, Rupert, 1964, *What Happened on the Mary Celeste* (Max Parrish, London). [186]

Gibson, G. P., and Taylor, R. J., 1945, *Analyst*, **70**, 449. [132]

Glenn, A. L., 1965, *PSG Bull.*, No. 16 (in press). [185]

— , see also Collaborative Tests (above). [184]

Goldring, L. S., 1950, *PSG Bull.*, No. 2, 39. [160, 212]

— , Hawes, R. C., Hare, G. H., Beckman, A. O., and Stickney, M. E., 1953, *Analyt. Chem.*, **25**, 869. [208]

Goulden, J. D. S., 1961, *Brit. J. appl. Phys.*, **12**, 456. [217]

— , 1962, *PSG Bull.*, No. 14, 386. [217]

Gridgeman, N. T., 1951, *PSG Bull.*, No. 4, 67. [190]

— , 1952, *Analyt. Chem.*, **24**, 445. [208, 213]

— , 1955, *PSG Bull.*, No. 8, 197. [166]

— , 1966, *New Scientist*, **29**, 91. [195 n.]

Halban, H.v, Kortum, G., and Szigeti, B., 1936, *Z. Elektrochem.*, **42**, 628. [178]

— and Litmanowitsch, M., 1941, *Helv. chim. Acta*, **24**, 44. [178]

— , 1944, *Helv. chim. Acta*, **27**, 1032. [178]

Hales, J. L., 1953, *PSG Bull.*, No. 6. [79]

Hantzsch, A., 1911, *Ber. dtsch. Chem. Ges.*, **44**, 1783. [140]

Hartley, W. N., 1885, *J. chem. Soc.*, **47**, 685. [140]

Hartree, E. F., 1951, *PSG Bull.*, No. 4, 94. [200]

— , 1963, *PSG Bull.*, No. 15, 398. [153, 164]

Haupt, G., 1952, *J. Res. nat. Bur. Stand.*, **48**, 411. [188]

Herrmann, E., 1919, *Z. wiss. Photogr.* **18**, 253. [140]

Hiskey, C. F., 1948, *Analyt. Chem.*, **21**, 1440 (and several later papers, *ibid.*). [166]

Hogness, T. R., Zscheile, F. P., and Sidwell, A. E., 1937, *J. phys. Chem.*, **41**, 379. [207]

— and Zscheile, F. P., 1947, *J. phys. Chem.*, **51** 903. [188]

Holiday, E. R., 1937, *J. sci. Instrum.*, **14**, 166; and 1950, *Disc. Faraday Soc.*, **9**, 484. [36]

— and Beaven, G. H., 1950, *PSG Bull.*, No. 3, 53. [153]

Johnson, E. A., 1962, *PSG Bull.*, No. 14, 394. [224]

Kayser, H., 1905, *Handbuch der Spektroskopie* (Herzel, Leipzig). [22]

Kendall, C. E., and Lloyd, D. G., 1956, *PSG Bull.*, No. 9, 216. [218]

— and Huke, D. W., 1963, *PSG Bull.*, No. 15, 401. [167]

Ketelaar, J. A. A., Fahrenfort, J., Haas, C., and Brinkman, G. A., 1951, *PSG Bull.*, No. 8, 176. [190]

Knowles, E., 1952, *PSG Bull.*, No. 5, 120. [217]

Kortum, G., 1937, *Angew. Chem.*, **50**, 193. [166]

Lipsett, F. R., 1959, *J. opt. Soc. Amer.*, **49**, 673. [88]

— , 1961, *Rev. sci. Instrum.*, **32**, 840. [200]

— , 1965, *PSG Bull.*, No. 16 (in press). [200]

Lothian, G. F., 1951, *PSG Bull.*, No. 4, 86. [190]

— , 1956, *PSG Bull.*, No. 9, 207. [166, 211]

— , 1958, *Absorption Spectrophotometry*, 2nd ed. (Hilger & Watts Ltd, London). [19, 21, 35, 109, 134]

— , 1963, *Analyst*, **88**, 678. [11, 67, 216]

Martin, A. E., 1950, *PSG Bull.*, No. 3, 50. [153]

McNicholas, H. J., 1928, *J. Res. nat. Bur. Stand.*, **48**, 411. [100]

Mellon, M. G., 1950, *Analytical Absorption Spectroscopy* (John Wiley & Sons Inc., New York). Chapter 5 by K. S. Gibson is relevant. See also Konen, 1909, *Z. Elektrochem.*, **15**, 165; Henri, Victor, 1913, *Phys. Z.*, **14**, 515; Finger, 1909, *Z. wiss. Photogr.*, **7**, 320, 369; Stücklen, 1924, *Z. Phys.*, **30**, 24; Schaum, *Z. wiss. Photogr.*, **24**, 86; Angerer u. Joos, *Ann. Phys.*, *Lpz.*, **74**, 743, and Weigert, Fritz, *Optische Methoden der Chemine*, page 43 (Akademie Verlag, Leipzig) for these and other references to the under-water spark. [100]

Moon, P. B., 1960, *Times sci. Rev.* (Summer), 13. [10]

Moroney, M. J., 1951 (and onwards), *Facts from Figures* (Pelican A 236, London and Baltimore). [237]

Morton , R. A., and Gouveia, A. J. A. de, 1934, *J. chem. Soc.*, 916. [136]

— , 1949, *PSG Bull.*, No. 1, 15 [124]

— , 1951, *PSG Bull.*, No. 4, 65. [190]

— and Stubbs, A. L., 1946, *Analyst*, **71**, 348. [197, 218]

Neal, W. T. L., 1956, *PSG Bull.*, No. 9, 204. [166, 206]

Ovenston, T. C. J., 1953, *PSG Bull.*, No. 6, 132. [221]

Perry, J. W., 1950, *PSG Bull.*, No. 3, 40. [153]

Pritchard, H., and Ward, R. J., 1957, *Unicam Spectrovision*, No. 3, 1. [19]

Rao, C. N. R., 1961, *UV and Visible Spectroscopy: Chemical Applications* (Butterworths, London). [21]

Reichmann, W. J., 1964, *Use and Abuse of Statistics* (Pelican A 707, London and Baltimore). [238]

Reilley, C. N., and Crawford, C. M., 1955, *Analyt. Chem.*, **27,** 716. [166]
Ringbom, A., and Sundmann, F., 1939, *Z. anal. Chem.*, **115,** 332, 402. [166]
— and Ostenholm, K., 1953, *Analyt. Chem.*, **25,** 1798. [166]
Sanders, E. T., and Edisbury, J. R., 1955, *PSG Bull.*, No. 8, 187. [96–9]
Sargrove, J. A., 1947, *J. Brit. Instn Radio Engrs*, **7,** 86. [104]
Shaw, C. H., and Foreman, W. T., 1959, *J. opt. Soc. Amer.*, **49,** 724. [164]
Slavin, W., 1962, *J. opt. Soc. Amer.*, **52,** 1399. [180]
— , 1963, *Analyt. Chem.*, **35,** 561. [153, 158, 189]
— , 1965, *Appl. Spectrosc.*, **19,** 32. [213]
Smith, W. O., 1943, *J. Res. nat. Bur. Stand.*, **30,** 449. [88]
Spruit, F. J., and Keuker, H., 1965, *PSG Bull.*, No. 16 (in press). [143, 146, 228]
Sutton, C. G., 1950, *PSG Bull.*, No. 2, 19. [39]
Tarrant, A. W. S., 1953, *PSG Bull.*, No. 6, 143. [79]
— , 1965, *PSG Bull.*, No. 16, (in press). [148, 193, 216]
Taylor, R. J., 1942, *Analyst*, **67,** 248; also Kreider, H. R., 1945, *Industr. Engng Chem. (Anal.)*, **17,** 694. [178]
— , 1955, *Analyst*, **80,** 438. [19]
Turk, W. E., 1952, *PSG Bull.*, No. 5, 100. [115]
Twyman, F., and Lothian, G. F., 1933, *Proc. phys. Soc. Lond.*, **45,** 643. [206, 213]
UV, *Atlas of Organic Compounds*, 1966 (Butterworths, London; Springer, Berlin). [248]
Vandenbelt, J. M., Forsyth, J. F., and Garrett, A., 1945, *Industr. Engng Chem. (Anal.)*, **17,** 235. [178]
— , 1954, *J. opt. Soc. Amer.*, **44,** 641. [188]
— , 1961, *J. opt. Soc. Amer.*, **51,** 802. [175]
— , 1962, *J. opt. Soc. Amer.*, **52,** 284. [180]
— and Spurlock, C. H., 1955, *J. opt. Soc. Amer.*, **45,** 967. [178]
— and Henrich, C., 1953, *Appl. Spectrosc.*, **7,** 171. [220]
— — , 1954, *Analyst*, **79,** 586. [221]
Veszi, G. A., 1941, *Electron. Engng*, **14,** 436. [107]
— , 1953, *J. Brit. Instn Radio Engrs*, **13,** 183. [104]
Waldofogel, E. A., 1954, *Statistical Shortcuts* (MLM-956, from Tech. Services, Washington 25, D.C.). [237]
Walker, S., and Straw, H., 1962, Spectroscopy, vol. 2 (Chapman & Hall Ltd, London). [21]
Walsh, A., 1955, *Spectrochim. Acta*, **7,** 108. [170]
— , 1965, *XII Colloquium Spectroscopicum Internationale*, pp. 43–65 (Hilger & Watts Ltd, London). [171]
Wilkinson, K. R., 1957, *Unicam Spectrovision*, No. 3, 4. [21, 23]

INDEX

An index is never *complete*